DEVELOPING
A
HEALTHY
MIND

A practical guide
for any situation

DEVELOPING A HEALTHY MIND

A practical guide for any situation

JULIÁN MELGOSA

Doctor of Psychology. Dean of the School of Education and Psychology
at Walla Walla University, Washington State, USA.

Editorial safeliz

Collection: **New Lifestyle**
Title: **Developing a Healthy Mind**
Original title in Spanish edition: *Cómo tener una mente sana*

Author: Julián Melgosa
Illustration credits: See page 331
Design and project development: Editorial Safeliz team

Translation: Annette D. Melgosa

Copyright by © **Editorial Safeliz, S. L.**
Pradillo, 6 · Pol. Ind. La Mina
E-28770 · Colmenar Viejo, Madrid, Spain
Tel.: [+34] 91 845 98 77 · Fax: [+34] 91 845 98 65
admin@safeliz.com · www.safeliz.com

April 2009: 4th edition in English language (also available in Spanish)

ISBN: 978-84-7208-168-0
Legal Deposit: TO-536-2009

Printing: Artes Gráficas Toledo, S.A.U.
Jarama, 128, polígono industrial
E-45007 Toledo, Spain
PRINTED IN THE EUROPEAN UNION

'Happiness
is not a station
you arrive at, but
a manner of traveling.'

Margaret Lee Runbeck

General layout

 **PAGE 12**

Chapter 1: Learning to live

 PAGE 82

Chapter 2: Self-centred problems (I)

 PAGE 142

Chapter 3: Self-centred problems (II)

of the work

Foreword

Dr. José Luis Pinillos

Professor Emeritus at the Complutense
University of Madrid.
Awarded doctorates honoris causa
by over ten universities.
Awarded the Gold Medal of the
Centre for University Studies.
Awarded the Gold Medal of Madrid.
Prince of Asturias Prize of
Social Sciences (1986).
Member of the Spanish Royal Academy.
Member of the Spanish Royal Academy
of Moral and Political Sciences.
Member of the *Academia Scientiarum
et Artium Europaea*.
Author of multiple works in Psychology.

*D*EVELOPING A HEALTHY MIND, in Professor Melgosa's own words, 'is a book for the popular press, wherein everyone, regardless of their knowledge of psychology and the behavioural sciences, can understand and apply principles to help themselves and others.' While this is true, the phrase 'popular press'—a branch of publishing that makes something available to the general public—does not do justice to the originality and special talent used by the author to make the complex themes of mental health accessible.

The author develops his work around three important thematic points: mental problems focused on *oneself*, problems one has with others, and ways to face both. From the very beginning, the book elicits in the reader an excellent impression. Each unit begins with a brief but clear and rigorous scientific explanation of the topic supported by the most competent research. A suggestive clinical case setup follows, helping the reader to identify with the *patient's* inner attitudes and feelings. Lastly, there are always interesting guidelines for alternative measures that the subject may choose to solve his or her problem. This bears close resemblance to the daily clinical visits to their patients that good physicians conduct with their interns.

Take for example, the six-page unit, 'Living with hope', which deserves to be read and reflected upon. It includes: references to Martin Seligman, the main proponent of positive psychology; accounts from Victor Frankl of the Nazi concentration camp prisoners who, because of their hope against all odds, survived until the end; research from Daniel Goleman, creator of emotional intelligence, on hope levels and their influence upon academic achievement. All these contribute, amidst other observations, to reinforce the conviction that hope is perhaps *the most important source of human motivation*. In the twilight of my life, I believe this with increasing firmness.

I close, but not without noting the excellent photos and graphs that continually illustrate and enliven the text. They not only provide added value, but are central to the work. As true image semantics, they are indispensable, penetrating the inner human soul. This was already known by artists of ancient Greece, Egypt, and other Eastern civilisations, who decorated clay with scenes from myth, fantasy, and daily life, enticing the viewer to experience more than the words. In sum, whether or not the reader has a background in the behavioural sciences, I am sure that no one will regret reading this excellent book. It will not protect them from all pain, but it will prevent evil from taking over their spirit.

It is for me a great satisfaction that a former student of mine, to whom I had the fortune of teaching some psychology at the University of Madrid many years ago, has written a book such as this that the reader now has in hand.

José Luis Pinillos
Spanish Royal Academy
Madrid, Spain
December 2006

Introduction

S ometimes, as soon as physical symptoms of a contagious disease appear, we look for the possible cause. Most often we simply limit ourselves to seeking a remedy to cure those annoying symptoms that harass us. The same thing happens with any digestive tract dysfunction. We try, as quickly as possible, to find the right medicinal resource to soothe ourselves and to restore our health.

With major ailments, such as chronic and degenerative diseases, we intensely search for the therapy that may help us maintain, as much as possible, a normal lifestyle. Or if we suffer from an accident affecting any part of our body, we rush to heal ourselves and to restore normality if possible.

We refuse to feel disheartened by such circumstances. Our organism requires attention. If we have an accessible and quality health system, we approach a variety of health professionals who are willing to help, especially in the case of more severe illnesses. Sophisticated equipment becomes available to us in order to find a cure. Specialists present their opinions on how to heal the affected organism.

On the other hand, if we acknowledge that health does not only encompass the physical dimension but also our mental, and social well-being, the challenge is even greater. In this case, our state of health includes a three-dimensional scheme that includes the physical organism, social interaction, and our mental state, each of them playing a crucial role in health.

With this premise in mind, it becomes necessary to find adequate information to attain and maintain our health. And when our mental state is the focus, we must search for the best sources to learn whether or not we are reasonably well and whether we need help.

We know that everything touching our existence affects our lives positively or negatively. What we see or listen to, what we read, whether attentively or superficially... all im-

pacts us. As happens with diet and food ('we are what we eat'), so it is in the mental realm.

This volume, as is tradition in this publishing house, has been carefully prepared to offer the key elements to maintain a healthy mind. In choosing Dr. Julián Melgosa as the author, this house has not only considered his theoretical and academic background, but also his practical wisdom accumulated over years of experience in several countries. His style is also distinguished by an attitude of respect, without any type of prejudice, in all topics covered in his work.

As with any publication, we do not ignore this book's limitations—at times, it will become necessary to seek professional mental health care. But its value lies in that many problems arise from interpersonal situations of daily life, or from events that happen in our lives, all so well stated and described throughout the pages of this volume.

Rigorous information and prevention are the basic tools utilised by the author in each of the thematic units included in this book. The book is conceived as a contribution to society, which is today characterised by a continuous flooding of bad news, fraudulent events, threatening climatic variations, and a whole array of personal circumstances that affect mental functioning.

We are constantly expected to use our abilities to the maximum, and it continues to be the intention of the publishers, via this New Lifestyle series, to offer a service to a society that is increasingly being challenged. To this purpose, we recommend that the readers peruse and reflect upon these pages without any prejudice. In this way, as they walk through the book's content, they will realise that they have in their hands the formula for *Developing a Healthy Mind*.

The Editors

Chapter Summary

Learning to live

1

For the first thirty years of her life, Arlene thought that enjoying life was a matter of luck. Some have it, some don't. But based on her own experience, she has recently found out that everybody has much to choose in life. She has also learned that a great deal of happiness is attained through personal decision-making.

Arlene has learned a lot from a friend at work. For instance, now she knows that she can set her own mood, whether good or bad. When self-deprecating thoughts assail her and when she feels that everyone is better than herself, she rejects these ideas and thinks of the many good traits she possesses. Arlene can now deal positively with friends; she is able to pass happiness and courage onto them, instead of sadness and grief. When she relates to others, she does not transmit the dark and gloomy side of life, but a positive outlook.

She is still amazed at how beneficial it is to forget about oneself. When she feels sad or discouraged, she goes to her elderly neighbour and says: 'Anne, shall I run an errand for you? Can I clean your house?' Straight away, she starts helping the aged friend. When the task is finished, she feels wonderful!

Arlene is now convinced. Happiness is made by each person and she practises this every day.

Chapter Highlights

- Positive thinking must be an ongoing, permanent **style of mental activity**. It should also extend to all (or almost all) life aspects.

  - Self-esteem development comes from **two basic sources**: Persons we interact with and ourselves.

    - The **words we pronounce** and listen to end up carrying pleasure or pain, security or insecurity, closeness or rejection, encouragement or sadness.

    - Being happy consists of **choosing appropriate acting, feeling, and thinking options**. Grasping happiness is a matter of will.

    - Unlike conventional intelligence, which possesses a strong innate component, emotional intelligence is **susceptible to great changes and improvements**.

  - Hope is perhaps *the most important source of motivation*. This quality, together with optimism and the ability to keep good relations, are the major features to prevent mental illness.

- Mental health promotion can be carried out by **avoiding negative emotions** (hatred, envy, rage, frustration, pessimism, sadness, impatience, despair...) and **focusing on positive** emotions. Also, where appropriate, opting for **natural remedies**.

Experiential learning

True knowledge of life is not learned in school. Life is learned through living. The school of life contains more subject matter and usefulness than all educational programmes together. However, life events leave certain fundamental aspects untouched. This chapter targets basic topics necessary to attain skills required to live a reasonably healthy life.

We **learn to think adequately** (units 1 and 2) because thoughts are the tools to solve problems and to face situations wisely. Thoughts bring about emotions that may affect behaviour—the way we perceive the quality of our relationships, work and school achievement, and eventually our mental health and our happiness.

Learning to live presupposes a good understanding of how to obtain **holistic development** (unit 3). Human existence has multiple facets (physical, mental, social, spiritual) and all of them need a balanced and harmonious development. The excessive growth of one or two aspects without the corresponding development of the others may produce limited individuals who find great difficulty enjoying life.

Self-esteem development (unit 4) also adds to life's happiness. Everybody can nourish his or her self-concept as well as help others to shape a good self-esteem. This psychological trait affects almost every perspective of thinking and behaviour.

Learning to live means to a great extent enjoying everything in the surroundings. The **senses** (unit 5) are the channels that link us to the external world. All senses may become a source of pleasure and their enjoyment can contribute to mental health. **Sexuality** (unit 6) is an experience where all senses come together; an extraordinary gift where a man and a woman who love each other exchange sensual pleasure.

Life problems and difficulties cause tension that needs compensation with corresponding **relaxation** (unit 7). Sleep—an indispensable state—may not be sufficient. In order to free ourselves from mental and emotional burdens, we need to learn how to relax using adequate exercises and mental-rest techniques.

One cannot be reasonably happy without **learning how to communicate** with others (unit 8). Communication is the key factor to build up and maintain relationships. Hurting words can damage friendships in minutes, whilst wise words, used with the appropriate emotional tone, affirm people and contribute to lasting mental health.

Being **optimistic and living happy lives** (unit 9) can be learned. Whether by imitation, by habit or by inertia, people tend to make a pessimistic analysis of situations. This is a step towards depression and other mental disorders. Learning to be an optimist, to put aside what has been previously learned (unit 11), and to eliminate habits leading to our own or others' unhappiness (unit 12) are goals that everyone should seek.

It is well known today that conventional intelligence is insufficient. **Emotional intelligence** (13), on the other hand, is being seen as increasingly valuable as this type of intelligence is closely associated to happiness. In order to develop this basic characteristic, one needs to learn perseverance, self-motivation, control of impulses, mood self-regulation, understanding and trust in others. It is also necessary to live **hopefully** (unit 14) and to truly desire **happiness** (unit 15). Being happy is a choice and those in search of happiness must explore the path leading to it.

Lastly, **a healthy mind is linked to a healthy body**. In fact, both concepts share so much that body and mind (unit 10) are difficult to separate even when studied. Mental illnesses (unit 16) precede many bodily diseases. Therefore, preventing mental disorders (unit 17) avoids bodily ailments. It is true that there are very powerful barriers (unit 18) to the attainment of mental health, but being aware of these problems will help to overcome such barriers.

The power of thoughts

Although somewhat exaggerated because of its absolute tone, the maxim 'where there's a will there's a way' holds a great deal of truth. Athletes know that beating a record is not a matter of mere physical training, but of nourishing the mind and thought. Likewise, to a great extent, the behaviours we adopt, the emotional states we experience, and even the illnesses we suffer from find their root in thoughts and thinking.

The chart on the next page shows the effects of thoughts, how begin, and the results to which they lead. Environment (people, places, circumstances...), personality (optimism, suspiciousness, aggressiveness...), together with memories and past experiences are the stimuli resulting in thoughts. People process them at will, and these thoughts lead them to an eventual reaction that may become of great significance to their lives.

Mental content and its processing can be the origin of quite opposite consequences (see the chart again).

Thoughts and behaviour

With the exception of automatic reactions or repetitive acts, behaviours find their root in the preceding thoughts. Consider these three cases:

- Before going to the time-share agency, Mark never thought he would end up buying property. However, the environment, the kindness of the salespersons, the beautiful images of the apartments, the attractive financial plans, encouraged him to consider the option. Once at home, Mark reflected on the offer, fantasised on the exotic holidays he would be enjoying along with the idea of selling the property or passing it on to his children and grandchildren. He signed the contract two days later.

- Elaine went out for some refreshments together with two old girlfriends from high school. They thoroughly enjoyed talking about endless memories from the past as well as present life. Once at home, Elaine contrasted her life with that of her friends. She pondered the details, went over the conversation, and concluded that her friends were luckier than herself. Soon she was taken by a strong feeling of sadness, mixed with disappointment about her own accomplishments. This mood stayed with Elaine for several days.

- Victoria enjoyed a good relationship with everyone. However, a few months back, she had had

→ **Thoughts can lead...**

From...	To...
• *reconciliation*	• *aggression*
• *restitution*	• *theft*
• *love*	• *hate*
• *peace and confidence*	• *anxiety*
• *happiness*	• *sadness*
• *a bright smile*	• *a headache*
• *general well-being*	• *sweat and palpitations*
• *energy to work*	• *back ache*

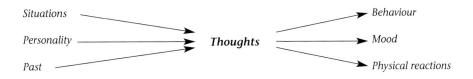

The origins and influence of thoughts

Situations ⟶
Personality ⟶ ***Thoughts*** ⟶ Behaviour
Past ⟶ ⟶ Mood
⟶ Physical reactions

a serious confrontation with her brother and they stopped talking to each other. She refused to reconcile as she had been deeply hurt by her brother's offence. When, in her mind she rehearsed the moment of the row, she experienced anger, her heart beat wildly and at times she felt nauseous.

The three cases above show a clear connection between thought and behaviour (or mood). What would have happened if Mark, Elaine and Victoria had changed the course of their thoughts? Their conduct would have probably been very different!

In the end, everyone is in charge of their own thoughts. And, therefore, everybody can, with more or less difficulty, harbour, channel, elaborate, reduce or reject their thoughts.

GET USED TO CONTROLLING YOUR OWN THOUGHTS

In this way you will avoid inappropriate behaviours, will adapt better to situations, and will enjoy better physical and mental health. In sum, when you are governing your thoughts you are building up your own happiness. (See also page 146).

How can you identify your negative thoughts? How can you know whether they will lead you to an undesirable conduct or mood?

In order to avoid adverse thinking, choose a lifestyle that is guided by universal principles and values, such as:

Honesty
Responsibility
Justice
Respect for others
Integrity
Truthfulness

Those adopting these ideals will end up harbouring positive and edifying thoughts in a natural and spontaneous way. They will also experience the positive effect of this type of thinking.

 self-help

TRACKING SITUATIONS, EMOTIONS AND THOUGHTS

As a preventive measure, it might be very useful for you to identify and control emotions as well as undesirable thinking. If you wish to avoid an undesirable behaviour (for example, getting angry at your family, being unable to concentrate or becoming nervous), try the following clinical psychology procedure:

- For two or three days, keep a **written record** of a sample of five or six daily situations.
- Following the example given below, write down circumstances, emotions and thoughts.
- Check the list of positive and negative emotions included in the table in order to verify the emotions you have experienced (lower part of the table).

This exercise will help you know yourself better and gain practice in the management of your thoughts. Harbour positive thinking and positive emotions and reject the negative ones. You will find additional ideas in the next two units.

	Situations	Emotions	Thoughts
1.	*A fight with my sister-in-law*	*Tension*	*'This woman never gives up'*
2.	*Observing Charlie's play*	*Pride*	*'If it weren't for my children...'*
3.	*Someone jumps the queue...*	*Anger*	*'I would slap him'*
4.	*Irene finished the report on time*	*Joy*	*'I'd like to give her a good present'*

Negative emotions	Positive emotions
Anger	*Understanding*
Envy	*Generosity*
Aggression	*Acceptance*
Fear	*Trust*
Sadness	*Happiness*
Frustration	*Patience*
Agitation	*Serenity*

The physical benefits of a positive mind

David Sobel and Robert Ornstein (2000) obtained empirical evidence on the benefits of positive thinking, optimism, and the sense of personal control over the following areas of health:

- **Immune system.** Human saliva contains chemicals that protect us from infections. The level of protection offered by these substances becomes most effective on days when persons feel happy and satisfied as compared with sad days.
- **Cancer.** In one study, a sample of patients with cancer of the pancreas was taught to think in a positive and edifying manner. They also received instruction on relaxation techniques. The antibodies of patients under instruction were found to be much more active than those in patients who had not been taught to think positively and to relax.
- **Longevity.** A group of elderly folk living in a retirement home were given the opportunity to make small choices—type of breakfast, the day to watch a certain movie, etc.). Having the ability to choose made them happier and more satisfied. One year later, the mortality index of the participants was 50% less than those who had not been given options to choose from. (See box on page 73).
- **Recovery from surgery.** Data was collected on the personality of patients who had undergone cardiac surgery. According to the results, the group was then divided into optimists and pessimists. Optimists took less time to recover from the intervention, suffered from fewer complications, returned to their posts of work more quickly and retook their hobbies up earlier than the pessimists.
- **General health.** Participants were asked to create a list of positive and negative events that, in their estimation, would be happening in their lives over the next few years. Their general health was assessed two years later. Researchers found that those looking at their future optimistically showed fewer symptoms of illness than the pessimists.

THOUGHTS ARE NOT THE ANSWER TO EVERYTHING

Positive thinking is an excellent option in order to preserve mental health and reach goals. But let us not think that every problem can be solved with positive thinking. Remember the following limitations:

1. Optimistic thinking is inappropriate in certain contexts: The death of a dear one, a natural disaster or a medical test (see pages 248, 244 and 282) result showing probable cancer.
2. Optimistic thinking is impossible in the midst of shock or a very critical situation.
3. Optimistic thinking may sometimes become deceiving and make us lose the perspective of certain sad realities.

There are times when we need to be prepared to suffer. In the middle of those circumstances we can wait (time heals a lot), trust (faith in God can be a source of support), and find relief with the presence of a dear one.

Gems of Ancient Wisdom

'Do not those who plot evil go astray? But those who plan what is good find love and faithfulness' (Proverbs 14:22).

1.02
Positive thinking

Positive thinking results

Why is there so much variation in the way persons react? Why do similar circumstances bring about different reactions? To a great extent, this is due to the fact that different persons perceive and process information in very different ways. Markus gets upset when it rains: 'Rain makes me nervous; umbrellas are a nuisance, traffic slows down, people slip and hurt themselves...' On the other hand, Lucy assesses the fact differently: 'I like the smell of wet soil, rain cleans the air, birds are happier, and plants and flowers grow.' Their respective attitudes touch their work, family, friends, and everyday events. As a result, Markus experiences the bitter side of things and Lucy enjoys the sweetness of life.

Healthy and optimistic thinking:

- Causes good mood.
  - Helps maintain optimal social interactions.
  - Increases school achievement and work performance.
  - Blocks anxiety.
  - Enhances self-esteem.
  - Reduces pain and other somatic symptoms.
  - Strengthens the immune system.
- Helps patients recover from illness and from surgical treatments.

How to think positively

To reject negative thoughts and substitute them with alternative positive options constitutes a good way to obtain a positive thinking style. Pessimistic thoughts tend to take over the person automati-

AVOID BEING IRRESPONSIBLE!

Being optimistic does not mean being careless and irresponsible (see page 151). Certain people fall into the habit of taking things too lightly with the excuse of avoiding worry.

Being an optimist means not being overwhelmed with negative interpretations but being able to transform problems into challenges and to understand that something good may come out of adversity.

• **Positive thinking about people and the environment.** Put on your 'rose-coloured glasses' and look around. Not everything is perfect, but there are beautiful things and pleasant experiences. Do not grow suspicious of other people. Trust them and respect them and make efforts to feel affection towards them. Try to understand the problems of others. Help them and you will see how your attitude becomes sweeter.

Many are dominated by **irrational beliefs**—ideas without logical sense that are able to cause unhappiness and even disorders. For example:

continued on the next page

cally and without following any logical pattern. It is therefore important to learn to identify such thoughts and to change the thinking style (see the Self-help box on page 23).

Positive thinking must be an ongoing, permanent style of mental activity. It should also extend to all (or almost all) life aspects. The following areas need consideration:

• **Positive thinking about oneself.** Try and avoid building your self-concept by comparing yourself with TV stars and individuals from public life. They all portray unreal images. Accept your limitations and do something to improve these. Above all, do not forget to underline your values and abilities. Stop and reject self-deprecating thoughts.

• **Positive thinking about the past.** The past cannot be changed. Accept it even though it may contain unpleasant events. But do not blame the past for your present difficulties. That is useless. Never get obsessed with a disagreeable past. And as far as past positive events and anecdotes, remember them and enjoy them. Your attitude will improve and turn more positive.

• **Positive thinking about the future.** The future can be changed. Your attitude today affects tomorrow's events. When you think with confidence and hope about tomorrow, you are increasing the probability of a much more successful future. And if something negative approaches, make plans now to prevent it instead of becoming anxious.

RESEARCH RESULTS

Worry and chronic fatigue

A team of researchers (Taillefer *et al.*, 2003) at the University of Montreal (Quebec, Canada), compared a group of 45 patients diagnosed with chronic fatigue with a group of 45 multiple sclerosis patients. They studied their illness anxiety.

The result of psychometric tests showed that worry levels in chronically fatigued patients were significantly higher than their counterparts.

It was not clear whether the excessive worry was the cause or the effect for chronic fatigue. In any case, it is not a good thing to fall into the fear of illness, as there seems to be a risk of suffering from chronic fatigue (see page 188).

- 'We are permanently surrounded by dangers and risks; it is natural to always feel worried and fearful.'

- 'Unhappy and unfortunate people can do nothing to improve their situation.'

- 'In order for me to be happy and to live in peace with myself, I must be loved and receive approval from everyone who knows me.'

- 'There is always a perfect solution to every problem and if that solution is not realised, disastrous consequences follow.'

The above statements are fallacies and those living by them may experience psychological pain and even unhappiness. Make every effort to identify and analyse your favourite irrational beliefs. Reason logically in order to reject these thoughts and accept better alternatives.

Hope as a factor in good thinking

Filling our mind with spiritual thoughts and themes can be a safe way to attain mental peace. A peaceful conscience and a serene mind bring about an optimal mood. Meditation in the sacred messages contained in the Bible produces mental peace (read the quotes included in the following tables several times). Try praying to God and tell him of your painful experiences. Trust in God. He will take care of you.

RESEARCH RESULTS

Positive emotions enhance defences

Sheldon Cohen and his team (2003) at Carnegie Mellon University interviewed 334 healthy individuals to ascertain their level of optimism in regards to their strength, well-being and inner peace. They also assessed depression, anxiety and hostility. Next, they administered doses of the human rhinovirus (the virus most frequently causing a cold) via their nostrils.

The most pessimistic individuals had the highest propensity to contract the infection and manifest the symptoms—congestion, cough and headache. On the other hand, optimists managed to successfully resist the virus.

Sayings of Jesus

'Do not let your hearts [thoughts] be troubled. Trust in God; trust also in me' (John 14:1).

'The good man brings good things out of the good stored up in his heart, and the evil man brings evil things out of the evil stored up in his heart. For out of the overflow of his heart his mouth speaks' (Luke 6:45).

Gems of Ancient Wisdom

'Cast your cares on the LORD and he will sustain you; [...] I trust in you' (Psalm 55:22-23).

'The cords of death entangled me, the anguish of the grave came upon me; I was overcome by trouble and sorrow. Then I called on the name of the LORD: "O LORD, save me!"' (Psalm 116:3-4).

'In my anguish I cried to the LORD, and he answered by setting me free. The LORD is with me; I will not be afraid. What can man do to me?' (Psalm 118:5-6).

MIND CONTROL

People carry a general tendency to either positive or negative thinking. This tendency depends, to a great extent, on the continuous and automatic inner dialogue style that takes place within the person.

In order to eliminate adverse thinking habits and search for positive alternatives to help solve situations, it is absolutely necessary to know the type of dialogue within ourselves.

Consider the following thoughts and their alternative options. Then think of your own typical mental reactions and write them down together with a good thinking alternative:

Negative self-dialogue	Alternative
'All this is horrible'	'It is not all that bad. It could be worse'
'This is useless'	'There must be something good...'
'This man is a pain'	'I can learn something from this man'
'My cold will end up in pneumonia'	'I'll soon recover from my cold'

TEST YOURSELF ::

To know if you are optimist or pessimist, answer True or False to the following statements, based on whether you agree or disagree with them:

Am I an optimist or a pessimist?	T	F
1. I like to think about pleasant things of the past.		
2. I like to look at the future in hope.		
3. I have a tendency to look at the positive side of everything.		
4. It is good to bring some humour to tragic situations.		
5. My past has been a disaster.		
6. I am unlucky.		
7. I bring doom to everyone.		
8. It is always safe to mistrust others.		

Scoring:
Count 1 point for each T of statements 1-4.
Count 1 point for each F of statements 5-8.

Interpretation:

7-8 points	5-6 points	3-4 points	0-2 points
Definitely optimist.	Tendency to optimism.	Tendency to pessimism.	Definitely pessimist.

1.03
Whole person development

An indivisible whole

Human beings were considered in terms of dualism in the past. It was understood that man was made up of two distinct components, one physical (body) and the other immaterial (soul). It was also understood that the soul had life in itself even after the body's death. In fact, many religions today teach this idea of the immortality of the soul (which is foreign to the Bible). Only Judaism and some minority Christian denominations, together with the greatest theologians, understand the nature of man in a **holistic and unitary sense**.

Current science also sustains the idea of man as a natural unit. Back in the early twentieth century, Medicine Nobel Prize winner **Alexis Carrel** wrote: 'Soul and body are inventions of our own observational methods. Those methods divided an indivisible entity into two.'

The **psychosomatic nature of illness**, the body-mind fusion, the narrow line between physical and mental functions, and the neurological explanations of human performance, together with the emotional and spiritual facets, are evidence of a united and indivisible nature.

This idea is not incompatible with the existence of different human dimensions, as is explained in the box, pages 26-27. Even the Gospels refer to four dimensions in human development.

Very briefly, the Gospel narrative summarises the growth of young Jesus of Nazareth (the prototype of the ideal human being) listing wisdom (intellectual development), stature (physical development), favour with God (spiritual development) and favour with men (social development).

Balanced and harmonious development

If you wish for a life of total health, choose to nourish each and every one of its facets. This will

> **Gems of Ancient Wisdom**
>
> *'And Jesus grew in wisdom and stature, and in favour with God and men' (Luke 2:52).*

also help you develop as a person and increase your potential. Avoid focusing on only one aspect; otherwise, you may end up with a significant imbalance.

- **Take care of the physical aspects of your life.** The physical dimension is basic and affects all the others. Exercise every day, especially if your job is sedentary. Sleep sufficient hours and eat rationally. Seek contact with nature and do not use substances known to be dangerous to your body.

- **Cultivate your mental development.** This is perhaps the most important facet, as the brain (mind) directs all aspects of existence. If your professional activity is physical, compensate it with mental tasks—reading, study, critical analysis of issues, and participation in deep conversations. General control of your thoughts is of even greater importance. To attain this, use your mind to develop clear ideas, distinct objectives, and get into the habit of making effective decisions. Nourish positive thinking, control your

character through your thinking, improve your interpersonal relationships through loving and respecting others. All responsible behaviours develop in your mind.

- **Nourish your social relationships.** The joys and pains of life are magnified by the effect of relationships. It is therefore most important that you devote time and effort to strengthen links with your family, friends, neighbours, relatives, and peers. Good social relationships are also a safeguard that prevent a variety of mental disorders.

- **Do not forget the spiritual dimension.** When you seriously consider this dimension, you will be reaching the highest level of personal development. In the area of morality, reflect on good and evil actions. In aesthetics, exercise a taste for beauty, art and even for daily cleanliness and orderliness. Lastly, in the religious area, search for God, reconcile with your Creator and enjoy a beautiful and lasting relationship, which is the result of the association with Deity.

RESEARCH RESULTS

Social factors affect physical health

David Williams' sociological study (2003) at the University of Michigan (USA) confirmed that males have a higher probability of suffering from illnesses and premature death than females (this is a well-known fact). However, the contribution of this study has to do with the reasons for the difference, which have nothing to do with biology or genetics but rather with **beliefs and expectations** rooted in society:

- Unemployment and lack of security at work produce in men a stronger feeling of failure (with risk to contract illness) than in women. This is due to societal and institutional expectations that men will provide income for the maintenance of the family.
- Professional advancement and stress (with the corresponding health risks) affect men more than women due to societal expectations.
- Men run greater risk than women of getting trapped by and suffering from the health hazards of chemical substances, especially alcohol and drugs. This is because society tolerates and facilitates addictions in men more so than in women.

This study points at the need to eliminate prejudices and social differences through an educational system based on scientific data and not on traditional stereotypes.

A COMPLETE HUMAN BEING INVENTORY

The holistic and indivisible nature of the human being is finding increasingly greater scientific and philo-sophical support. Yet, it seems clear that there are several dimensions that meet in the person.

PHYSICAL DIMENSION

Human beings possess the necessary resources to maintain a healthful balance.

Our organism is programmed with a number of **biological clocks** that indicate the beginning of organic processes. For instance, when some-one reaches puberty, endocrinal glands initiate the secretion of estro-gens in girls and of androgens in boys. This triggers a sequence of physical changes that takes place at the right time for each individ-ual.

The physical dimension is so basic that some end up believing that the human being is only physics and chemistry. This may seem an exaggeration, but it entails a principle that cannot be discarded. **Good, healthy habits** (physical exercise, adequate rest, balanced di-et, contact with nature…) are at the heart of a satisfactory life in all its aspects.

MENTAL DIMENSION

This dimension is even more complex than the physical one. It is rather intri-cate and therefore less known. Partly because of its complexity, partly be-cause of its exclusiveness to the human being, it is the most valued di-mension. It was mental life that triggered traditional philosophies to search for the 'soul' somewhere external to the person's body.

Today, it is known that the mind (located in the brain) has a **physi-cal substrate** and controls all behaviours of the person. In fact, the brain is made up of one hundred thousand million neurons or nerve cells that carry information, initiate and maintain mental processes, retrieve memories, process data… Any mental activity of the human organism is associated with the work of these neurons.

The interconnections of this immense network of nerve cells are al-most infinite, and the more connections are made possible, the more mental capacity will be attained. **Continuous mental activity** to strength-en existing neural connections and to establish new ones is therefore rec-ommended.

SOCIAL DIMENSION

Paradoxical as it may sound in the overpopulated world in which we live, there are deficiencies in the social dimension. This is so not only because of the **lonely** feeling experienced by millions of people in the big cities, but also due to the loss of family **identity** and to lack of social solidarity.

It is very important to understand that human beings, social by nature, are not really human until they integrate fully in their communities. The other dimensions feed from the social dimension, as it provides a unique source of neural connections, a breeze of continuous 'oxygen' to the body and a means to the challenging demands of **loving** relationships.

SPIRITUAL DIMENSION

First, it should be noted that spirituality and religiosity are not synonymous. Spiritual persons may not necessarily be religious, or vice versa.

'What is thought, that strange being, which lives in the depths of ourselves without consuming a measurable quantity of chemical energy? Is it related to the known forms of energy? Could it be a constituent of our universe, ignored by the physicists, but infinitely more important than light? The mind is hidden within the living matter, completely neglected by physiologists and economists, almost unnoticed by physicians. And yet it is the most colossal power of this world.' (Alexis Carrel, Physiology and Medicine Nobel Prize Winner, *Man, The Unknown*, p. 64, New York: Harper & Brothers, 1939).

Although embedded in the mental function, the spiritual dimension deserves separate treatment. **Moral, aesthetic, and religious functions** can be considered part of spirituality. The spiritual human facet, relative to the discernment between good and evil (moral), beautiful and ugly (aesthetics), and the relationship with God or transcendence (religion), is an undeniable component that has been present in all civilisations.

1.04
Self-esteem

How does self-esteem affect behaviour?

An adequate self-esteem brings psychological well-being to the person: personal worth, safety, self-respect and strength to face challenges. Those with the right self-value achieve the highest attainment at work, in the family, with friends and in their communities. On the other hand, those with low self-esteem feel inadequate to face problems and are bound to fail.

An impoverished self-esteem affects people adversely in different ways. It may:

- Cause depression.
- Affect school and work achievement.
- Deteriorate interpersonal relationships.
- Lead to anorexia and bulimia.
- Be related to the use of alcohol and drugs.

Traditionally, it has been said that social recognition and status are primordial sources for the nourishment of self-esteem. Thus having intelligence, wealth, a good house, a luxury car and a prestigious job are sources of self-esteem. However, recent studies point to non self-centred motivation, more specifically, the willingness to help others and the possession of ideals and cherished values (see the box on the adjoining page) as more proven sources of self-esteem.

HOW TO SUPPORT CHILDREN'S SELF-ESTEEM

Children are especially vulnerable to feelings of inferiority because they place too much emphasis on comparison with their friends and schoolmates. Other children are perceived as stronger, more intelligent, more attractive and with more resources than themselves.

The next suggestions are useful to enhance children's self-esteem:

- Use frequent words of approval and encouragement.
- Be positive in your messages.
- Avoid comparisons.
- Do not tease them on their limitations or defects.
- Prevent the development of undue guilt.
- Decide to be in a good mood.

The best sources of self-esteem

Jennifer Crocker, a researcher from the University of Michigan (USA), conducted a self-esteem study (Crocker, 2002) among 642 college students. Many subjects stated that their self-esteem came from their academic achievement. Interestingly, those who tracked academics as their source of self-esteem did not have the best grades. This can be explained by the fact that the need to feed self-esteem with personal achievement makes people more apprehensive and doubtful of their success.

The study concluded that the best sources of self-esteem are activities targeted at others. In other words, both self-esteem and achievements will be greater if, for example, students focus on **high ideals** like serving humanity, instead of short-term and personal ideas such as obtaining good grades. Likewise, self-esteem improves when part of our effort is targeted at **helping and supporting others** instead of only ourselves.

How to attain healthy self-esteem

It is important to know how to develop self-esteem, as this improves one's ability to be happy. Self-esteem development comes from two basic sources: Persons we interact with and ourselves. Messages from people close to us, even incidental comments and non-verbal indicators, constantly shape our self-esteem. Here are a few pieces of advice to enhance a balanced development of self-esteem in others:

- **Emphasise positive features in others.** Words of approval for the correct actions of others can enhance self-esteem. Praise and congratulations (which must be true and well earned) do not only contribute to the self-esteem of the recipient, but also of the one who offers them.

- **Recognise the special needs of everyone.** There are significant differences among people, especially between men and women. For example, men appreciate positive comments about their professional ability and their character traits, and they hope for demonstrations of respect. On the other hand, women welcome demonstrations of affection and comments on their looks, tact, and sensitivity. Of course, there are always exceptions.

- **Do not joke with or mock the other person.** Those inclined to low self-esteem suffer greatly when others tease them. Try to joke only with those who know how to take it.

- **Provide family support.** Feeling loved and accepted by family members anchors one's esteem and smooths out many self-concept deficiencies. Having children contributes (especially in women) to a favourable feeling leading to healthy self-esteem.

- **Ask for forgiveness when appropriate.** If the opponent feels offended, his/her self-esteem will suffer.

Self-esteem may also be enhanced on a personal level. Try the following suggestions to help yourself develop self-esteem:

- **Keep fit and healthy.** Sports and diet benefit health and make you feel well with yourself.

- **Look at your strong and positive features.** Do not forget your personal achievements and be aware of the areas that need improvement.

- **Be in control of your thoughts.** Stop and reject self-deprecating mental messages. Think rationally of yourself.

- **Forgive yourself.** Do not continuously blame yourself for the past mistakes or problems that

Self-esteem in the couple

The following areas are affected by the self-esteem of each of the partners in the couple:

- **General mutual relationship.** Daily relationship between a man and a woman may deteriorate in the presence of a deficient self-image. Dialogue, decision-making, and relations with others outside the couple become difficult and fill the relationship with barriers that make the couple feel dissatisfied.
- **Sexuality.** Women with low self-esteem feel sexually exploited and believe that the only purpose of sexual intercourse is to satisfy the man's desire. Men attempt to compensate their sense of inferiority by adopting a macho attitude.

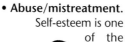

- **Abuse/mistreatment.** Self-esteem is one of the

most significant factors in family violence (see page 222). The husband with low self-esteem practises violence against his wife in order to set up greater control and establish power and dominance. The victim with a low self-esteem submits herself thinking that she does not deserve better treatment.

- **Jealousy.** Unfounded jealousy (page 204) in the couple is frequent among those with feelings of inferiority. Men and women with a low self-concept become obsessed with their partner's infidelity, even when there is no indication of such behaviour.
- **Guilt.** Feelings of guilt (page 164) aggravate low self-esteem, as it represents a source of moral reproach.

A woman sincerely praised by her husband feels good and enjoys positive self-esteem that allows her to function well in the mentioned areas. A husband admired by his wife can build up sufficient self-esteem to nourish and develop their mutual relationship. **Forgiveness** and **willingness to reconcile** in case of conflict also favour self-esteem and mutual admiration.

you may have caused others, especially if you have already taken appropriate steps to resolve them.

- **Find support in your family.** As seen before, good family relationships provide the ideal context in which to grow and develop a healthy self-esteem.
- **Choose your friends.** Avoid those given to criticise others and make friends with those who are positive and affirming to their neighbours.

- **Revive your success.** List your past achievements and reflect on them. Read your list often and review it once in a while.
- **Nourish the spiritual dimension.** God cares for you. Even if everyone rejects you, God does not. The Bible calls those who accept God and his salvation 'chosen people, a royal priesthood, a holy nation, a people belonging to God' (1 Peter 2:9).

EXAGGERATED SELF-ESTEEM

Although low self-esteem affects many people, an exaggerated concept of oneself is a danger that can become pathological (see the unit 'Narcissism' on page 172). If you have the tendency to overestimate your abilities, decide to follow the advice of the apostle Paul: 'Do not be arrogant' (Romans 11:20).

Sayings of Jesus

'Are not five sparrows sold for two pennies? Yet not one of them is forgotten by God. Indeed, the very hairs of your head are all numbered. Don't be afraid; you are worth more than many sparrows' (Luke 12:6-7).

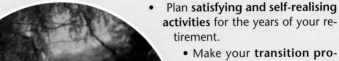

DO NOT FORGET TO PREPARE YOUR SELF-ESTEEM FOR RETIREMENT

Many make good financial provision for retirement, but only a few understand the **risk of suffering lowered self-esteem during old age.** The transition from an active professional life to retirement causes an important loss of self-esteem in many, especially in those whose job was the only source of self-esteem.

Try the following counsels to prevent deterioration of self-concept:

- Plan **satisfying and self-realising activities** for the years of your retirement.
  - Make your **transition progressive**, leaving your profession gradually, taking several years if possible.
  - Make sure to carry out a **variety** of activities. If you were to put all your strength in a single task, you would be unprotected if that activity were to fail.

(See also page 176).

self-help

TO KNOW THE IMAGE OTHERS HAVE OF YOU

As with other qualities that are learned in concert with other people, self-help becomes especially strong if practised with others. Try the following exercise, which will help you discover the image you portray. This will also give you sufficient information to usefully channel your behaviour.

Together with your partner or in a small group where everyone knows one another, follow these steps:

1. Distribute blank sheets of paper with the name of each participant. Everyone will have as many sheets as individuals in the group (except his/her own).
2. Participants write down on their papers positive qualities and traits of the person whose name is written on the sheet.
3. Notes may be classified in positive character qualities, personality qualities, skills, conversation, way of treating others…
4. Notes are to be written in capital letters to preserve anonymity.
5. Notes must be positive. Negative attributes do not belong to this exercise.
6. When all annotations are finished, each participant receives the sheets containing his or her name and reads them silently.
7. The activity may stop here or continue with a second part where each reads aloud the notes others have written and there are general comments.

1.05
Enjoy your senses

Senses are the communication channels between a person and the outer world. They provide very useful information, which is the foundation of our learning. They also warn us instantly of possible environmental dangers and provide endless mechanisms of personal protection.

In addition to their utilitarian functions, senses provide satisfaction, pleasure, and physical and psychological well-being. Observing a forest in the midst of rocky mountains, listening to a concert, enjoying the beauty and aroma of flowers at dusk, tasting an exotic fruit shake, or feeling the ocean waves caress our back at the beach... are all experiences that contribute to our mental health.

We will do well to enjoy our senses in order to attain mental balance. But, be careful with extremes! Too much pleasure may make us lose our sensibility or may even hurt us. (See the box on the bottom of this page).

Vision

Your sense of vision is the greatest window to the outer world. It also provides the most of all the sens-

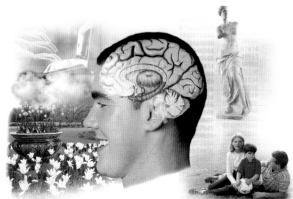

es. Through vision one can contemplate the beautiful things in the environment. Vision can be entertaining and bring about mental peace, especially when contemplating things in nature, in their original state. Make plans to go out to the country. Surround yourself with natural environments and use time to enjoy the sea, trees, plants, the skies, clouds, mountains, rivers, animals...

The city dweller can also enjoy a clean and balanced urban landscape, through buildings, monuments, art and other man-made objects. The **mix of shapes and colours** will directly affect your mood (see the adjoining page).

It is not always possible to surround ourselves with beautiful things. Sometimes, we will be forced to witness unpleasant landscapes and situations. The effect that these have upon our minds depends on ourselves. Although we will not always see happy people and a clean environment, we can supply happiness and personal cleanliness, as well as a healthy acceptance and understanding that life in this world is not perfect.

ABUSING THE PLEASURE OF THE SENSES...

Enjoy the senses. It is right and necessary. But if you fall into excesses, the pleasurable feeling will fade away until it disappears. Consider the following examples:

- **Enjoy your sense of hearing.** Listen to music that uplifts you and brings you satisfaction. Do it at sufficient but not excessive volume. **Excessively loud music will deaden your sensitivity** and may permanently damage your auditory system.

- **Enjoy your sense of taste.** Choose a delicious and healthy dish. Eat with appetite and in the right amount. This will please you. Your body will welcome it and it will be profitable. But **if you eat excessively** in search of repeated satisfaction, **your perception will become saturated** and you will lose the pleasure. Besides, the stomach may refuse to accept it. Determine the ideal amount of food you need to attain maximum pleasure. Then set up your limit.

COLOURS FOR A BETTER LIFE

Light and colour are basic elements in life. Colours can relax you and stimulate you. Thus they affect your be-haviour. It is known that certain colours generate sensations that help gland secretions and variations in blood pressure. This is called colour therapy.

Choose the appropriate colours. Allow them to surround you or search in nature for those tones that help you enhance your mood:

Orange
A mix of red and yellow, it softens the strength of red without cancelling it. It favours optimism and activity. An energetic, brilliant and cordial colour.

Yellow
Because of its brightness, it is ideal for the depressed person. It is inviting when combined with some red tone. Its liveliness entices optimism. Too much of it, like that of light, may produce fatigue.

Red
Warm colour that favours adrenaline secretion, raises blood pleasure and stimulates circulation. It entices the senses, causing one to remain active and dynamic. It is recommended for shy people or those experiencing a low mood.

Green
Made up of blue and yellow, it is a very balanced colour, and produces a serene mood. It is nature's colour, favouring rest and serving as an antidote against stress.

Blue
Cold colour that invites serenity and relaxation. It reduces blood pressure and slows down metabolism. It is advisable for persons who feel nervous to surround them-selves with blue-tone objects.

Black
It actually is the absence of colour. It portrays sobriety, limited tones and therefore discipline and self-determina-tion. Black causes sorrow, since, like all dark colours, it limits space and makes it appear smaller. This colour may produce dis-comfort and even tiredness.

Purple
It is widely utilised in religious contexts, as it invites silence, serenity, and concentration. Excessive exposure to this colour may cause depression as this is an intimidating colour.

White
Unlike black, white contains all colours in the same proportion. It is therefore equated to balance. It makes defects obvious and offers the impression of purity and simplicity.

An aquarium kept at home with a variety of fish and living plants may offer the ideal combination to nour-ish your visual sense fully.

Hearing

Nature provides a source of spirit-soothing sounds. A river or waterfall, the wind, the rain and the singing of birds... are all examples of relaxing sounds that bring about not only pleasure, but also serenity.

Music is also a blessing to mental health. Since ancient times (see the Biblical Example box below), music has been utilised to lift up the spirit, bring about mental peace or set up a specific emotional state (see the box at the bottom of this page).

Music also affects a number of physiological functions, such as blood pressure, the dilation of the respiratory pathways and the production of hormones.

Under experimental conditions, several effects of music upon patients with a variety of ailments have been observed. Results were amazing (see the adjoining page).

BIBLICAL EXAMPLE

David plays for Saul

The Bible contains the first case of **musical therapy** in the beginning of Israel's monarchy (around the year 1000 BC). **Saul**, the first king of Israel, was rejected by God because of his open disobedience. This circumstance caused him serious symptoms of mental disorder. His counsellors recommended that he search for a musician who could play good music on the harp at times when his spirits were down. The chosen one was young David, the future king, who alternated between his job of shepherd and that of musical therapist. The result: 'David would take his harp and play. Then relief would come to Saul; he would feel better.'

The full story is in 1 Samuel, chapters 15 and 16.

 self-help

THERAPEUTIC MUSICAL SUGGESTIONS

Music for relaxation
- Debussy's *Claire de Lune*
- Albinoni's *Adagio*
- Vivaldi's *Oboe Concerto*

Stimulating Music
- Verdi's *Triumphal March*
- Handel's *Water Music*
- Mendelssohn's *Midsummer Night's Dream*
- Tchaikovsky's *Swan Lake*
- Elgar's *Pomp and Circumstance March No. 1*

Music to sleep
- Massenet's *Meditation of Thais*
- *Nocturnal* (by several composers)
- Brahms' *Cradle Song*

Music to soothe anxiety
- Vivaldi's *Four Seasons*
- Rodrigo's *Aranjuez Concerto*
- Mozart's *Linz Symphony*

Healthy effects of music

There are many studies showing the positive effect of music upon various areas of health. These are a few examples.

Music has been utilised in clinical settings in the following cases:

- **Pain reduction** in geriatric patients with **arthritis** (McCaffrey, 2003). Participants in this study were administered a 20-minute musical session every day and they were compared to a control group exposed to environmental silence during the same time. The elderly people who had been under the music condition attained 66% pain reduction according to themselves, and 50% reduction according to the researchers, as compared to the control group that experienced pain at the same level.

- **Stress treatment** of elementary teachers (Cheek *et al.*, 2003). A team of researchers carried out a comparison among teachers undergoing clinical psychological treatment for stress. Half the group received psychotherapy accompanied by music. The other half received the same intervention but without music. The first group achieved stress reduction in a significantly greater extent than the second group.

- **Control of anxious responses to coronary angiography** (Campbell *et al.*, 2003). This study was carried out at the Kingston General Hospital (Ontario, Canada). Music was present before, during, and after the performance of coronary angiography. The experiment confirmed the soothing effect of music against the anxiety and pain that normally go along with this procedure.

- **Treatment of migraine in children** (Nickel *et al.*, 2002). This study established the effectiveness of musicotherapy for the psychiatric treatment of children suffering from migraine. This was especially manifested in the case of outpatients.

- **Anxiety reduction** and **increase of well-being in children** diagnosed with cancer (Barrera *et al.*, 2002). The study took place in a Toronto (Canada) hospital among children with cancer exhibiting hospital anxiety. Young patients were exposed to interactive musical parts. Their mood was assessed. Parents also evaluated the playful behaviour of their children. Both evaluations showed the positive effect of music.

Taste

Taste has a basic protective function: It alerts us of food in bad condition and may even guide the nutritional needs of someone suffering from malnutrition. Moreover, taste is a **source of pleasure**.

In order to take maximum advantage of this sense when you eat, try the following things:

- **Be moderate.** The secret of enjoying food is to eat moderate amounts. Gourmets preserve an exquisite palate because they know to stop eating on time.

- **Practise simplicity.** Exercise the taste of simple flavours. Salty, sweet, sour or spicy foods in excess saturate taste, leading to lack of sensitivity and preventing the enjoyment of natural and simple food.

- **Eat slowly.** Chew slowly; eat in a relaxed mood, with good company and without any rush. This will help you enjoy and notice the satiation point on time.

- **Enjoy each and every bite.** Experience the ingredients and the variety of tastes and colours.

- **Focus on your meal.** Avoid reading or watching TV while eating. It will help you enjoy your food to the maximum.

- **Integrate other senses.** Besides taste, make sure that food is presented beautifully (sight) and that it provides a good aroma (olfaction). When you eat fruit, for example, take advantage of tactile influences: hold the piece and experience the sensation of its shape, texture and temperature.

- **Avoid noxious substances.** There are products that provide the sensation of enjoyment but have adverse effects. Alcoholic beverages, for instance, may be enjoyable, but their side effects are definitely unhealthy.

Gems of Ancient Wisdom

'Do not gaze at wine when it is red, when it sparkles in the cup, when it goes down smoothly! In the end it bites like a snake and poisons like a viper. Your eyes will see strange sights and your mind imagine confusing things' (Proverbs 23:31-35).

Touch

The sense of touch reaches all corners of the body surface. It is extremely useful to alert us of any danger coming from extreme environmental temperature or direct contact. It may also be a source of pleasure, as its coverage is so extensive.

There are many **pleasurable sensations that promote physical and mental health** and are directly related to the tactile sense: water baths, sunbathing, wind, breeze… The use of these sources of life and pleasure should not be discounted. Instead, they can be promoted in a systematic way, since many common lifestyles tend to reduce these options.

Touch also contributes to **emotional closeness** and to deepening relationships. Holding the hands of your partner or child when taking a walk shows closeness, acceptance, commitment and enjoyment. Use touch in your relationships and also as a way to achieve personal satisfaction. (See the box on the right).

HEALTHY TOUCH

Touch is a source of interpersonal warmth. Although it varies from culture to culture, touch is generally acceptable in family and couple contexts. Try the following ways to bring it into them:

Interpersonal
- Massage with your couple.
- Hug your children and family.
- Walk holding hands.
- Practise physical contact games.
- Display kind and warm greetings with others (shake hands, kiss, hug, according to what is acceptable in each cultural context).

Personal
- Bathe with water at pleasant temperature.
- Enjoy breeze or soft wind on face and body.
- Go out and sunbathe.
- Spread hydrating cream over your body.

Olfaction

This is the **sense with the greatest emotional charge**. The olfactory nerve connects the nasal terminals directly with the olfactory area of the brain; and this area is in the midst of the most relevant emotional centres.

The sense of smell may be utilised to prepare a **special ambience** that can be remembered for many years. The use of air fresheners and perfumes can be strongly associated with life experiences and memories that can be retrieved easily with the presence of the odour (see the box on the right).

In order to create this type of link, make plans to live your joyous experiences accompanied by certain enjoyable aromas and enjoy the perception thoroughly. In the future, the sole presence of the aroma will retrieve pleasant memories.

AROMATHERAPY

Treatment with pleasant smells is based on the known **physiological effects** of aroma upon the body.

Before reaching the lungs and passing into the bloodstream, smell molecules stimulate the olfactory cells (a type of neuron) found inside the nasal cavities. The relation between the olfactory nerve, the thalamus, the hypothalamus, and the pituitary gland may explain the known regulatory effects of aromas over the neurohormonal system.

In order to create a healthy environment, using **a single essential oil** is better than mixing several. For example:

- A **balsamic environ** to sooth sinusitis, pharyngitis, and other respiratory ailments: eucalyptus, pine, thyme or rosemary.
- A **relaxing and sedative environ** to help with nervousness and insomnia: lavender or orange.
- A **toning effect**: lemon, rosemary, peppermint or winter savoury.

Sayings of Jesus

'When the disciples heard this, they fell facedown to the ground, terrified. But Jesus came and touched them. "Get up," he said. "Don't be afraid."' (Matthew 17:6-7).

1.06
Healthy sex

A mental health factor

A balanced sex life is a source of mental health. People with a healthy sexual life enjoy better mood, a closer and intimate connection with their partner, and a reduced risk of depression and anxiety. Besides its reproductive function, sexuality provides pleasure and enjoyment to the couple, causing a deep emotional closeness and a desire to please each other.

Healthy sex is much more than sexual intercourse. It includes erotic foreplay, tenderness, and humour. But above all, it is based on mutual love and respect. In addition, sexuality must be practised **responsibly** as it carries risks and consequences (see the box below).

Improve your sexuality

Try the following counsels:

• **Discuss the topic of sex with your partner.** It may be a little embarrassing at the beginning, but you can talk of your preferences and try to understand the wishes and desires of your part-

AVOID IRRESPONSIBLE SEX

Consider the following things:

• **Beware of changes of partner.** Change of sexual partner is attractive to many, but a stable relationship offers deeper satisfaction. A change of partner brings about significant risks: Sexually transmitted diseases, psychological pain, guilt, disarray in practical and family arrangements, etc.

• **Sex may become an obsession.** Sexuality is a very strong force that needs to be governed by the will.

Uncontrolled sexual impulses can absorb most of one's available time and energy.

• **Do not use sexuality as a coercive tool.** Sex must be given and received lovingly and liberally, without tying it to other intentions or to blackmail. Statements such as: 'We will not make love until you…' expose a lack of ethics and of sexual understanding.

Male-female differences in sexuality

An evaluation (Peplau, 2003) of a large number of sex investigations clearly reveal four fundamental differences between men and women:

1. **Sexual impulse** is stronger in men than in women.
2. Women attach utmost importance to sexuality in the context of a **committed** relationship and not based on casual encounters.
3. There is a **relationship between aggression and sexuality**, but this link is only relevant in men and not in women.
4. Women do have a greater capacity than men to **adapt and modify** their sex life.

The knowledge of these gender differences in sexuality is quite important to reach mutual agreements within the couple. Love and mutual understanding will help to smooth out differences in order to attain a more satisfactory sexual experience.

ner. Discussion will help you reach the most satisfying middle point.

- **Remember the differences.** Sexuality in men is different than in women. But it can be complementary. If you are a woman, remember that sex is passion to men. If you are a man, understand that sex is romanticism to women.

- **Invest time and effort.** It is not possible to enjoy sexuality if one is not willing to invest in it. Time is very important to women (and often to

men as well). Pleasure builds up little by little and reaches its summit after a prolonged time of foreplay, kisses, and caresses. Besides, sexual foreplay is optimal when the relationship is free from conflict and pressure.

- **Nourish your self-esteem.** Self-esteem is closely tied to sexuality. Thus make efforts to nourish your own self-esteem (see page 28), avoiding feelings of inferiority or superiority. Also make sure that your partner feels good about himself/herself and possesses a good self-concept. Comment on his/her achievements, his/her qualities, and do not get tired of declaring your love for him/her.

- **Avoid monotony.** Break the habit of monotonous and predictable lovemaking. Try a variety of places or different positions and surprise your partner with unexpected advances, always avoiding abusive ones.

CYBER SEX

Sex on the Internet (cyber sex) is a significant, high revenue activity. Many people go to Internet in search of pornography, a sexual partner, or to conduct online sex chats with others. The **Griffin-Shelley** report (2003) alerts us of the following dangers of cyber sex:
- It is addictive and compulsive.
- It adversely affects work and work performance.
- It deteriorates family and marriage relationships.

Full sexuality is attained through an open and direct relationship between a man and a woman who love each other. Alternatives may seem partially satisfactory, but they run the risk of significant dangers. Therefore we recommend responsible sexuality in the context of mutual commitment.

Gems of Ancient Wisdom

'May your fountain be blessed, and may you rejoice in the wife of your youth. A loving doe, a graceful deer—may her breasts satisfy you always, may you ever be captivated by her love' (Proverbs 5:18-19).

1.07

Simple relaxation techniques

These days effective work methods make labour lighter and more dignified. Physical fatigue and repetitive tasks are practically eliminated from all professions. However, people complain of tension and tiredness and wish to free themselves from this load. It is therefore necessary to know simple and practical methods of relaxation.

Body relaxation

The human organism is impacted from stress, thus producing muscular pain, stomach discomfort, headaches, alteration of the cardiac rhythm, etc. Here are some ways to attain relaxation:

- **Breathing.** This is the fastest and most accessible method to free oneself from rage and tension. Practise breathing deeply, expanding the belly (not the chest) and breathing out little by little. Repeat this four or five times and return to normal breathing. Do this five or six times a day, wherever you are: in the car, at work, in your conversation with someone, in the waiting room, or before going to bed. When performing breathing exercises, make efforts to smile, putting aside matters that worry you.

- **Physical exercise.** Any form of physical exercise, as long as it is adequate for age and personal fitness, brings about physical and mental relaxation. Physical exercise should be done systematically and to the taste of everyone, as some people attain relaxation through intensive sport while others achieve it through a calm walk.

- **Bathing.** Water at various temperatures provides a beneficial effect over muscular relaxation. A simple bath or shower adds tone to the muscles. Hydrotherapy, based on the alternation of cold and warm water, has a superior relaxing effect over arterial and capillary circulation. Because of its high mineral content, sea bathing stimulates the body's internal glands as well as the general metabolism thus relaxing the body.

- **Muscular relaxation.** In addition to the methods mentioned above, muscular or progressive relaxation ensures, in a systematic way, the loosening of muscles suffering from stress (see the box on the adjoining page).

self-help

MUSCULAR RELAXATION METHOD

Practise relaxation lying down on your bed or mat. Rest your head on a small pillow. Spend about 20 minutes in this activity. Breathe in deeply before starting, in the middle of the session, and at the end. Soft environmental music may help you achieve better relaxation.

Carry out the following tension-relaxation sequences with the following muscles:

1. Tighten fists. Relax them.
2. Bend forearms against arms. Relax them.
3. Press arms against mattress. Relax them.
4. Pull arms along body. Relax them.
5. Turn hand palms outward. Relax them.
6. Turn hand palms inward. Relax them.
7. Pull shoulders towards ears. Relax them.
8. Pull shoulders forward. Relax them.
9. Turn head right. Return to original position
10. Turn head left. Return to original position.
11. Lift head from pillow. Lower it.
12. Open eyelids and eyebrows to the maximum. Relax them.
13. Close eyes tightly. Relax them.
14. Press tongue against teeth. Relax it.
15. Clench jaws tightly. Relax them.
16. Make a tight muzzle with lips. Relax them.
17. Open mouth with strength. Relax.
18. Push belly inward. Relax.
19. Push belly outward. Relax.
20. Tense thighs and buttocks. Relax them.
21. Pull feet and legs down. Relax them.

Note: Keep tension for 4 or 5 seconds, and relaxation for 5 or 6 seconds.

Mind relaxation

Mental tension means a heavy psychological burden to many persons. Obsession over problems, uncertainty towards the future, mental fatigue, loss of memory and slow reasoning are associated features of the tense mind. What can one do to prevent these mental states and obtain peace and relaxation? Try the following:

- **Thinking.** Reject catastrophic thoughts and focus your mind on positive and happy things. Learn to put aside sour and tense issues, albeit temporarily, until such a time as you can provide solutions.

- **Visualisation.** It will be much easier to reject unwanted thoughts if you have a theme or themes to substitute them. Use imagination to visualise your chosen topic in detail. Some think of the place where they grew up or in their adolescence and youth. Others concentrate on a certain experience of peace and happiness, or in past moments spent with a dear one.

Choose your own images and enjoy the details, put some colour and movement; walk in those places and situations. You will soon realise that your mind and mood find a point of quietness and serenity.

- **Self-instruction.** Encourage yourself to reject troubling thoughts. Instruct yourself with commands such as 'Do not think of it, Mary,' 'Don't exaggerate, George,' 'You can take care of it tomorrow, Louise; think of something pleasant now.'

- **Social interaction.** Seek the company of friends and relatives in order to distract yourself. If you have an introverted personality, avoid the natural tendency to remain alone with negative thoughts. Call a friend and chat; get out of the house and attend a social function where you are forced to converse with others.

- **Hobbies.** When faced with mental tension, practise activities such as home repairs, gardening, collections, games and, very particularly, sports. Watching a funny movie or reading an easy book is also a good method to achieve mental relaxation.

- **Music.** Choose a CD or audiotape that elevates you with music that has brought relaxation and mental peace to you in the past. Get comfortable, close your eyes and focus on listening to the music. Do not permit the intrusion of unwanted thoughts.

- **Prayer.** You may have never prayed in your life, but sincere prayers facilitate a great deal of mental relaxation for those using them. Some use repetitive chanting. But it is better to avoid repetitions, as Jesus advised (Matthew 6:7-15) and pray by talking to God as one talks to a father. Express your uncertainties, sorrows, and conflicts through a prayer. Ask God for blessings and he will grant you the best.

Prayer is a highly spiritual experience and it must be tested in order to know its benefits (see the box at the bottom of this page).

- **Other options.** There are a number of ways of bringing mental relaxation into your life, depending on your personal preferences. Try these:

  ✓ Sing a song or whistle a melody.

  ✓ Forgive wholeheartedly someone who has offended you.

  ✓ Go to a park or natural setting and listen to the birds singing.

  ✓ While seated or lying down, observe the water in a fountain, river or sea.

  ✓ Pay attention to cloud movement for a period of time.

  ✓ Rub your eyes with both hands and leave them closed for a few minutes.

  ✓ Look for an ant farm and observe their bustle.

  ✓ Carry out a conversation with a 4- or 5-year-old for a few minutes.

  ✓ Play with the dog or the cat.

RESEARCH RESULTS

The effects of prayer

Herbert Benson is a physician, professor and researcher at Harvard University School of Medicine. For years, he has investigated the effects on illness of several alternative methods, such as prayer. One of the basic conclusions of his studies is that prayer brings about a relaxing response. In his book *Timeless Healing* (Benson, 1996), he explains how prayer:

- Slows down metabolism.
- Reduces cardiac rate.
- Reduces breathing rate.
- Expands the brain wave frequency.
- Slows down blood pressure.
- Causes feelings of peace and calm.
- Improves health.

RELAXATION OPTIONS

Dietary habits affect the ability to attain mental relaxation. There are foods and drinks that stimulate the central nervous system and should be *avoided*:

- **Coffee**, **tea**, and **caffeine**-containing beverages, as caffeine causes nervousness and prevents relaxation.
- **Alcoholic drinks**, because their use over time damages the nerve cells and blocks any form of relaxation.
- **Refined sugar** in pastries, chocolate, sweets…, as sugar causes hyperactivity, which is incompatible with relaxation.

However, there are dietary ingredients that are ***beneficial*** to enhance nerve and muscular relaxation:

- **Oats** may be taken in the form of porridge or as muesli. The active relaxation ingredient is avenin, an alkaloid with calming effects.
- **Lettuce**, commonly used in salads and as an ingredient in sandwiches, also provides a sedative effect.
- **Cashews**, delicious nuts rich in magnesium, favour the prevention of nervousness and irritability.

Gems of Ancient Wisdom

'I have set the LORD always before me. Because he is at my right hand, I will not be shaken. Therefore my heart is glad and my tongue rejoices; my body also will rest secure' (Psalm 16:8-9).

Sayings of Jesus

'Come to me, all you who are weary and burdened, and I will give you rest' (Matthew 11:28).

1.08

Good communication

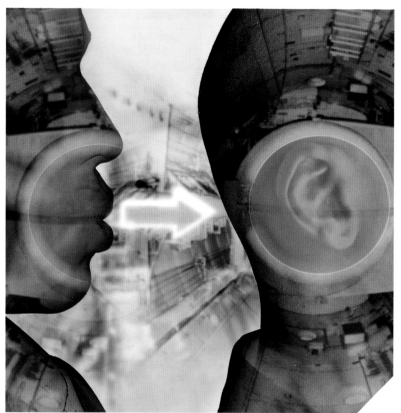

How does communication affect us?

We may not realise often enough the importance of communication. However, every time we contact people, we send and receive messages. Communication affects the image we portray to others and it establishes the emotional tone of each encounter. A great deal of success and failure directly depend on the quality of communication. Good communication makes us feel accepted and understood, while deficient communication causes disappointment and misunderstanding.

Communication is particularly important in **interpersonal relationships**—family, friends, neighbours, colleagues, acquaintances and strangers. The words we pronounce and listen to end up carrying pleasure or pain, security or insecurity, closeness or rejection, encouragement

or sadness. And beyond words, there are other messages deeply affecting others and ourselves, such as looks, gestures and tones.

How to listen

The first and most important item in any exchange of communication is to listen. Sufficient attention stimulates communication, encourages the speaker and keeps the listener active.

In fact, the recipient of the message has the most communication power, since without his participation communication breaks down.

When you wish for communication to happen, make sure you listen. Consider the following tips to increase your listening ability:

• **Find support in non-verbal language.** Take care of your posture, your looks, your smile and your head motions. They should be warm and able to transmit a message of interest and attention. This will maintain vibrant communication.

• **Avoid distractions.** In order to listen with maximum attention, try by all means to reject thoughts or problems unrelated to the conversation and focus on what you are being told. Use your imagination to focus on the ideas and messages you are hearing. This will help you not only to maintain attention, but also to understand better.

• **Ask for clarification.** When you do not understand or if you have doubts, ask for clarification. Speak with simplicity (What do you mean? I do not quite understand…) and avoid nagging messages (Why are you late? Why do you speak like this? Are you suggesting that…?).

- **Confirm what you have heard.** Make sure that your understanding is thorough, especially in very important matters. One good way to do it is to paraphrase or summarise the message. This will let the other know that you have understood. For instance: 'You are telling me that you need to return to your town because your family situation is unbearable, correct?' 'I see you are willing to lose out on income because of your convictions...' 'In other words, your children have evaded all responsibility on the matter...'

- **Find out the feeling of the other person.** Try and find out the mood of your opponent. What does he/she feel? What is the reason for his/her talking in that way? Why is he/she raising the volume of his/her voice? Why isn't he/she looking at me while he/she speaks?

- **Offer your help, if possible.** In addition to improving your own attention, if you offer help you will notice that communication will become more complete and meaningful.

Watch out for the replication instinct

The replication instinct is one of the most common barriers of listening. It consists of mentally preparing your reply while the other person speaks. This causes a **complete breakdown in communication**, as messages are not received but only sent. Avoid this practice using the following tips:

- Make a firm decision to listen.
- Bear in mind that your reply will only be adequate once you fully understand the other's message.
- Make eye contact.

- Imagine that you are expected to give account of everything you are told.
- Think that, sooner or later, it will be evident that you have not listened.
- Instruct yourself with the idea that it is not ethical to drop your attention when you are being talked to.

'He who answers before listening—that is his folly and his shame' (Proverbs 18:13).

Research Results

Fatigue and interpersonal relationships in women

Laura Dzurec (2002) reviewed medical research of the last few years together with her own studies on women's fatigue. She concluded that interpersonal relations, where communication is the principal component, affect the way in which women perceive fatigue. When relationships are optimal, tiredness is borne with happiness and good disposition, whilst in the middle of adverse relationships, work and fatigue are perceived as painful. Dzurec proposes that the state of relationships should be part of the definition of fatigue, at least in women.

'Pleasant words are a honeycomb, sweet to the soul and healing to the bones' (Proverbs 16:24).

How to speak

Kind and respectful words, clearly pronounced, establish an emotional tone that favours comprehension. Make sure that your ideas are clear before you speak, especially when it is time to utter important messages. Consider the following advice:

- **It is sometimes best to be quiet.** If you suspect that your statement will hurt someone or if you are angry, do not say anything. A Castilian proverb says: 'Word or stone that has been shot cannot be stopped.' Postpone the conversation until a better moment.

- **Organise what you are about to say.** Jot down (or make a mental note of) your three or four basic pointers and arrange them in logical order. This will make your message more understandable.

- **Use kind, not hurting words.** Practise the habit of expressing your ideas with courtesy and good manners. Show respect to your counterpart and experience the satisfaction of being polite. You will soon realise that communication becomes easy and helpful.

- **Avoid 'always' and 'never' messages.** Expressions such as 'You always forget my things,' or 'You never let me speak' load conversations with emotion and make communication difficult. Besides, these statements tend to be untrue, as they are radical and absolute.

- **Use praise.** Even though the topic of conversation may be controversial, recognise something good in your opponent and in truth and honesty, comment about it. This will eliminate hostility in the other person and will improve communication.

- **Apologise.** Do not be too proud to fail to recognise your mistakes. Ask for forgiveness whenever you have erred. This will cause a soothing effect upon communication, apart from enhancing the generosity of your opponent.

Gems of Ancient Wisdom

'Kind words appease rage, but harsh messages make it worse' (Proverbs 15:1).

self-help

LEARN TO SAY 'NO'

Good communication should bring about mutual satisfaction. However, sometimes one of the parties remains unsatisfied because he/she has not been able to say 'No' and thus experiences frustration and defeat. Consider the following options before the communication encounter:

- **Do not rush to say 'Yes.'** If in doubt, simply say: 'Give me extra time to think about it.' Then take your time to reflect and do not commit yourself until you are certain.
- **Explain your position.** Whenever you are not sure to accept a proposition, explain your situation and the current challenges. In this way, you will under-line your own difficulties and your opponent will remain well informed.
- **Offer alternatives.** If you have difficulties accepting the other's request, suggest different options or names of persons with better preparation.
- **Do not argue.** If in your inner self you wish to say 'No,' avoid argumentation, including logical reasons, as to why you are not accepting. Simply be firm after having explained your position. If your opponent insists, express yourself kindly but firmly: 'Please, I beg you not to insist. My answer is "No."'

TEST YOURSELF ::

In order to avoid the passive response (which implies submission) or the aggressive one (harassment), you should seek the middle point, called assertiveness. Read the following case and choose the most appropriate responses.

Cecile and Cathy are very good friends. They often go out and enjoy their mutual fellowship. But Cecile is not punctual and this bothers Cathy greatly. One day Cathy decides to speak out on the matter and she is considering the following messages. Imagine you are Cathy; choose what you would say to Cecile:

Am I assertive?
1. You are inconsiderate and must correct your habit of always being late.
2. Observe that oftentimes you do not arrive on time to our appointments.
3. You think that your time is more valuable than mine.
4. I believe that punctuality is a most desirable trait.
5. If you arrive late again, look for another friend who is willing to endure you.
6. When you come late I am left with a feeling of rejection.
7. You do not have any respect for others.
8. I would like to ask you to be more punctual.

Interpretation:
If you have chosen the even statements, you are assertive; but if you are leaning to the odd ones, you have the tendency to verbal aggression.
Consider speaking in first person; do not nag, do not sermonise, do not judge and do not make general statements about the other person. For assertive communication, state your observations, thoughts and feelings in a kind and courteous manner. Lastly, communicate your desires.

1.09
Live happily and optimistically

Some people think that joy and happiness are random, the product of circumstances or luck (see case on page 13). However, above and beyond randomness is personal choice. To be happy is an option. Some seem interested in being unhappy and miserable (see page 58), but it is possible to choose optimism and to enjoy a reasonably happy and satisfying life.

Simple and committed decisions such as 'I have decided to be happy,' 'Today I will enjoy life... I am not going to permit the bad mood to take over,' 'I am going to look at the bright side of things' are personal decisions. Taken with determination, these decisions bring about great strength and prevent discouragement.

RESEARCH RESULTS

Study on happiness

Researchers at the University of London conducted a study (Cheng and Furnham, 2003) on happiness with 88 university students as participants. Extensive data were collected on their explanations about their joyous events as well as their misfortunes. They were also administered the *Oxford Happiness Inventory*. After corresponding statistical analysis, the following results were obtained:

- There is a close relationship between the **personal interpretation** of the events that happen in one's life and happiness. Those who perceive events as something that can be changed and controlled, enjoy a higher level of happiness than those who see things as being outside their control.

- Those with a **balanced self-esteem** (no inferiority complexes) perceive happenings as something under their own dominion.

It is therefore necessary to exercise one's personal sense of security along with skills to act upon events that happen in our surroundings (see page 28 on self-esteem). Failure to do so leads to a condition of helplessness and despair because of the impossibility of transforming circumstances into something positive. In sum, viewing surrounding events optimistically and seeing oneself with the ability to influence circumstances leads to happiness and psychological well-being.

HOW DO YOU FACE FAILURE?

Consider the following example and compare it with your own thinking style. Do you tend towards the first applicant's style? Or do you identify yourself mainly with the second one?

Alice and Amanda prepared themselves thoroughly for a government post based on competition. They took their examinations but neither was chosen. When they learned their results, reactions were very different:

Alice	Amanda
'I am useless'	'Exams were more difficult than usual'
'I have such bad luck'	'There have been many failing grades'
'I fail in everything I set out to do'	'The examining board was tough in their verdict'
'Surely I am the worst'	'These exams count among the most difficult'
'If I try again, I will flunk again'	'I will do better next time'

The fundamental difference between Alice and Amanda is that the first applicant attributed her failure to herself, whilst Amanda attributed it to external circumstances, although she admitted that she needed to do something to improve her chances.

If your thinking style is similar to Alice, you should understand that the reasons for your failure are not only inside you, but also outside. Likewise, the explanations for your success should not only be in terms of luck and random events, but also because of your own abilities and values.

How to improve the state of mental well-being

Being happy and enjoying life joyfully and optimistically is a desirable aim and happens through personal initiative, not by chance.

Twenty-five-year-old Emma considered herself unlucky in almost everything. But she became friends with a peer from work who had the ability to see things in a positive way. This influenced her life. Emma's attitude changed through her learning new behaviours, as explained below:

• **Exercise in positive thinking.** Do not fall into the trap of focusing only on negative aspects, or your life will be bitter. Consider everything in general, but focus on the positive. Whenever you face a problem, apply the corresponding solutions and put it aside for a while. Then, retrieve pleasant memories

from the past, such as people you admire, jolly friends, or a funny anecdote that may help draw a smile to your face. Think of these things while you perform routine tasks. This will help you displace adverse thoughts related to your problem.

• **Feel reasonably satisfied with yourself.** Self-esteem is closely related to the ability to enjoy life. If you feel inferior, your behaviours will tend to mediocrity and low performance. Seeing the poor results will affirm your belief and, in the end, you will fail. Self assurance is a good emotional habit that needs to be cultivated in order to obtain further achievements, to nourish self-esteem and to enjoy greater happiness and satisfaction.

In order to improve your self-esteem, focus your thoughts on your positive traits. Encourage yourself, think about your past triumphs and trust in a prosperous future.

List your virtues and praiseworthy traits. Ask a good friend about your strong points and add them to your list. Carry the list with you and look at it occasionally. In general, neither entirely blame yourself for your failures, nor remove from yourself the merits of your accomplishments.

- **Nourish good interpersonal relationships.** The greatest satisfactions and happy experiences in life tend to be associated with other people. Likewise pain and displeasure come from interpersonal relationships.

  In the absence of disagreements and difficulties, when relationships are excellent with your spouse, boss, partners, friends and neighbours, happiness and mental health seem to overflow. But when things go wrong with people, life turns bitter, and sadness, discouragement and uncertainty set in.

  In order to improve relationships, try this:

  ✓ Practise pleasant relations with your colleagues. Show yourself willing to cooperate with your peers. Be courteous and respectful to your superiors.

  ✓ Always keep your good mood and an open smile to prevent others from avoiding you.

  ✓ Organise your free time in such a way that relationships with family, friends and relatives may be fostered. Instead of watching TV or playing on the computer, go and visit a friend, take a walk with your spouse, or play with your children.

  ✓ Surprise your dear ones with an unexpected gift or with words of praise and approval.

  ✓ Make efforts to be fun. This will make you loved and accepted by others and it will bring about further happiness and mental health.

  - **Look at the funny side of things.** Add a pinch of humour to life's difficulties. Laugh at the stressful situations in order to release tension.

    A great barrier that prevents many from experiencing happiness is the tendency to 'catastrophise' or exaggerate problems. A sense of humour minimises the importance of sombre things and helps to adopt a more realistic and balanced perspective.

- **Do something to help others.** It is a widely accepted fact among mental health professionals that altruism fights depressive symptoms and adds satisfaction and happiness to the lives of those practising it.

  Try to volunteer in an association to help the needy, teach classes in a marginal neighbourhood or cooperate in an ecological project. Or perhaps, in a private manner, make plans to visit members of your family or old friends. Visit them to support them and give them the satisfaction of your being the one seeking their friendship and well-being.

- **Practise a healthy lifestyle.** Those in good health tend to have a greater chance of experiencing happiness. When physical discomfort is present, it is difficult to enjoy mental well-being. Keeping healthy is a simple process, enjoyable and easy for everyone to attain:

  ✓ Maintain a balanced diet including **whole grains, vegetables, fruits, beans and nuts**. Avoid animal foods or use them moderately.

  ✓ **Drink plenty of water** every day, especially outside of regular meals. Avoid the use of sugar drinks, beer and coffee. They only supply empty calories—no nutritional value.

  ✓ **Exercise regularly.** Double your effort if you have a sedentary job. Practise a sport or an enjoyable, vigorous activity.

  ✓ **Adequate rest** follows regular exercise. Keep to 7-8 hours of sleep. It is absolutely necessary to preserve your physical and mental health.

  ✓ **Do not use psychoactive substances—** drugs, alcohol, tobacco, etc., as they affect the central nervous system and your mood. Although they may cause satisfaction in the beginning, they ruin good mood in the end.

- **Keep a hopeful attitude.** One of the greatest secrets to happiness is to look at the future with hope. Reflect on the past and how problems were solved. Adopt the confidence that this time they will also be solved.

  Dispel ideas of misfortune and calamity from your mind. If you are a believer, trust in God and you will notice that a great burden is removed and you will start enjoying God-given blessings.

Gems of Ancient Wisdom

'Finally, brothers, goodbye. Aim for perfection, listen to my appeal, be of one mind, live in peace. And the God of love and peace will be with you' (2 Corinthians 13:11).

'Make sure that nobody pays back wrong for wrong, but always try to be kind to each other and to everyone else. Be joyful always; pray continually' (1 Thessalonians 5:15-17).

1.10
Mind-body connection

From very old times, it has been understood that body and mind work closely together and that the failure of one means loss of health for both. **Aristotle**, addressing a team of physicians said:

'In the same way that we do not attempt to cure the eyes without the head, or the head without the body, neither can we treat the body without the soul.'

Nowadays, with so much experimental evidence of the interaction between mood and physical health, we do not have any doubt of the mind-body interrelationship (see a sample of this in the box on the adjoining page).

Roman lawmaker **Juvenal** (60-140 AD) coined the famous sentence *Mens sana in corpore sano* (A sound mind in a healthy body) in order to emphasize the intimate relationship of these two aspects. It is therefore necessary to tackle both in order to enjoy total health.

'Mens sana...'

- **Laugh often.** It has been demonstrated that roaring with laughter has an instant and beneficial effect upon the majority of vital organs. Laughter relaxes tissue and muscle, and diminishes anxiety, depression and worries.

  It is also known that roaring with laughter increases the respiratory function, oxygenates the body, lowers blood pressure and acts as a pain killer.

- **Practise optimism.** Try by all means to see the positive side of things. Without falling into a simplistic attitude, observe the good things and try to enjoy life. Optimists suffer from less illness than pessimists.

- **Use memories to relax.** Retrieve experiences, anecdotes, and events from the past that bring about relaxation. They will cause good mood and will displace sombre thoughts about yourself, the surroundings, and your future.

- **Look at the future in hope.** Positive anticipation reinforces self-confidence, promotes personal ability and helps achieve a general state of well-being.

- **Be sure to have an adequate social support system.** Do not neglect this very important aspect of your existence. Initiate solid friendships to share your sorrow as well as your joys. Optimal social support does not only prevent illness, but also helps restore health once one has contracted an ailment.

- **Maintain anger control and practise assertiveness.** Today it is well known that displaying anger is useless since the advantage of releasing

Gems of Ancient Wisdom

'A cheerful heart is good medicine, but a crushed spirit dries up the bones' (Proverbs 17:22).

pressure is lost to remorse, deterioration of relationships, and cardiac risk.

It is best to use assertive communication, sharing things calmly, with respect and true care towards others.

- **Practise religion and spiritual life.** A few years ago, religious and spiritual matters were not considered. Today, a variety of studies (Olive, 2004) demonstrate that religious belief and practice reduce mortality in hospital patients, help to achieve better post-surgery recovery, reduce the risk of dependencies, strengthen the immune system and result in fewer visits to the doctor.

Sayings of Jesus

'I am the bread of life. [...] If anyone eats of this bread, he will life for ever' (John 6:48, 51).

RESEARCH RESULTS

Emotion-ridden diseases

Nicholas Hall and his associates (1996) present scientific evidence showing that mental states (attitude, serenity, hope, social relations, feeling well with oneself, etc.) significantly affect the course of the following illnesses:

- **Tuberculosis.** The emotional state of patients with tuberculosis affects the course of the disease in such a way that fear and worry hinder proper medical treatment and increase the risk of death in the youngest patients.
- **Common cold.** Stressful events make the person vulnerable to infection of the upper respiratory passages. Mental states cause significant changes of the hormones epinephrine, norepinephrine and cortisol. These variations weaken the immune system, causing the person to be more prone to contract the disease.
- **AIDS.** The loss of a friend or lover in the gay community causes in the bereaved a lowering of defences and allows the disease to take over, following an adverse course. Likewise, the threat of losing one's own life also complicates the development and action of the AIDS virus. Hence the necessity to practise a positive and hopeful attitude.
- **Melanoma (cancer).** A specific mental disposition alters the developmental course of the disease. Behavioural intervention into a group of patients caused the increase of CD-57 lymphocytes, the cells that fight cancerous cells. The same beneficial effect was observed in cancer patients who were in a good marital relationship.
- **Breast cancer.** Patients with breast cancer who were willing to discuss their problem during the post-surgery period and receive the support of relatives and friends had a lower mortality rate than those who isolated themselves or had a poor social support system.
- **Chronic fatigue syndrome.** The presence of this illness causes symptoms of a psychological nature. If not tackled, chronic fatigue syndrome will interrupt the normal course of recovery. It is known that patients suffering from the illness secrete 30% less cortisol over a period of 24 hours, and that 46% of these patients suffer or have suffered major depression.
- **Multiple sclerosis.** All multiple sclerosis patients know that stressful situations cause attacks or crises in their illness. This is due to a complex process of internal secretion (caused by the reaction of the person facing stressors) that lowers defences and favours the outbreak of the disease.

'...in corpore sano'

- **Get regular exercise.** Physical exercise (see page 322) brings about an extraordinary state of well-being. In addition to the toning and stimulation of all vital organs and muscles, physical exercise causes the production of endorphin, a hormone serving as pain killer that stimulates good mood and well-being. In addition, physical exercise successfully compensates for the effect of anxious and depressive thoughts.

- **Eat with balance and moderation.** Foods close to their natural state, prepared in simplicity and with taste and taken in a moderate amount facilitate clear thought and reasoning. Heavy meals, with much spice, fat, or sugar negatively affect not only the body but also the emotional and cognitive functions.

- **Drink what is good.** Water is the best drink and it is sufficient for all vital needs of fluid. Drink it abundantly (one to two litres every day outside meals). It will help you renew organic fluids, think clearly, and feel better overall. Other healthy drinks, such as juices and blends of fruits and vegetables are delicious and healthy.

- **Do not neglect rest.** The regular and systematic activity-rest cycle is a constant in nature and must not be ignored by human beings if they wish to enjoy mental health. Therefore, accomplish your work and guard your rest. Sleep the necessary hours without falling into the mistake of sleeping too much or too little. Remember that, in addition to sleep, rest is also achieved through free time and pastimes. If your job is sedentary, seek vigorous physical activities for hobbies. If your occupation is physically active, read or practise a quiet activity.

- **Reject all unhealthy substances.** Psychoactive substances (drugs, alcohol, tobacco, etc.) directly affect your central nervous system and your mood. They also adversely intervene upon cognitive functions: memory, reasoning ability, and the capacity to discern between good and bad.

- **Use breathing as a relaxing method.** Seek pure air and breathe deeply two or three times in a row, two or three times each day. Breathe in, expanding your belly (not the thorax) and breathe out slowly. Have no misgivings about the relaxing efficacy of such a simple remedy.

'AN HONEST AND SIMPLE LIFE...'

José de Letamendi was born in Barcelona, Spain, in 1828. He studied medicine at the University of Barcelona and at 26 he already was assistant professor of Anatomy at the School of Medicine. He obtained the professor chair position in 1857 and trained hundreds of physicians in the Catalonian capital. From 1878 he continued his teaching and research career in Madrid as professor of Pathology until his death in 1897.

Letamendi also developed projects in anthropology, philosophy, pedagogy and music. He authored several books and thousands of articles. His multi-faceted style made him complex and at the same time simple, but wise, as the poem below shows. If this advice were to be practised to the letter, everybody's health would soon improve:

An honest and simple life;
use just a few remedies
and by all means try
not to worry about anything.
Moderate food;
fun and exercise;
out to nature for a while;
little time alone,
much with people
and constant activity.

Practise the advice of this poem and observe how your total health improves.

Gems of Ancient Wisdom

'Dear friend, I pray that you may enjoy good health and that all may go well with you, even as your soul is getting along well' (3 John 1:2).

1.11
Self-improvement: Unlearn

We spend our lives learning, but not only at school or university. The surrounding context and events also teach us a great deal and shape us in one form or another. We also teach ourselves through reflection and practice.

But learning is not limited to the knowledge of data and facts. It also includes a variety of ways to think, behave and even to feel. **Problem-solving** is a task of great importance; this does not only include problems of mathematics or physics, but also of interpersonal relations, home finances, health, doubts and fears, faith crisis, and the choice of alternative ways in life.

How to uproot what has been learned

A way to perfect oneself is to unlearn certain habits that cause problems. The box on the adjoining page offers you a sample of undesirable behav-iours with the corresponding suggested alternatives in order to substitute such conducts, thoughts or feelings by more adaptive ones. At the beginning, it will be hard to eliminate the old habits, but as time goes on and as you practise the new ones, there will be less probability of repeating them.

Learning habits is very important in order to carry out tasks without much thinking or worry. They happen without noticing. Therefore, we need to change those harmful behavioural habits. Even though changes are difficult due to the strength of habits, it is not impossible to eliminate them.

Habits and customs may be accompanied by thoughts or wishes. Other times, they are made up of repetitive acts with devastating effects, such as the habit of smoking, drinking alcoholic beverages, or using other substances that affect the thinking process.

BIBLICAL EXAMPLE

The story of Zacchaeus

Zacchaeus was a tax collector. He gathered taxes from the people to pass on to the central administration of the Ro-man Empire. He was not alone; he was in charge of a body of professional tax collectors who paid commission to him. Zacchaeus had the authority to vary the rates according to his personal criteria, thus retaining a good portion of the mon-ey raised. Then he transferred a fixed amount to the Empire. He had done this during years and was very skilful. It was extremely dif-ficult for Zacchaeus to change direction or to unlearn what had been learned.

But a teacher of his time, Jesus of Nazareth, impressed Zacchaeus with his messages and willingness to help people. One day, both men met and Zacchaeus was amazed that Jesus treated him so well—a very different attitude from his other fellow citizens, who hated him. Zacchaeus changed so much that in the presence of witnesses, he said: 'Look, Lord! Here and now I give half of my possessions to the poor, and if I have cheated anybody out of anything, I will pay back four times the amount.' Zacchaeus un-learned his well-learned lack of ethics.

The complete story is found in the Gospel (Luke 19:1-10).

UNLEARN INADEQUATE BEHAVIOURS

Write down your own behaviours and how to eliminate them:

I have learned to...	Alternatives
... get extremely irritated whenever they make me wait. Then I lose my temper and am in a bad mood for hours.	I'll take with me a funny book to read in case I must wait. I will observe the people passing by.
... scream and get upset when my children leave everything on the floor.	I will change tactics: I will teach them with patience and care and will reward them when they do the right thing.
... think that my fellow workers are spreading slander against me, even though I have never found any proof.	I will stop those thoughts and will reflect on the positive things my peers may have done for me.
... ruminate often about a family incident that happened years ago.	I will reject that thought and will make up with the persons with whom I had the argument.
... eat too much and then feel guilty for my excess.	I will decide beforehand how much to eat. If I ever overeat, I will forgive myself.
... often think how much I dislike my brother-in-law and to wish something awful would happen to him.	I will not wait any longer to think of his positive traits and I will learn to accept the things I don't like in him.
... feel inferior whenever I hear of my old peers' achievements.	I will convince myself that things are not as they appear and that I have also obtained success.

Gems of Ancient Wisdom

'I will instruct you and teach you in the way you should go; I will counsel you and watch over you. Do not be like the horse or the mule, which have no understanding but must be controlled by bit and bridle or they will not come to you' (Psalm 32:8, 9).

Basic rules to be miserable

Being happy consists of choosing appropriate acting, feeling, and thinking options. This unit offers many examples of bad choices, precisely those adopted by unhappy people (almost always without realising) who live a miserable life. Try to avoid such choices, for, when permitted as part of one's existence, they take root and are difficult to eliminate.

Emotional dependence

Emotional dependence may carry the appearance of love and care between two persons. But it may actually be the unfortunate cause of unhappiness. Emotional dependence happens when someone clings excessively to another and perceives the relation as the only way to obtain personal security. The dependent one understands the relationship as exclusive, feels anger (or depression) when the other person is absent, has extreme interest in the other's preferences, appearance and problems, and experiences lack of interest for any other relationship.

This unhealthy association may happen in relationships between two friends, psychologist and client, husband and wife, or parent and child. One is usually 'strong,' while the other is 'weak.' The latter tends to manipulate the relationship because of his/her need for the other. The strong also has his/her needs, especially that of being indispensable.

If you are trapped in an emotional dependence relationship (sometimes referred to as co-dependence), consider the following pieces of advice:

- **Open the relationship to others.** Although, at the beginning, it may be uncomfortable, invite others to join in your activities and to share moments together. Dialogue with them and learn of their counsel and ways to live their life.

- **Put time aside to be by yourself.** Learn to enjoy occasional solitude and use it to find yourself. Try to solve your problems without having to go to the dear person all the time. Recognise your inner fortitude and your ability to provide solutions.

- **Develop your self-esteem.** Try to feel good about yourself. Recognise your strengths and

follow the advice of unit 1.04 (page 28) in order to strengthen your self-esteem.

Self-denial

Self-denial has much of noble, healthy and heroic. It is a good thing to sacrifice one's own interests and desires. But there is a risk of the fragmentation of one's ego. Denying oneself to the point of hating oneself is highly dangerous and it requires some action to avoid ending up on the path to dejection and depression. So, try these tips:

- **Practise assertiveness.** Your ideas, opinions and solutions count and you should make them

known to others. You need to do this adequately but with consideration. Express your ideas and thoughts in a cordial and peaceful manner. State your disagreements with respect.

- **Protect yourself and care for yourself.** Be careful not to enslave yourself for others and learn to say 'no' when necessary. Take care of yourself, grant time to yourself, and give yourself some gift or satisfaction. Forgive and ask for forgiveness when appropriate, and pardon yourself for past mistakes.

Gems of Ancient Wisdom

'Show me, O LORD, my life's end and the number of my days; let me know how fleeting is my life' (Psalm 39:4).

'Teach us to number our days aright, that we may gain a heart of wisdom' (Psalm 90:12).

Not finding sense to life

Some do not think about the reason for their existence; they do not find sense to life, nor do they set up clear aims and goals. This ends up in frustration and disgust. State transcendental questions and attempt to find answers for them:

- Is there more than materialism in life?
- What is the purpose of my existence?
- Where does a person go at the end of his or her life?
- Will there be justice someday with so much unfairness and suffering?

Not everything has a simple answer, but the Scriptures (the Bible) offer sufficient information to respond satisfactorily to each of those questions. Study the Bible and search for answers so that you may live your life with sense.

UNHAPPINESS MAXIMS

If you wish to be *unhappy*, pay much attention to each and every one of the maxims included on this box. Adopt them as a rule of conduct. Once they are well rooted, they will remain with you for a long time:

- Choose a topic of worry and ruminate on it from morning to night.
- When meeting a person or situation, focus on defects, mistakes and shortcomings. Overlook strong, good, useful and beautiful aspects.
- Remember that your position is the correct one and the others are wrong.
- Mistrust everyone; do not believe anyone and never confide your intimacies to any person.
- Flee from a sense of humour. Always be serious and avoid laughing and smiling.
- Nourish addictive habits: smoking, drinking, sleeping pills, bingo…
- Take as an insult anything others say; consider it as a personal offence and do all you can to take revenge.

- Meditate on the misfortunes of the past and the wrongdoings others did to you. Review them regularly, lest they be forgotten.
- Lose your temper, scream, shout, and nag and insult your spouse and your children (or your best friend). Do the same with your companions at work.
- Do not be polite. Do not use kind messages: 'Please,' 'I'm sorry,' 'Thanks,' 'Forgive me.'
- Repeat to yourself many times: 'Everyone hates me; I am a failure; I don't have remedy and will never have it.'
- Avoid kind messages such as: 'How thoughtful you are,' 'What a good job you've done,' 'I admire your perseverance,' 'You have been a great help.'
- Annoy others before they annoy you.
- Make sweet promises to look well. Then never fulfil them.

Gems of Ancient Wisdom

'Above all else, guard your heart [mind], for it is the wellspring of life' (Proverbs 4:23).

A healthy emotional intelligence

The traditional idea of intelligence as general capability to predict success is being questioned today. As an alternative, a more complete explanation has emerged—emotional intelligence. Feelings, emotions, motivation, and social interaction have, in practice, more relationship with success and failure than pure intelligence.

Daniel Goleman, in his book *Emotional Intelligence* (1995), broke the traditional pattern on the authority of intelligence quotient (IQ). Without diminishing the importance of cognitive and intellectual tasks, Goleman considers them insufficient and suggests the following components of emotional intelligence. Without these components, the greatest talent would become useless:

- **Ability to motivate ourselves**, which allows us to carry out any important task.

- **Perseverance to achieve our goals**, without which even those with the highest natural intelligence would abandon their tasks.

- **Impulse control** in order to prevent undesirable behaviours that may be contrary to one's principles or inappropriate to the occasion.

- **Ability to postpone rewards**, a trait found in truly mature individuals who can make the necessary effort even though the reward may be delayed.

- **Self-regulation of mood** (see page 150), useful to escape from discouragement, irritability, jealousy, impulse of revenge, despair, and many other moods that adversely affect physical and mental health.

- **Empathic ability**, very useful to achieve optimal relations with others and, in the end, to reach success.

- **Ability to trust**, a basic trait to obtain tranquillity, safety and satisfaction.

- **The use of reason in intense emotional moments**, absolutely essential to avoid the excessive influence of emotions.

→ Two types of intelligence in men and women

Conventional intelligence	Emotional intelligence
Conventional intelligence includes a logical and rational style together with thoughts and behaviours dissociated from emotions. On the other hand, emotional intelligence suggests a more complete and human reality. The most notable traits of both intelligences are outlined in the two columns below.	
Man's traits: *Ambitious, predictable, productive, tenacious, critical, apprehensive, inhibited, uncomfortable with sexuality, inexpressive, distant, cold and tranquil.*	***Man's traits:*** *Socially balanced, extroverted, happy, responsible, ethical, pleasant, kind, and caring.*
Woman's traits: *Intellectually confident, good communicator, theoretical, interested in ethical and intellectual matters, introspective, predisposed to anxiety, worry and guilt.*	***Woman's traits:*** *Energetic, good communicator of feelings, positive vision of herself, open, sociable, able to resist tension, socially balanced, rarely anxious, possible feelings of guilt and apprehension.*

How to nourish emotional intelligence

Unlike conventional intelligence, which possesses a strong innate component, emotional intelligence is **susceptible to great changes and improvements**. The following are tips that cover the different areas for the development of emotional intelligence. Try them and observe whether they cause changes in your life.

- **Know your emotions.** You need to start observing your emotions. How do you feel, what type of thoughts go through your mind, how do various events affect you? Write down in a notebook the feelings and emotions you experience: upset, nervous, mistrusting, self-assured, apprehensive, generous, etc. Write down their duration and the internal and external experiences that make changes possible.

- **Learn to control your emotions.** Flee from sorrow and make the decision to improve your mood. If you become anxious about the future,

learn to change your thinking theme or do something to distract yourself. If you tend to lose your temper, practise ways to speak in a calm manner, breathe deeply and think of something funny. If these things do not work, get out for a moment, to allow the situation to cool down, and return once you are calmed down. If you feel inferior, think of your achievements and your strengths. Whenever you are irritated, encourage yourself: 'Charlie, relax... The keys will appear... and if they don't, there will be a solution.'

- **Practise self-motivation.** Lack of motivation freezes situations. The lack of an attractive aim or goal disorients and achievement is affected. Reject discouraging and depressive thoughts. Practise self-confidence and perseverance. Cultivate the delight for simple and ordinary things. Learn to enjoy what may not be attractive in the beginning, especially if it is something you must go through. Exercise discipline. Be realistic in your expectations; do not set up goals that are too ambitious or not ambitious enough.

continued on page 63

TEST YOURSELF ::

Answer the following questions with 'YES, in general' or 'NO, in general':

What is my emotional intelligence level?	YES, in general	NO, in general
1. Do you stay calm during times of irritation?		
2. Do you feel guilty or excessively uncomfortable for past mistakes?		
3. Can you love and respect anyone if you decide to?		
4. Do you worry excessively about the future?		
5. Are you patient and tolerant with others?		
6. Are you jealous?		
7. Are you pleased with the way you are?		
8. Do you tend to become angry and irritated?		
9. Do you attain success in your relationships with other people?		
10. Do you criticise yourself too much?		
11. Do you come up with good solutions to interpersonal problems?		
12. Do you tend to be sad and discouraged?		
13. Do you easily identify the true intentions in others?		
14. Do you often experience shame in yourself?		
15. When you are affected or discouraged, can you pinpoint the reasons?		
16. Is it quite difficult for you to talk about your feelings and emotions?		
17. When you are affected or discouraged, do you know how to overcome this state?		
18. Do you have the impression that stress never ends?		
19. Do you use words of approval and praise towards those deserving them?		
20. When something goes wrong, do you blame yourself harshly?		

Scoring
Odd questions: Add 2 points for each YES and 0 points for each NO.
Even questions: Add 2 points for each NO and 0 points for each YES.

Interpretation:

0-15 points	16-30 points	Higher than 30 points
You have a weak emotional intelligence and should take the steps to improve it, according to the advice offered in this chapter as well as other more specialised resources. You may also find help in others who can guide you and advise you to improve your emotional intelligence.	You are in the average zone of emotional intelligence. Of course, you can improve yourself, especially if your score is in the lower area of the range. Study the questions of this test and identify the behavioural areas that would give you extra points. Organise your life towards better relations and a greater knowledge of your emotions.	You are endowed with a very good emotional intelligence and with a great opportunity to attain a balanced emotional life.

continued from page 61

Gems of Ancient Wisdom

'Rejoice with those who rejoice; mourn with those who mourn' (Romans 12:15).

- **Identify other people's emotions.** Practise this very important skill, as it is the origin of empathy. Observe non-verbal messages in others: their tone of voice, facial gestures and appearance. Make every effort to feel like the other person. This is not only useful to attain compassion and understanding, but also to reach appropriate agreements, diplomacy and successful mediations.

- **Nourish your relationships.** Make every effort to live together in peace and harmony with people. Join hands with others in their projects and avoid clashes. Be happy, kind, nice, and use words of approval. Be courteous, and willing to help any person. Do not consider yourself superior to others in your attitude or words.

- **Practise the following social arts in your relationships:**
  - ✓ Try to give a touch of organisation to the group.
  - ✓ If there is conflict, offer yourself as mediator, peacemaker or negotiator.
  - ✓ Connect with people and make them feel good.
  - ✓ Recognise and respect their feelings and interests.
  - ✓ Sense and identify the feelings and motives of others.
  - ✓ Accept the other person, even though her/his ideas are contrary to yours.

- **Avoid the following practices in your relationships:**
  - ✓ Continue with a conversation when the other person has sent signals to finish.
  - ✓ Speak repeatedly of yourself.
  - ✓ Insist on discussing a topic that your opponent shuns.
  - ✓ Ask indiscrete questions.
  - ✓ Openly and directly oppose the other person's ideas.
  - ✓ Any form of provocation.

Sayings of Jesus

'Blessed are the peacemakers, for they will be called sons of God' (Matthew 5:9).

RESEARCH RESULTS

Happiness and emotional intelligence

A sample of 88 young people of an average age of 20 participated in a study (Furnham and Petrides, 2003) conducted at the University of London. They were given psychometric tests.

An extensive multivariate analysis of the data clearly showed that emotional intelligence is strongly linked to happiness. In this study, the effect of emotional intelligence was so relevant that it surpassed other traits traditionally linked to happiness, such as mental stability, extraversion and willingness to try new experiences.

Emotional intelligence in this study explained 50% of the variance. This means that a well-developed emotional intelligence constitutes a significant step to happiness.

1.14
Living with hope

Hope is perhaps *the most important source of motivation*. Most people work because they hope to get their salary; students will prepare whole-heartedly for an examination because they hope for a good grade; and athletes compete intensely because they have the hope of winning.

Hope is the principal emotion towards the future (see the table below). This quality, together with optimism and the ability to keep good relations, are the major features to prevent mental illness.

Resilience (see chapter 5, page 240) is an interesting benefit of hope. Whenever a natural catastrophe or a personal misfortune happens, those firmly believing in a solution experience an additional measure of strength that helps them compensate for the material losses incurred and to recuperate from their current weakness.

As explained by psychologist **Viktor Frankl**, almost all survivors of Nazi concentration camps made it because they kept their hope of liberation

Past, present, and future emotions

Martin Seligman, the principal founder of Positive Psychology (see page 311), lists emotions as they relate to our past, present, and future (Seligman, 2003). Hope is precisely the most central emotion related to the future.

Emotions related to the PAST	Emotions related to the PRESENT	Emotions related to the FUTURE
Satisfaction	Joy	Hope
Contentment	Ecstasy	Optimism
Fulfilment	Calm	Faith
Pride	Zest	Trust
Serenity	Ebullience	
	Pleasure	
	Flow	

The daily practice of positive emotions is the right way to obtain and maintain happiness and mental health.

until the very end. They also refused to accept that the camp was the end of their lives and focused on the hope to some day be rescued from such hell.

Hope can also affect a variety of daily tasks. The Research Results box on the next page, for example, shows how the hope factor can influence the academic achievement of college students.

To enhance hope

If hope is so important and it affects so many areas of our present and future, we should know how to maintain it and increase it. A list of tips to enhance and develop hope is suggested below. Try some of them; if they work, make them part of your daily life.

- **Engage in hopeful thinking.** When you contemplate the future, make efforts to see good results and satisfactory experiences. What you expect from the beginning determines the final outcome. And when you run into a positive event, expand your thoughts on the stable qualities that make it possible.

(See the box below).

THOUGHT AND HOPE

	Positive event *'I got an A in Mathematics'*	**Level of hope**
1.	*Thought:* *'I work and I am a good student'*	*High*
2.	*Thought:* *'The test was easy and the teacher too generous'*	*Minimal*
	Adverse event *'I had a car accident last night'*	
3.	*Thought:* *'It was night, there was fog and I had a headache'*	*High*
4.	*Thought:* *'I am an awful driver; besides, it is impossible to escape from traffic accidents these days'*	*Minimal*

How to think in a more hopeful way and avoid pessimistic thoughts?

- Whenever **something positive** happens to you, think of the stable qualities that made possible such an event (for example, item 1). This will help you face the future with hope, as stable qualities will produce good future results.
- Whenever **something adverse or negative** happens to you, focus on the transitory circumstances that caused the adversity (for example, item 3). Transitory events can be changed and future adversities thus prevented.

Avoid thoughts like those of items 2 and 4. Do not explain the good happenings with transitory and random reasons (such as item 2) because you need to be in control so that good things may happen again in the future. Likewise, do not interpret negative occurrences in stable and durable terms (such as item 4), as this will discourage you and diminish your hope.

- **Reject negative thoughts.** Many pessimistic thoughts contain mistakes of logic and we need to learn how to refute them. If your vacation goes wrong, you cannot conclude saying that all future attempts of vacation will go wrong. You should look for specific, modifiable, and transitory reasons to regain control over past failures and place hope in the future. (See the box on the previous page).

- **Reflect on the past with serenity.** Look at past events with calm. Focus especially on the pleasant things and revive your appreciation and gratitude for your experiences. If you do this, you will see the future in a more positive way, as there are enough blessings in the past to look at the future with hope.

Hope improves academic achievement

Daniel Goleman, the creator of the concept of emotional intelligence, cites a study (Goleman, 1995) conducted at the University of Kansas among first-year college students.

Participants decided they would obtain a B-letter grade in a specific subject. At the end of the first term, results were C grades.

What happened from that point on to the end of the school year?

The level of hope was crucial to raise their grades. Students who kept a high level of hope found ways to work harder and achieve their goal. On the other hand, those having low levels of hope lost their motivation.

In addition, the statistical analysis revealed that hope levels were a better predictor of final grades than the results of a standardised achievement test (Scholastic Achievement Test – SAT) given to all students at the beginning of the school year.

- **Break the cycle.** In moments when despair surrounds you, find some way to break the routine. Get out to a distant natural setting, breathe new air, entertain yourself with something different, call up a friend from school whom you have not seen for years, listen to new music… These variations will renew your spirit and you will be able to look at the future with hope.

- **Practise optimism.** Hope and optimism are closely linked together. There are two ways to interpret the same fact: 'It is probable that my headache is a tumour;' and 'It is probable that my headache is nothing.' In the absence of further information, choose the second alternative. Everything, absolutely everything, has a positive and a negative side. Look at both, but relish the positive side and enjoy the results.

- **Use self-instruction.** Sometimes you may fall into despair. Send encouraging messages to yourself: 'Julia, things will work out. Anxiety does not help; it takes away energy from you and things will turn out wrong. Remember how everything was solved last time.'

- **Read and meditate on maxims of wisdom.** Get books of proven reputation, books containing elevating themes and profound maxims of wisdom. Meditate on them and find peace and strength to nourish your hope. The Gospels, the Book of Psalms and the Book of Proverbs are inspired texts that have provided support and guide to strengthen many people's sense of hope.

Pandora's box

Hesiod tells that Zeus swore to take revenge on Prometheus because he stole the gods' fire. To do so, he sent Pandora (the most beautiful and first woman according to Greek mythology) to his brother Epimetheus.

Pandora, as dizzy as she was charming, opened a box she had received with the specific warning to keep it shut. It contained all evils: Old Age, Fatigue, Illness, Vice, Madness, and Passion. When the evils left the box, all humanity was contaminated. Only False Hope remained in the box. This made man believe (in vain, according to Hesiod) that with hope it was possible to overcome all those evils.

This curious legend shows the negative and fatalistic concept of hope that paganism had. A very different idea, for instance, from the Judaeo-Christian worldview.

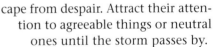

- **Seek a good social circle.** Hope does not only increase through your own influence. The presence of hopeful and positive people does produce a benign effect. Look for those who enjoy hope and become friends with them. Spend time being with healthy people. Offer your help in whatever you can. You will see how well received you are and what a vision of hope you will gain.

- **Transmit courage and hope to other people.** Part of your personal growth includes approaching others and exerting a positive influence upon them. Whenever you speak with someone going through trials, give them courage and help them to es-

cape from despair. Attract their attention to agreeable things or neutral ones until the storm passes by.

- **Take care of your physical well-being.** Keeping yourself fit, healthy and in comfort are conditions that help you to look at the future with hope. Take care of yourself so that your thinking may be hopeful. Follow the simple but effective advice to improve and maintain your health: simple and varied diet, rest, exercise and activity, pure air, plenty of water, absence of toxic substances, and trust in God.

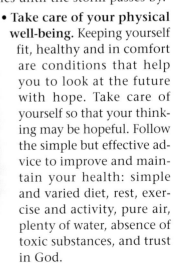
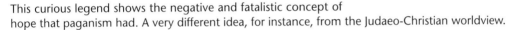

Religious hope

Aside from favouring a positive attitude towards the future and being a source of mental health, hope is a quality closely related to religious faith.

The majority of religions are founded in hope or consider it as an important part of religion.

To the believer, hope is a gift from God. It links past, present and future, offering an eventual and definite end.

These are the most relevant features of hope in the religious context:

1. Hope refers to **salvation**. Religious hope provides an ultimate solution to the problem of human suffering. It culminates in eternal salvation according to a plan worked out by God himself:
   'Resting on the hope of eternal life, which God, who does not lie, promised before the beginning of time' (Titus 1:2).

2. It is **essential to survive**. In a world touched by injustice and suffering, we need to find refuge in the psalmist's words, which offer hope in God as the means of vital support:
   'I am still confident of this: I will see the goodness of the Lᴏʀᴅ in the land of the living. Wait for the Lᴏʀᴅ; be strong and take heart and wait for the Lᴏʀᴅ' (Psalm 27:13, 14).

3. It takes **more than human effort** to attain it. In the biblical context, it is not only interest in hope and individual perseverance, but **divine intervention** that makes this wonderful gift possible. The apostle Paul testifies that true hope comes free from God:

'May our Lord Jesus Christ himself and God our Father, who loved us and by his grace gave us eternal encouragement and good hope...' (2 Thessalonians 2:16).

4. It brings about **joy.** Religious hope has nothing to do with contrition, suffering and penance. True hope causes joy, happiness and well-being. Paul freely uses this concept: 'Be joyful in hope, patient in affliction, faithful in prayer.' (Romans 12: 12). 'May the God of hope fill you with all joy and peace as you trust in him, so that you may overflow with hope by the power of the Holy Spirit' (Romans 15:13).

5. It extends to the **return of Jesus** or the end of the world. Hope, according to the Bible, culminates with Jesus' return to this earth, which marks the end of fear, injustice and suffering: '... while we wait for the blessed hope—the glorious appearing of our great God and Saviour, Jesus Christ' (Titus 2:13).

6. It entails the **certainty of resurrection.** After an unfair life ending in death, the Christian hope encourages believers to know that one day they will be raised up to attain eternal salvation: 'Brothers, we do not want you to be ignorant about those who fall asleep, or to grieve like the rest of men, who have no hope. [...] For the Lord himself will come down from heav-en, with a loud command, with the voice of the archangel and with the trumpet call of God, and the dead in Christ will rise first' (1 Thessalonians 4:13, 16).

7. It focuses on a **perfect and eternal reward.** Religious hope goes into a totally different stage, another dimension, a new order to reach the global and ultimate solution. 'Praise be to the God and Father of our Lord Jesus Christ! In his great mercy he has given us new birth into a living hope through the resurrection of Jesus Christ from the dead, and into an inheritance that can never perish, spoil or fade—kept in heaven for you' (1 Peter 1:3, 4).

If you have not yet made religious hope a part of your life, we invite you to try. Study and accept these promises as a hope of salvation and eternity for your life.

This acceptance will cause changes that will bring about more sense to your life and a much more complete hope.

Gems of Ancient Wisdom

'Anyone who is among the living has hope—even a live dog is better off than a dead lion!' (Ecclesiastes 9:4).

'Know also that wisdom is sweet to your soul; if you find it, there is a future hope for you, and your hope will not be cut off' (Proverbs 24:14).

'Because when the plowman plows and the thresher threshes, they ought to do so in the hope of sharing in the harvest' (1 Corinthians 9:10).

1.15

The wish to be happy

Everybody wants to be happy. While it is true that perfect happiness does not exist, it is possible to attain a reasonable amount of it and maintain it most of the time. What does happiness depend upon? Does it have to do with money or possessions? Is it dependent on genetic endowment held by some and not by others? Is it plain luck or good fortune?

The available evidence does not point to a certain social class, a geographic location, or high or low purchasing power. Instead, it indicates that the decision to be happy is a personal choice. Yes, grasping happiness is a matter of will, of wanting and learning to be happy, and of keeping it throughout life.

Who is happy?

There has been a great deal of studies focused on happiness over the last ten years—what is the cause of happiness, who is happy, how happiness can be attained. Based on these results and attempting to answer the question: 'Who is happy?', we find the following that tend to be happy:

- **Those with friends.** A lively and positive social context is a great factor in achieving happiness. Isolated individuals do not enjoy the company of others and are among the least happy.

- **Those with good humour.** Good sense of humour and laughter are cause and consequence of happiness (see the box on the adjoining page.)

Fable of the happy man's shirt

(or the importance of a positive attitude towards life)

Happiness is an internal (rather than external) state. A great Indian prince had anything his heart desired. However, he was not happy. He possessed money, palaces, servants that made his life comfortable, entertainment… But he did not enjoy life. One day, he decided to find a solution to his problem and consulted his wise men.

–What should I do to be happy?

–Nobody is happy. Your Highness is asking for the impossible.

The prince was left in sadness. Soon one of the wise men approached and offered his advice:

–If Your Highness wishes to be happy, Your Highness must put on the shirt of a happy man.

Straightaway, the Indian prince started the search for a happy man through his entire kingdom. But everyone offered excuses:

–I do not have enough to feed my family and I am sad.

–I am unhappy.

–I feel tired and ill.

Everybody seemed to lack something and the happy man could not be found. Rich and poor, young and old, men and women…, nobody was happy.

One day, the Indian prince walked by a cave, the dwelling place of a hermit. He had nothing, lived eating whatever he found, and spent his life in contemplation and meditation.

–Are you happy? –Asked the Indian prince.

–Completely happy! –was the answer.

—Then give me your shirt –asked the prince.

The hermit looked tenderly into the prince's eyes and said:

–I would gladly give it to you, but I am so poor that I do not have even one shirt.

(Pierre Babin)

charity work for the benefit of the needy.

- **Those committed to a religious faith.** Religious parishioners show superior levels of happiness when compared with those not holding any religious belief (see the box on the next page).

Decide for happiness

A great deal of happiness depends on the desire to be happy, a conscious and firm decision to reach that state. **Martin Seligman**, the creator of the learned helplessness theory and of positive psychology, proposed the following happiness equation:

Happiness = Heredity + Circumstances + Will

There is, in fact, a significant part of being happy that comes to us through **heredity**. Many personality traits, mood, temperament and the way one judges situations are partly transmitted by genetic processes.

- **Those in good marriages.** A bad marriage is hell, but a good marital relationship brings about happiness to both spouses. Among married people, 40% assess themselves as 'very happy,' while only 24% of the non-married individuals (singles, widows and widowers, separated, and divorced) declare themselves 'very happy.'

- **The altruistic.** The highest happiness rates are found among those practising social help and

Smile, tomorrow will be better

Researchers of the University of California at Berkeley conducted a study (Harker and Keltner, 2001) where the main source of data was class photographs of 141 females who graduated in 1960. Based on a careful facial analysis, experts classified these photos into two groups:

1. Those exhibiting an open, natural and sincere smile.
2. Those who smiled in a forced manner or did not smile.

Personal data was collected from participants at the time they reached 27 years of age. Again, data was gathered at the age 43; and then at 52. It would seem difficult to believe that class pictures would be able to predict anything valuable. However, it was evident that women in group 1 had a greater probability of getting married, enjoying a happier marriage, and attaining a higher degree of personal satisfaction than women in group 2.

RELIGION AND HAPPINESS

Physical dividends of religion

- Persons regularly attending religious services live longer than non-attendants.
- Religion helps endure pain.
- Religiosity reduces the risk of arteriosclerosis and heart attack.
- People committed to their religious beliefs recover better from illness than the non-committed ones.

Emotional dividends of religion

- Religious faith is a preventive factor of suicide, psychotic behaviour, and anxiety.
- Religious people possess greater hope than non-religious ones.
- Believers enjoy a low risk of crime and substance dependence.

(Schumaker, 1992; Larson, 1992; Barker, 1995).

Religion can help you to be happier. Consider this option to live a fuller life. But make sure that your religiosity is serious and committed, not merely nominal or a formality.

Circumstances also determine happiness: the place where one grows up and lives, material means, age, position, civil state… all have something to do with the attainment of happiness.

But the factor that, according to Seligman, has the most weight in the happiness equation is **will, or the desire to be happy**, the firm belief that one wants and can be happy. (Read about the study referred to in the box on the adjoining page, one of the most relevant investigations on happiness and longevity).

If you wish to be happy, decide to be: 'I am going to be happy!' Once your decision is made, you will have to overcome (or simply not pay attention to) the many barriers intercepting happiness. You will also need to promote the pleasant aspects of your life and relish them.

Your life and experiences can be either a source of happiness or suffering. And depending on how you judge them, they may build up or destroy your happiness. Look at the past with satisfaction, contemplate the future with hope, and decide to be happy at present.

Satisfaction with the past

Many mental, emotional and personality disorders and disturbances happen because of events of the past.

Likewise, a great deal of joys and positive moods are linked to past events. But even of more importance than the events themselves, are **the way we judge** those memories.

Avoid regrets for past events. Nobody can ever change them. Use those past experiences as a learning tool to avoid future complications. And as far as the rewarding memories are concerned, treasure them, revive them and talk to your dear ones about them.

Happiness at present

'Enjoy the here and now,' says one of the maxims in psychotherapy. Many emotional ailments are caused by past events, or by anxious thoughts of the future. In the mean time, the present slips by, and the opportunity to experience happiness is gone.

Joy favours longevity

A longitudinal study (Danner, Snowdon and Friesen, 2001) with 180 participant nuns showed that, in spite of having basically identical environment and lifestyle, there were significant differences in longevity.

Some nuns died before the age of 60, others were almost 100 when the study was published.

The exhaustive analysis of their written autobiographies revealed an amazing fact. In their writings about their life and experiences, some often noted how work and service had brought about 'happiness' and 'joy' to their lives and how they experienced 'delight' realising this or that project.

Other nuns, however, did not refer to positive emotions when writing the same events in their diaries.

According to these data, researchers (without knowing at the time the nun's age or whether they lived or not) classified the texts into **two groups according to the degree of happiness evident** by their writings. After studying their personal data, these were the results for each of the two groups:

- **High-rate-of-happiness group:** 90% of nuns were alive at 85 years of age. Nine years later, 54% of them were still alive at the age of 94.
- **Lesser-rate-of-happiness group:** 34% of nuns were alive at 85 years of age. Nine years later, only 11% of them were alive at the age of 94.

To be happy at present, learn to enjoy the simple things of today, the environment, people, flowers, children, animals, a smile, the good mood of some people... Use and enjoy your senses. If one of them does not offer a pleasant experience, ignore it and focus on the others. Put aside the fast pace and make a pause to experience tranquillity, serenity, and fluency. Relish the reading of a good book, visit an elderly person or give a hand to someone in need. In your duties, take difficulties as challenges and you will receive satisfaction as a result.

Optimism about the future

Nobody knows the future and therefore it is futile to suffer for what does not yet exist. But you can prevent many personal evils. In order to avoid an undesirable future, take control of your life with firm determination, shown in statements such as: 'I will do everything possible to avoid it; many have done it, I can also do it.' Avoid generalisations over negative and catastrophic aspects: 'It always turns out badly,' 'All men are the same,' 'I will never change for better,' 'Nobody cares for me.' Instead, use hopeful thoughts: 'I committed a mistake, but I will not repeat it again,' 'I must be very careful with certain men,' or 'What can I do so that others accept me and care for me?'

Gems of Ancient Wisdom

'Light is shed upon the righteous and joy on the upright in heart' (Psalm 97:11).

'Be joyful always' (1 Thessalonians 5:16).

1.16

Causes of mental illness

It is very difficult to pinpoint with precision the causes of mental disorders. Heredity and environment interact in such an intricate way that it is not possible to know for certain which is predominant. The origin of mental illnesses, especially the most common ones, is under constant study and conclusions are not always clear. Nevertheless, there are some general trends about their origin. Let's outline them for each disorder:

Anxiety

There is evidence that bio-chemical processes in the brain undergo changes in people with generalised anxiety disorder and with phobias. This is constantly verified by the use of medication. However, there are manifestations of anxiety, such as panic attacks, that are due to highly stressing experiences that trigger the crisis.

Psychoactive substance abuse

What makes some people fall into dependence and not others? Studies on twins, as well as studies among siblings and adoptive children, show that many of those ending up in trouble with substances have a genetic predisposition. However, the example that parents set for their children (even adopted ones) and the influence of the social environment are crucial factors in the onset and course of the problem.

Depression

The influence of heredity upon depression is significant and this has been firmly established through twin studies. Biology also has its part. It is a proven fact that excessive levels of dopamine and norpinephrine seem to trigger the depressive symptoms. Yet, many psychotherapeutic treatments clearly demonstrate that personal attitude, positive thoughts, rational analysis of events, or hope toward the future prevent and combat depression.

Schizophrenia

The root of this severe mental illness seems to be of genetic nature. However, psychological intervention, together with a careful pharmacological treatment, affects positively the course of the disorder.

Eating disorders

Disorders such as anorexia nervosa and bulimia nervosa seem to have their exclusive origin in cultures and societies where the value of slimness is overestimated, particularly in women.

Traumas

Traumas are rooted in some past, purely environmental event. Avoiding such events is a sure way to prevent these long-lasting problems.

SELF-HELP IS NOT FOR EVERY PROBLEM

There is an increasing tendency to emphasize mental state, attitude, positive thinking, serenity and optimal interpersonal relationships. We believe in this and much advice contained in this book is based on these principles. However, whenever we have to face mental disorders of a clinical nature, such as schizophrenia, depression or anxiety, we need to seek a good professional (psychiatrist or clinical psychologist) to receive the appropriate treatment.

A well-understood self-help strategy will not hurt anyone but, while it may provide support, it can be insufficient.

Does gender affect mental health?

A World Health Organization (WHO) study (Tansella, 1998) showed the following facts:
- During the years of development, boys are more prone to mental disorders than girls. On the other hand, adolescent girls are more at risk of behavioural disturbances than their male counterparts. These differences diminish at the end of adolescence.
- During the adult stage, men suffer from substance abuse (alcohol and drugs) more than women and women experience more anxiety, depression and eating disorders.
- The previous fact is not only certain in the highly industrialised regions of the world, but also in countries and cultures of Africa, Asia, Middle East, and Latin-America.
- Men are more given to crime and suicide (90% of them due to some kind of mental disorder) than women.

Gems of Ancient Wisdom

'You will keep in perfect peace him whose mind is steadfast, because he trusts in you' (Isaiah 26:3).

TEST YOURSELF ::

Answer YES or NO to the following questions:

Am I prone to mental disease?	YES	NO
1. Are you able to reject sombre thoughts with relative ease?		
2. Do you tend to look at the positive side of things?		
3. Do you tend to forget the offences others did to you in the past?		
4. Are you reasonably satisfied with the way you are?		
5. Do you often display laughter and good humour?		
6. Do you seek conversation with other people?		
7. Is it easy for you to open your intimate thoughts to someone you trust?		
8. Do you belong to a mentally healthy family?		
9. Do you practise altruistic help with someone in need?		
10. Are you satisfied with your employment?		
11. Do you know how to escape from too much stress?		
12. Do you practise hobbies and activity that help you to relax and make you feel well?		
13. Do you keep physically active?		
14. Do you enjoy good health?		
15. Do you look at the future with confidence and hope?		

Interpretation:
The more YES answers you have given, the more protection you have against psychological ailments. Examine each of the questions and consider what you can do to answer affirmatively to each of them. Read and learn (from this book and others) practical ways to improve your mental health.

1.17

Prevention
of mental illnesses

There are organic mental illnesses such as schizophrenia or bipolar disorder (manic depression) that carry a strong genetic component and are long-lasting.

During the last 100 years, the frequency of these disorders has kept constant and has affected a relatively small proportion of the population. It can be said that their prognosis and course is predictable and requires psychiatric care, aside from the corresponding psychotherapeutic intervention to manage the problem.

However, there are other ailments that have been subject to an alarming increase in the last 100 years, like depression, anxiety, substance dependence, or the effects of psychological stress. This **development of mental problems** has nothing to do with genetics and much relationship with **lifestyle** and **mental attitude**. Depression, for instance, is now affecting proportionally double the number than fifty years ago and it is endemic both in high-technology regions as well as in areas of primary economy.

What can we do to break away from this diabolic tendency to spread mental illness over extensive sectors of the world population?

Positive psychology (see page 311) would say that positive emotions do not visit us frequently, due to current circumstances. People live obsessed with tasks that cause a long inventory of negative emotions. As a result, most live unhappily and many end up suffering from mental disorders.

self-help

HARBOUR POSITIVE FEELINGS AND EMOTIONS

Love	Tenderness	Kindness
Trust	Good mood	Gratitude
Self-esteem	Helpfulness	Enthusiasm
Optimism	Generosity	Spirituality
Peace	Forgiveness	Serenity
Joy	Empathy	Hope

At the beginning of each day, plan not to accept any negative emotion. Choose two or three positive emotions (among the most needed ones) and remind yourself each hour of your goal to systematically give priority to them.

Positive feelings and emotions

Mental health promotion, as well as the prevention of mental disorders, can be carried out by avoiding negative emotions (hatred, envy, rage, frustration, pessimism, sadness, impatience, despair…) and focusing on positive emotions.

Any person who is conscious of this process may possess sufficient control to harbour one kind or another according to his/her will. The enclosed Self-help box (on the top of this page) offers a menu of positive emotions for the reader to use daily or as much as he/she can.

Preventive behaviours

A few simple but profound and effective activities are suggested below. They may be beneficial to everyone, especially to those wishing to prevent mental illness. Try all the pieces of advice offered and practise those providing the best and most lasting satisfaction:

1. **Think optimistically** (see pages 20 and 48) When something goes wrong in your life, consider explanations that include solutions, not those hopeless thoughts that will be a barrier to triumph in the future. Take courage to try again and be careful to provide the necessary precautions. As for your good accomplishments, congratulate yourself and adopt an attitude of gratitude. Think that there is something good in you (not just luck) when things have turned out well.

2. **Develop your self-esteem** (see page 28). When you feel inferior, you are lowering your defences against mental ailments. Practise the habit of increasing your self-confidence every day.

   Find your strengths (we all have them) and reflect on your accomplishments. If you cannot think of any, talk to someone you trust so that he/she may help you identify them. Write down these strengths and carry them with you. Review them once in a while and make plans to carry out useful tasks where you can put to work your resources and gifts. And when you achieve something, do not take away the merit you deserve.

3. **Find support in people.** The most frequent 'downs' of mental health come through the ad-

verse effect of people. In the same way, recovery takes place also through the personal intervention of others, either a professional or someone else providing support and help to the needy. Care for the best possible relationship with your marriage partner, boss, peers, neighbours... Get used to positive and cooperative relationships. Be courteous and respectful with everyone. Avoid remaining at home with the TV or computer. Instead, go out and spend time in interaction with others.

4. **Keep active** (see page 324). The most effective plans against depression (the most common mental malady in the world) almost always include an activity program. Besides, nearly all types of mental disorders are incompatible with activity. Grant a reasonable time to your work. Then, during your free time, supplement your professional activity with one of a different nature (if your employment is sedentary, practise a sport or get physical exercise).

   If you don't like a certain activity, try another— Do-it-yourself tasks, errands, shopping, visiting friends, pastimes... Do not stay home doing nothing

5. **Face guilt** (see page 164). If you are invaded by this, whether true or unfounded, act quickly, for guilt is dangerous to your mental health. If

you have said or done something painful to someone else and the thought of it makes you feel guilty, go and talk to the offended person. Sincerely and humbly ask for forgiveness. The other person will most likely grant your request and the damage will be repaired.

Sometimes, the offended person may not be available or will not accept your apology. In that case, search for God and confess your transgression. The Bible tells that 'if we confess our sins

to God, he will keep his promise and do what is right—he will forgive us our sins and purify us from all our wrongdoing.' (1 John 1: 9).

6. **Take care of your physical health.** Mind and physical health are very closely knit together (see pages 52 and 180). When suffering from a physical ailment, you will not enjoy mental well-being. It is therefore necessary to keep your health in the best possible condition.

   • *Watch your diet.* Eat foods close to their original state. Variety is a sure guide: grains, vegetables, fruits, grains, and nuts in their many forms. Eating moderately will ensure good nutrition. The great majority of foods of animal origin are not necessary and they may be bad for your health.

   • *Exercise* (see page 322). Your body requires activity. Bones and muscles need movement to regenerate and to keep in good condition. Make a systematic plan for physical exercise through sport or play. If you cannot tolerate vigorous physical exercise, at least walk.

   • *Sleep regularly at night.* Make sure you get your 7 to 8 hours every day. If you have problems going to sleep, establish a pre-bed routine—warm bath, reading, pleasant temperature and comfortable bed. Avoid intensive exercise and abundant meals before going to bed. Turn the TV/music off, as nocturnal noise keeps the subconscious alert.

   • *Keep away from psychoactive substances* (see page 130). Drugs, alcohol and even coffee excite the central nervous system and alter your mood. In mental health, any preventive or healing plan should totally eliminate these substances. It is estimated that 15% of all cases of mental illness are associated or complicated with the use of alcohol/drugs. Remember that any chemical capable of altering the central nervous system increases the risk to develop a mental illness.

7. **Carry out humanitarian services.** Prepare or participate in support plans to help the indigent or needy. This will be helpful to them and also to you. In your free time, visit an elderly person, help a single mother, or join any project for the improvement of your neighbourhood. Do everything in good spirit and with gratitude. Seeing that others benefit from your

help, you will notice that your problems shrink and fade away.

8. **Keep a hopeful attitude.** This is one of the most useful resources to maintain good mental health. Do not be pessimistic about the future. Reflect on the past in a neutral manner, focusing on good, rather than unpleasant memories. Remove from your mind ideas of catastrophe, misfortune and calamity.

9. **Seek natural environments.** Mental disorders thrive in urban environments, while total health thrives in the midst of nature. If the work pressures prevent you from living outside the city, at least try and bring nature to your house—plants, flowers, a pet... Whenever you have the chance, go to the countryside, a big park or the mountains, and you will enjoy nature with all your senses.

10. **Bring the spiritual facet to your life.** The spiritual dimension may be fed through music, contemplative thought, the study of exemplary biographies..., but the most complete spirituality is attained by means of the religious experience, whereby God is accepted by faith. Not a tyrant god who enjoys punishing men to make them suffer, but a loving God who listens and responds to his children's prayers.
Through prayer and closeness to God you will obtain mental peace and serenity. Fill your life with faith and contemplate the hope of salvation and total happiness. If you have not done it before, try praying, but not as chanting. Use your own words to express your gratitude, hopes, and desires.

Gems of Ancient Wisdom

'Those who love your law have perfect security, and there is nothing that can make them fall' (Psalm 119:165).

1.18

Barriers to mental health

The prevention and treatment of mental illness find even more barriers than those in physical illness. This puts the mental health patient in a position of **manifest disadvantage**.

Being aware of the barriers to mental health may lead to the solution, albeit partially, of this difficult problem. This unit covers the most relevant obstacles:

1. **Social stigma.** Mental illness (especially when compared with the physical ailments) has been traditionally considered as shameful. This makes many who suffer from a mental disorder keep it hidden, thus depriving themselves from the benefits that could come from professionals or members of the community.

2. **Resistance to treatment.** Partly due to the previous barrier and partly to the condition of illness, the patient has a high resistance to treatment and a good chance of abandoning the intervention.

3. **Insurance coverage.** Many health insurance systems cover physical illness without including mental health problems. And those with full coverage often expect a full clinical diagnosis before authorisation of payment. In other words, to obtain a diagnosis of depression, for example, the patient must manifest five symptoms from the diagnosis manual. If four are displayed, the insurance will not take responsibility.

4. **The rise of mental illnesses.** The growing occurrence of mental illness is flooding

the health systems, which are left unprepared to cope with the volume of need.

The morbidity effect of mental illnesses is immediately below cardiovascular disease (see the box on the adjoining page). In a special way this rise is increasingly touching the senior sector with depression, dementia and schizophrenia.

Research Results

Mental maladies shorten the life span

The study entitled *Global Burden of Disease* (Murray and López, 1996) was carried out at the Harvard School of Public Health. This investigation was commissioned by WHO and the World Bank. The document specifies the ranking of diseases causing premature death throughout the world with an estimation of the years that life was shortened due to the effect of the particular illness. Mental disorders are in second place (after cardiovascular disease), with a loss of over 15 years of life.

	Diseases causing labour incapacitation and premature death	Mean years of life loss
1.	All cardiovascular diseases	18.6
2.	**All mental diseases (including suicide)**	**15.4**
3.	All forms of cancer	15.0
4.	All respiratory (including smoking-related) diseases	4.8
5.	All alcohol-related diseases	4.7

5. **The dissociation between research and practice.** Many health systems are anchored in ancestral ideas putting excessive emphasis on psychiatric hospitals and pharmacology, without paying much attention to psychotherapy or family and community support.

6. **Co-morbidity of mental disease.** Most mental disorders have co-morbid relationships with other mental problems. This means that many cases show a cluster of diagnoses, thus complicating the treatment.

7. **Lack of knowledge and information.** The majority of patients who begin experiencing symptoms of a mental and psychological nature do not know what to do or who to go to for help. In addition, there is a lack of knowledge of the maladies and the many remedies that may be applied. In numerous cases, simple self-help advice could prevent greater complications, but these solutions are not well known.

8. **Loss of employment.** According to the Global Burden of Disease report, sponsored by the World Health Organization and the World Bank, four out of ten reasons to grant labour incapacitation are of a mental nature (depression, obsessive-compulsive disorder, schizophrenia, manic depression, etc.). In other words, sufferers from mental conditions run a high risk of losing their employment. As a result, patients are deprived of one of the most significant sources of satisfaction: work. This condition often causes a worsening of the disease.

9. **The predominance of treatment over prevention.** Research in mental health is targeted to the treatment (particularly pharmacological) of diseases rather than prevention and mental health promotion. Thus, the knowledge of mental disease nowadays is much greater than the knowledge of mental health. This means that problems do not receive attention until they are formally diagnosed.

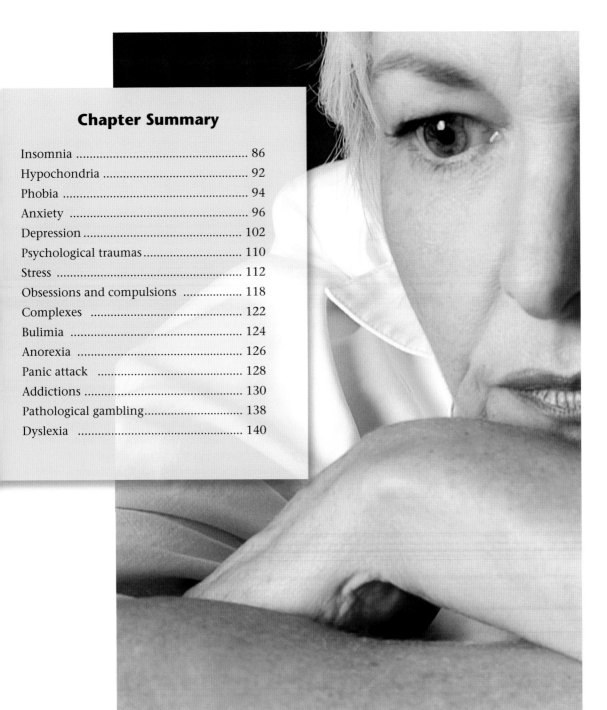

Chapter Summary

Self-centred problems (I)

2

Angela's children were already grownups when they left for the university. Her husband continued to be absorbed by work. Without knowing why, she started feeling useless, sad, discouraged and with very little energy.

She loved to cook and was very creative in the culinary arts. But suddenly, she began to feel repulsion for the kitchen. She did not feel like going out or travelling, which she enjoyed so much previously. She started to experience sleep difficulties, taking a long time to fall asleep and waking up very early. So she spent long nightly hours ruminating about the possibility of her children failing their studies or her husband losing his job. In addition, she started to lament the fact that her friends from school had completed higher education and she was just a mother, wife and homemaker.

Angela finally went to the doctor's, where she was diagnosed with depression. She was told that depression is quite common and that she could be healed with medication and psychotherapy. The departure of her children apparently triggered her problem. She felt such an empty spot in her life without them that she felt as if she had reached retirement age without wishing it.

She took her medication and went to a lady psychologist twice per week. Results were slow but notable. In four months, Angela saw life differently and started to look towards the future with hope.

Chapter Highlights

- People may not adequately face sleeping difficulties due to **widely accepted false ideas or beliefs**. Do not permit those myths to precondition you. Instead, tackle your sleeping difficulties based on your own experience.

- Anxiety medication, sedatives and tranquillisers are commonly used for anxiety treatment. However, these drugs have significant side effects. It is useful to consider **herbal and diet remedies** to soothe anxiety symptoms.

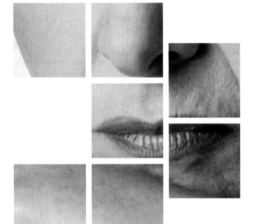

- Going through an upsetting experience or great worry does not necessarily mean depression. However, those emotional ups and downs may be the preamble. It is necessary to **be alert** to avoid that these events become prolonged.

- **Good time management** prevents stress; thus we need to know how to plan. Time is an asset given equally to everyone, and we make use of it according to our lifestyle.

- To fight bulimia **clinical psychological treatment** is the most adequate for bulimia. Diagnosed anorexia, in turn, calls for **strict medical treatment** and, in many cases, hospitalisation.

- Happiness has been defined as the total absence of addictions. We are not just talking about addictions to **'hard' or 'illegal' drugs**. There are ordinary and regularly-used addictive substances such as **alcoholic beverages**, **cigarettes** or **coffee**.

The most clinically relevant problems with oneself

A high proportion of conflicts and problems faced by human beings have to do with oneself. The knowledge of one's **strengths and weaknesses** helps to channel one's will, to prepare the environment and to take steps towards preventing or solving the difficulties.

Both this chapter and the next are devoted to dealing with **common problems centred around oneself**. Those with greater clinical relevance will be covered in this chapter and the remaining in chapter 3. Simple but effective solutions are offered as options.

Deep and restorative sleep contributes to the daily maintenance of mental health. **Insomnia** (unit 2.01) is the number one enemy of this daily need and must be solved definitively. **Hypochondriacs** (unit 2.02), who are extremely sensitive, fear disease and may even think they have contracted one when they have not; they need to learn how to eliminate this exaggerated perception. It is frequent to find individuals who suffer from **phobia and panic attacks** (units 2.03 and 2.12) towards a variety of objects, situations, or contexts to the point of becoming incapacitated or prevented from leading normal lives. They need to learn ways to free themselves from this burden.

This chapter also describes mental disorders common throughout the world—**anxiety** and **depression** (units 2.04 and 2.05). According to WHO, there are more than one hundred million persons with depression in the world. If we include those who have a depressive person nearby (family, peers, friends, etc.), we conclude that hundreds of millions of people suffer directly or indirectly from this problem. The reader will find this data helpful in better understanding these disorders and learning ways to prevent and cure them.

Stress (unit 2.07) is another problem affecting almost everyone. Knowing how to identify and face the causes of excessive stress is paramount. One should be prepared to tolerate a moderate amount of stress (which is necessary for achievement) without permitting intolerable levels.

A pressing problem over the last few generations is the growing use of **drugs** (unit 2.13). Addictive mechanisms are so powerful that they end up completely enslaving those who abuse these substances. We must also warn that people can become **addicts to sex, gambling** (unit 2.14) or any other habit-forming behaviour, which will considerably limit individual freedom. In such cases, tolerance, dependence, and withdrawal symptoms follow a pattern similar to that of chemical substances.

This chapter also includes a series of specific problems, such as **traumas** (unit 2.06), **obsessive-compulsive** disorder (unit 2.8), **complexes** (unit 2.09), **bulimia nervosa** (unit 2.10), **anorexia nervosa** (unit 2.11) and **dyslexia** (unit 2.15). Methods of primary assistance are suggested for all of the above. It is our goal to help readers identify attitudes and skills necessary to overcome these disorders, as well as enabling them to help others do the same.

2.01

Insomnia

Many people complain that they do not sleep well. Some take a long time to fall asleep, others suffer from intermittent wakefulness or early wakeup. Still others have a combination of these symptoms. Various statistics show that between 30 and 40% of the population complain of insufficient sleep quality, although only 3-4% are clinically diagnosed with insomnia.

Sleep is very important for health. Being deprived of it brings about serious problems of concentration and memory. In addition, insomnia causes drowsiness over the next day, slowness, poor achievement, and the lowering of defences with its corresponding proneness to illness. In fact, recent studies point out that there is a correlation between good sleep and **longevity** (see the Research Results box on page 88).

Unlike other disorders, insomnia has a clear **subjective component**. In other words, some people sleep relatively well, but they complain saying that they should sleep better and more. Others toss and turn in bed for an hour and are convinced that they have been several hours without sleeping. Perhaps due to the subjective nature of insomnia, false beliefs have developed (see the box on the adjoining page).

FALSE BELIEFS ABOUT INSOMNIA

People may not adequately face sleeping difficulties due to widely accepted false ideas or beliefs. Do not permit those myths to precondition you. Instead, tackle your sleeping difficulties based on your own experience.

- *'If you try hard to fall asleep, you will be able to do it with effort and perseverance.'* It is almost always **false**. In practice, whenever someone has lost the desire to sleep, he/she will remain awake for quite awhile. Sleep is not for us to catch, but for **it to catch us**.

- *'If you do not sleep well, the next day will be awful.'* It can be true, but this is generally due to **your own expectations** rather than to the lack of sleep. Poor sleep or no sleep at all one night is not as tragic as it may sound. Next day routine tasks can be performed, although it is true that we will have difficulty carrying out a new, difficult or very dangerous task. And, of course, achievement will become considerably lower when one accumulates several sleepless nights.

- *'Everyone needs eight hours of sleep per day.'* This depends on each person. It is true that most adults need between 7 and 8 hours of sleep, but there is a great variation, as 90% of the population sleep between 6 and 9 hours, and children more than that. **Study yourself to understand your real needs**. Sleeping too little is unhealthy and sleeping too much will diminish your well-being.

- *'People older than 60 need to sleep much less than younger adults.'* False. Sleeping needs lower with age, but only **slightly**. Sleeping **patterns** have been known to change after the age of 60; however, people at this age drift while they watch TV or when they travel by bus, coach or train, and they take naps here and there. For that reason, they sleep fewer hours at night, but the sum total varies very little.

- *'I did not sleep a wink last night.'* It is a doubtful statement as, according to multiple and controlled observations, it has been concluded that we perceive the vigil time as much longer than it actually is. Thus, it is not surprising that when a man complains to his wife of not having slept, she replies: 'Then, who was snoring last night?

Barriers to good sleep

Not everyone is endowed with a natural disposition to sleep well. However, everybody can keep away from products that make sleep more difficult. Study the following list. The more substances you avoid, the more probability you'll have to sleep well.

- **Caffeine.** Coffee, tea, cola drinks, analgesics and slimming products contain sufficient amounts of caffeine to alter your sleep. Caffeine is a strong stimulating substance and you should avoid it as much as possible.

- **Nicotine.** When compared with non-smokers, smokers take longer to fall asleep and wake up more frequently. This is due to a small withdrawal syndrome—not being able to fall asleep or waking up in the middle of the night almost always gets 'rewarded' with a cigarette. There are many reasons to quit smoking and insomnia is one more.

- **Alcoholic drinks.** There are people that have a drink before going to bed, as alcohol induces sleepiness. However, even though it may help to sleep, the presence of alcohol in the blood alters the sleep rhythms and causes intermittent or early waking.

- **Drugs.** Narcotics and amphetamines count among the substances impeding sleep. When the person manages to fall asleep, these substances alter the sleep cycle and produce undesirable waking.

- **Medication.** There is a long list of pharmacological drugs that produce insomnia, especially anti-depressants and steroids. Many pain killers

Sleep and longevity

According to a study published in *Psychosomatic Medicine* (Dew *et al.*, 2003) senior citizens that spend half an hour or more attempting to fall asleep during the night have more probability of shortening their lives than those who sleep during the time they lie in bed. Mary Amanda Dew and her colleagues at the University of Pittsburgh School of Medicine (USA) conducted a follow-up study during 19 years with a group of 185 participants (all healthy) aged between 58 and 91. With the help of electroencephalograms, researchers objectively followed the group's sleeping patterns.

At the conclusion of the study, 66 participants had already passed away. It was noticed that the deaths had no relationship to age, gender, or known disease, but with sleeping difficulties. Many of the deceased subjects were shown to have spent their nights with wakeful periods of thirty minutes or more or slept less than 80% of the time under observation.

This study points to sleep as a **source of health** and underlines the need to make every effort to improve sleep quality, especially during the senior years.

contain caffeine and interrupt sleeping. Read the instructions of every medicine you take and consult your doctor to find the best options for you.

- **Heavy meals.** A light meal may induce sleepiness, especially if it contains complex carbohydrates (bread, pasta, rice), as their serotonin content helps in falling asleep. However, heavy meals taken close to bedtime attract all organic energy to the process of digestion, thus interrupting sleep and causing gastric discomfort. Besides, if you drink too much before going to sleep, your body will wake you up urging you to urinate.

There are also **circumstantial obstacles** that contribute to insomnia. Most of them can be controlled and it is worth trying:

- **Stressors.** Your sleep will be affected during periods of excessive work, or when you may have lost a friend or dear one. The same will happen when you go through a relevant transition (wedding, beginning of a new job or change of address). Use this unit's general advice to bring relief to the problem. If the stressor is transitory, wait until it passes, but if it is likely to be of long duration, do something to put it aside.

- **Physical environment.** The place you sleep (or the time you retire to bed) may work against you to make sleeping difficult: noise, excessive heat or cold, an uncomfortable surface (too soft or too hard), or too much light. In these cases, you must do something to improve your environmental conditions. Invest in mechanisms or measures to eliminate these distractions and to promote the ideal environment conducive to sleep.

- **Social environment.** Sleeping with someone who moves too much, or who snores; or having children who wake up and need comfort may become exasperating. Persuade your spouse to have snoring treated or consider sleeping in separate beds (or rooms). Teach your children to become progressively independent... With tact, ability, and an open mind, dialogue with the members of your household and try out solutions knowing that sleep is one half of your life.

Tips to fight insomnia

Regularity of schedules and habits is a factor in sleep success. If you are prone to insomnia, bring some **order** into your life. Get used to a **fixed time** to go to bed (preferably early) and to rise. Follow a regular routine before going to bed. Avoid travelling in excess, as this brings much irregularity.

Watch out on weekends: do not overly delay your bedtime or your time to get up, as it will take you one or two days to return to the normal schedule.

Determine your **ideal number of sleeping hours** to avoid the frustration of thinking that you suffer from insomnia. Almost everyone needs 7 or 8 hours of sleep (some even more). But there are people who only need 5 or 6 hours and they insist that they need more. Since they do not manage to sleep more, they get frustrated and experience a bad temper. Avoid drifting or taking long naps during the day.

Sedentary life is one of the best friends of insomnia, as it produces little physical tiredness and much mental fatigue. Plan for **vigorous and regular physical activity**, as it will bring about well-being and a deep and continuous sleep. Exercise raises the daytime body temperature and lowers the nighttime temperature, thus inducing sleep. In any case, exercise at the right time of day (see the box on the right).

continued on page 90

THE RIGHT TIME TO EXERCISE

Gary sometimes loses his desire to sleep. So he does weightlifting for 20 minutes in the middle of the night.

Then, tired, he goes to bed with the hope of sleeping soundly.

But his method does not work. Heavy physical exercise does not immediately induce sleep. It is better to do it several hours before going to bed, or simply to take a walk before sleeping in order to combat insomnia.

Avoid vigorous exercise immediately before going to bed.

DIET AND SLEEP

There are food items with hypnotic and sedative qualities. They are common foods easily found in any home or in the shops.

- **Oats.** Oats contain avenin, a substance with a gentle sedative effect. Oats may be prepared in soups, breakfast cereal, crackers or in vegetarian hamburger mix.

- **Lettuce.** Lettuce produces a relaxing and sedative effect. A lettuce salad before going to bed may be the key to falling asleep.

- **Aromatic linden.** For centuries, linden tea has been used for its soothing and relaxing effects. A cup of linden infusion before going to bed will cause a light sedative effect.

- **Malt.** Malt causes an opposite effect to caffeine. As with linden, take it warm before retiring to bed.

  - **Honey.** Honey contains sedative ingredients that lead to sleep. Use it as sweetener in malt or linden tea in order to enhance their sleep-inducing effect.

Sleeping pills, relaxation and the power of suggestion

The effectiveness of hypnotic medicines is doubtful. Their **side effects** and **risk of addiction** are well known, but do they really work? **Carnwath and Miller**, in their handbook *Behavioural Psychotherapy—Primary Help* (1989), cite a study by Davidson and his associates where a group of patients with insomnia were participants. They were given sleeping pills and at the same time were taught to practise relaxation. Result: all of them began to sleep better.

Days later, the group was divided into two random halves. The first group was told that the real reason for their improvement was the effect of the pills. It was explained to the second group that the reason for their better sleep had to do with the effectiveness of relaxation, as the dosage of sleeping pills was insignificant (which was false). At that time the pharmacological treatment was interrupted. The summary of the results was that the first group went back to sleeping as badly as before and the second group continued to sleep better. The reason for the second group's improvement was either self-suggestion or relaxation, not the sleeping pills for they had been interrupted!

As mentioned before, **late and heavy meals** are barriers to quality sleep. The best advice is to have a light and early supper in order to get quality rest. Besides, strong or spicy foods block the sleep process. However, there are ordinary foods with sleep-inducing and relaxing properties (see the box 'Diet and sleep' on the previous page).

Gems of Ancient Wisdom

'I will grant peace in the land, and you will lie down and no one will make you afraid' (Leviticus 26:6).

 self-help

HOW TO QUIT TABLETS

If you wish to eliminate your sleeping pills, consult your physician and mention a progressive plan to quit, such as the following proposed by **Sobel and Ornstein** (1999):

1. **First week.** Reduce the doses to half, only once during the week.
2. **Second week.** Reduce the doses to half on two days of the week (not consecutive days).
3. Do the same for each week until **all days** have **half a dosage**.
4. Return to steps 1-3 to **reduce** the original doses to $^1/_4$ each day.
5. Return to steps 1-3 to **totally eliminate** the intake.

This plan spans over **21 weeks**. If during that time you put into practice the advice given in this chapter, it is likely that you will not need your pills any longer.

AROMATHERAPY AND SLEEP

The growing use of aromatherapy (see page 37) speaks for its effectiveness as a relaxing treatment and facilitator for a serene and peaceful mood. The plants listed in this box may be used in the form of essential oils. These **oils** are obtained by distillation of flowers and/or leaves. They are sold at herbal and other specialised shops.

For insomnia, use these oils **externally**. Massage the back and arms, or drop a small amount in a hot bath, in the air freshener or on the pillow.

- **Clary sage** (*Salvia sclarea*). Its scent acts as a regulator for the nervous system, relaxing, soothing and serving as an antidepressant. Its aroma is very pleasant and reminds one of walnuts.

Clary sage

- **Lavender** (*Lavandula angustifolia*). Lavender is considered one of the top healing essential oils. Its flowers are the base and its fragrance is used to treat stress, depression, insomnia and headaches. It also helps to keep tension under control.

Lavender

- **Roman camomile** (*Chamaemelum nobile*). It is a very mild oil, thus appropriate for children. Its scent soothes the central nervous system and induces sleep. It is also used against stress and anxiety.

Roman camomile

- **Ylan Ylan** (*Cananga odorata*). It comes from the flowers of a tree originating in Indonesia. Its scent is used as a sleep-inducer, sedative, anti-depressant, and to prevent high blood pressure.

Ylan Ylan

It is a well-known fact that **warm temperature** initiates and maintains quality sleep. Therefore, take a warm **bath** and a hot, caffeine-free drink before going to bed. Try **aromatherapy** (see the box on the left) and sleep in a cool room, covered with a blanket. Try by all means not to depend on sleeping pills. In fact, they are unnecessary many times (see the Research Results box on the previous page).

Additional advice includes the practice of **systematic relaxation** (see page 40) performed regularly before going to bed, positive thinking (page 20) (for example, avoid thinking of oneself as the desperate victim of insomnia), and planned exposure to natural light as much as possible: expose oneself to solar light, go to bed not too long after sunset and get up at sunrise.

Gems of Ancient Wisdom

'The sleep of a labourer is sweet, whether he eats little or much, but the abundance of a rich man permits him no sleep' (Ecclesiastes 5:12).

2.02

Hypochondria

Persons with hypochondria interpret any symptom of physical pain in an unrealistic and exaggerated manner. A headache may be perceived as a possible brain tumour, a pain in the abdomen may be interpreted as cancer of the colon and a simple cough as tuberculosis.

Many apprehensive and insecure persons, although not meeting the complete diagnostic criteria, have the tendency to experience some traits of the disorder that can be corrected with the right mental attitude, as explained in this unit.

What to do about this problem?

Hypochondria often finds its roots in **some psychological conflict**. It is therefore important to see if there is any lack of adjustment—a long illness in childhood, personal misfortunes, marital conflict, guilt, inferiority, feelings of inadequacy, fears…

Talking about the problem or traumatising memory is a good way to get to its root. A trusting friend, willing to listen and to keep respect and confidentiality, may be the solution. If the problem persists, it is necessary to consult a psychologist or psychiatrist. When the condition is extremely bothersome, tranquillisers and anxiety medicines are prescribed, but, most of the time, these are not necessary.

When there is no apparent underlying cause, the case is not likely to be serious and can be corrected with the **tips** offered below:

- **Go to a trusted doctor** and confide your fears and anxieties. If there is no serious illness, accept it and do not question the medical diagnosis anymore.

- **Do not change doctors** or go to a different clinic as if you were shopping.

- If you are under excessive stress, try and organise your life in a **calmer way**, as stress can be a trigger to the condition.

- If your life is low-paced or boring, keep **busy** and look for an additional activity you enjoy, or a humanitarian cause.

- **Supportive relationships** are basic. Your spouse, your friend or your counsellor can be the key for you to pour out your burden and find the right balance.

- Keep a **healthy lifestyle**. Do not smoke nor drink; eat healthy food and rest well… This will bring about well-being and faith in your own body's ability to restore itself.

TRUST YOUR DOCTOR

Due to their close and exacting view of things, persons with hypochondria get frustrated and angry when health professionals do not pay sufficient attention to their illness. If the doctor suggests that they are worrying too much for something that is 'not very important,' patients get offended and go to another physician to ensure that the 'illness' is confirmed.

If you tend to worry too much about your ailments, make the firm decision to **trust in the advice of your doctor**. Think that the background and experience of health professionals is adequate to do their job well. And, if, after all medical tests, there is proof that there is no illness, be happy instead of sad!

Useful techniques for hypochondria

Two reports, published in the *British Medical Journal* (Gottlieb, 2004) and the *Journal of the American Medical Association* (Barsky and Ahern, 2004), showed that cognitive-behavioural techniques are effective in the treatment of hypochondria. These are typical strategies from that psycho-therapeutic style:

- Modelling
- Self-control
- Thought control
- Self-instruction

(For further information, see units 6.02, page 296, and 6.03, page 302).

THINK OF RELATIONSHIPS

A well-known consequence of hypochondria is the deterioration of interpersonal relationships. The life of the family or couple centres on the 'illness.'

Friends start getting bored with the clinical analyses, tests, medical exams… People around grow weary of health complaints and move slowly away until they cut the link completely.

If you are inclined to project your worries upon your body, think of the devastating results that your attitude may bring to your work, social and family relationships. Make efforts to think of health rather than illness. This may save friendships.

Gems of Ancient Wisdom

'Do not be wise in your own eyes; fear the Lord and shun evil. This will bring health to your body and nourishment to your bones' (Proverbs 3:7-8).

TEST YOURSELF ::

Answer True or False to the following statements:

Am I hypochondriac?	T	F
1. I often feel weak.		
2. I have more headaches than others.		
3. I go to the doctor as soon as I have a common cold symptom.		
4. I read many magazines and publications dealing with illnesses.		
5. I keep the medical prescriptions from the last few years.		
6. When I don't feel well, my family and friends do not pay attention to me.		
7. I call in sick at work for any small ailment.		
8. I feel good when my companions show interest in my sickliness.		
9. My health worries me the most.		
10. I am afraid that some day I will get cancer.		
11. I feel comfortable explaining to others the symptoms of my illnesses.		
12. I feel a strange sensation if I go for several days without feeling any ache.		

Interpretation:

If you have answered T to more than four statements, you should seriously reconsider your excessive worry about illness. Go to the doctor to have a medical check-up. If there is no pathology, accept it and focus on feeling well and healthy. Keep a healthy and balanced diet, get moderate exercise and maintain a positive attitude towards your physical state. Make every effort to enjoy good health for the rest of your life.

2.03
Phobia

There are people who experience fear in some places or situations (crowd, hospital, aeroplanes, open spaces…), others become frightened of certain objects or animals (syringes, insects, snakes…), still others feel generalised anxiety (see page 96) not focused on anything specific. In most cases, these fears are mild and not pathological, but other times the dimension reaches the level of phobia, and they prevent the individual from functioning at work, in relationships and personally.

In the past, there were many types of phobias with complicated names (see the table on the adjoining page), but nowadays reference is simply made to 'specific phobia' and then the object or situation is mentioned. The most common phobias are agoraphobia, social phobia and specific phobia.

Agoraphobia

People with this disorder are afraid of being by themselves in public places where it would be difficult to escape in case of emergency. For example, living alone, being in the midst of a large crowd in a market, walking by a congested street, travelling by public transportation or being in the middle of a tunnel or bridge. Agoraphobia may be accompanied by panic attack (see page 128). The person starts feeling tension at the fearful situation or even at the thought of it. Fear grows rapidly un-

til the moment when somatic symptoms start—rapid breathing, sweating, palpitations…).

Social phobia

Persons with social phobia experience an **irrational or unfounded fear of social situations** such as attending a party, eating in a restaurant, using public lavatories or speaking in public. They try by all means to avoid these encounters, often cancelling appointments and excusing themselves from attending events. This seriously affects professional life and important social complications arise.

Specific phobia

Specific phobia is a **persistent and irrational fear to any object or situation**, apart from agoraphobia or social phobia. Phobic objects/situations include animals (snakes, spiders, dogs…), natural phenomena (heights, storms, wind…), blood or medical procedures (sores, health professionals, hospitals, injections…), or situations (public transport, lifts, enclosed or dark places…).

How to overcome phobia

Phobia and **anxiety** have many common features and tend to come from the same origin. See the treatment options for anxiety in page 96, and

THE VICIOUS CIRCLE OF SOCIAL PHOBIA

The course of social phobia feeds itself in a dangerous way:

1. The person is afraid of social situations and **avoids** them.
2. Since there are no relationships, he/she **does not develop social skills**.
3. Attempts bring about **poor results** (due to lack of practice).
4. **Doubts about oneself** take over and fear grows.

With increasing fear, the person grows more fearful and returns to point 1.

Perhaps due to this reason, statistics show that between 50 and 70% of social phobia patients experience **depressive episodes** (Lucribier and Weiller, 1997; Stain *et al.*, 1999).

Alcoholism (Lepine and Pelissolo, 1998) is another risk as the individual uses alcohol to 'push' himself/herself into social relations.

panic attacks in page 128. In any case, the following pieces of advice can be followed:

- **Speak of your problem with someone you trust.** Verbalise your fears of situations or objects with someone who knows how to listen to and respect you. This is in itself a great step towards the healing of phobia.

- **Join a self-help group.** Seek a psychotherapeutic group where you can find people with the same problem. This will give you the chance to hear from others their practical ideas on how to overcome fears and you could even help others to deal with their own fears.

- **Practise relaxation.** Avoid constant tension and learn how to apply a good relaxation technique, especially before you face a fearful situation.

- **Seek professional counselling.** There are techniques, such as systematic desensitisation, with proven and amazingly quick and effective results. However, their application requires the intervention of a professional.

- **Consult your psychiatrist.** Medical/psychiatric treatment oftentimes includes the use of tranquillisers and anxiety medication. These can act as supporters of psychotherapeutic methods to soothe the unpleasant symptoms.

→ Types of specific phobia

Phobia	Fear of...	Phobia	Fear of...
Acrophobia	Heights	Graphophobia	Writing
Aerophobia	Flying	Helmintophobia	Worms
Ailurophobia	Cats	Hematophobia	Blood
Androphobia	Men	Hydrophobia	Water
Apiphobia	Bees	Hypophobia	Horses
Aracnophobia	Spiders	Ophydophobia	Snakes
Bibliophobia	Books	Pyrophobia	Fire
Claustrophobia	Confined spaces	Tachophobia	Speed
Spermophobia	Germs	Xenophobia	Foreigners

Gems of Ancient Wisdom

'So do not fear, for I am with you; do not be dismayed, for I am your God. I will strengthen you and help you; I will uphold you with my righteous right hand' (Isaiah 41:10).

2.04
Anxiety

The anxious person experiences a **general sense of apprehension and worry** that considerably alters normal life. The most frequent worries centre on interpersonal relationships, work, finances, health and the future in general. This state escapes the control of affected persons and tends to disable them.

Anxiety may appear without any apparent physiological manifestation or with somatic evidence that may reach the level of panic attack (find more information in page 128). The symptoms of anxiety appear in the table below.

Anxiety and depression are the most common mental health problems and they are on the rise. Unfortunately, the conditions of life today seem to favour these problems and cause much suffering to those affected and to people near them. It is therefore necessary to understand how to prevent and cure anxiety as outlined in this unit.

How to prevent anxiety

Symptoms of anxiety disorders often remain **latent** until a stressful event takes place and a **crisis** develops. There are easy preventive **tasks** capable of avoiding and also soothing the symptoms when they appear:

- **Talk about your problems.** Seek the close company of people. Interact with a person or persons to share your experiences widely.
  Those living alone run a higher risk of anxiety. If this is your case, make sure you keep good relations with a member of your family or with a friend who can meet your companionship needs.

→ Types of anxiety and symptoms

Generalised anxiety	Anxiety with panic attack
• *'Nerves' or a fidgety feeling* • *Fatigue* • *Difficulty with concentration* • *Irritability* • *Muscular tension* • *Sleep disruptions* • *Decrease in sexual desire*	• *Palpitations* • *Rapid breathing* • *Cold sweat or hot flash* • *Sensation of horror* • *Nausea* • *Dry mouth*

- **Practise relaxation.** Tension goes along with any form of anxiety and it is necessary to know how to attain relaxation frequently and in a systematic manner. Find more about this in page 40.

- **Use breathing as a calming method.** It is amazing how simple breathing exercises can bring about so much relief and avoid complications in a situation of anxiety. Practise abdominal, deep, and slow respiration, breathing in and out little by little. Do it two or three times in a row and repeat it four or five times throughout the day.

- **Eat adequately.** Research (Rippere, 1983) shows that avoiding hypoglycaemia and having a protein-rich breakfast maintains the biochemical body balance and prevents preoccupying thoughts. Therefore, eat food with plenty of complex carbohydrates (all types of grains and their derivatives) and start your day with a good breakfast: soya milk, wholegrain bread, fresh fruit and nuts.

- **Look for self-help groups.** These are groups of people with similar problems (see page 316). In many towns you can find this type of organised therapeutic group. In this context, you will learn much from the experiences of others and they will be able to understand your difficulties as well.

- **Keep yourself informed of your problem and possible solutions.** There is plenty of information through books, magazines, pamphlets, the Internet, CD/DVDs, etc., that will help you understand your condition better. If you are knowledgeable, you can make a difference.

A recent study (Bachofen *et al.*, 1999) has demonstrated that many suffering from anxiety are able to apply successful treatment via a handbook and telephone access to an information system of counselling and orientation.

Sayings of Jesus

'Peace I leave with you; my peace I give you. I do not give to you as the world gives. Do not let your hearts be troubled and do not be afraid' (John 14:27).

Deep causes of anxiety

It is known by experience that **personal insecurity** and **feelings of failure** are deep causes of anxiety. It is also common to find feelings of guilt as ultimately responsible for anxious manifestations.

The two first causes have to do with feelings of **low self-esteem** (see page 28 and the box on next page). As for the person with guilt feelings, she/he needs to examine the past and try to obtain forgiveness from those offended; or else, take care of her or his life direction, if that is the cause of distress.

The believer who has accepted God as the source of forgiveness can receive great benefit from prayer. It is a reconciling experience that completely erases the past and offers a new beginning.

How to overcome anxiety

Clinical research (Hohagen *et al.*, 1998; O'Connor *et al.*, 1999; Salaberria and Echeburua, 1998; Stravynski and Greenberg, 1998) concludes that the most successful treatment techniques for anxiety are cognitive and **behavioural therapies**. These are a few examples:

- **Self-instruction.** These techniques may be practised by oneself (see page 303). First, try words to encourage yourself ('Calm down, nothing is going to happen,' 'I am not going to lose it,' 'I am going to overcome this'). When facing the moment of tension, breathe deeply and repeat the practised words. Persons of faith use self-instruction of religious content ('My God, give me peace, take away my fear…') or the retrieval of a Bible promise of strength, help and sustenance. This brings an ineffable calm to the believer.

- **Thought stopping**. This technique has proven to be very effective, especially when there are thinking topics that favour anxiety. For example, if my anxiety comes from the fear to contract a deadly disease, thoughts connected with this fear are identified (say, my sister-in-law's disease) or any other thought capable of triggering the cascade that ends up in anxiety. At the first sign of the thought, one says: 'NO!' and holds on to other thoughts or activities to distract oneself (see pages 306 and 146 for a fuller description).

- **Systematic desensitisation** (see page 303). It consists of learning relaxation techniques to be able to face the feared situation in a relatively tranquil state. The confronting task begins with the thought level, followed by a symbolic confrontation to the anxious situation. Finally, the real object of anxiety is confronted. Success level is very high and the procedure is fast; however, it requires the support of a psychologist.

These techniques can be quite effective yet superficial. Anxiety problems may have deep roots and it is necessary to tackle the cause and not just the symptoms. The box on the previous page shows examples of these problems.

 self-help

SELF-ESTEEM ENHANCING CARDS

Many need to remind themselves of their **positive aspects** in order to improve their self-esteem. One way to do it is to write in a small card specific personal values:

I am compassionate	I am a good cook
I have a pretty handwriting	I sing well
I have good physical health	

These small cards are carried in the pocket and read once in a while to remind ourselves that we possess many valuable traits and that we should not consider ourselves inferior or unfortunate.

Plants and food to fight anxiety

Anxiety medication, sedatives and tranquillisers are commonly used for anxiety treatment. However, these drugs have significant side effects.

Some are addictive and quitting them causes insomnia and anxiety as a rebound effect; others cause dry mouth, blurred vision, urinary retention, constipation, seasickness, insomnia, lowering of sexual potency, weakness, sweating, etc.

Others seem harmless but negatively interact with a long list of medicines and foods.

Consider the following herbal and diet remedies to soothe anxiety symptoms:

- **St. John's Wort** (*Hypericum perforatum*).
- **Kava Kava** (*Piper methysticum*).
- **Valerian** (*Valeriana officinalis*).
- Foods high in calcium, magnesium and group-B vitamins. Dairy products, oranges, almonds, cabbages, turnips and leeks are all high in calcium.

St. John's Wort

Soya beans, coconut, melon and cashew nuts are nutritional sources of magnesium.

Sunflower seeds, beans, wheat germ, eggs and low-fat milk contain significant amounts of vitamin B in various forms.

Valerian

Sunflower seeds

Kava

> **Research Results**

Kava Kava, an especially valuable herb

Kava Kava (Piper methysticum) is a plant originally from the South Pacific region. It has been used for social and ceremonial purposes for centuries. It is relatively new in the western world but it has become increasingly available in herbal shops and pharmacies in the form of extracts, tablets or tincture.

The study carried out by **Yadhu and Nirbhay Singh**'s (2002) confirmed the effectiveness of the Kava Kava root for anxiety treatment. Its medicinal properties are carried out by the blocking effect of **kavalactone** (Kava's active ingredient) upon several neuronal connections that are responsible for anxiety symptoms.

There are **minimal side effects**, such as skin alterations, when taken in high doses for long periods.

Due to the multiple side effects of anxiety drugs, this remedy is being increasingly utilised in anxiety treatment as a substitute for anxiety medicine, sedatives and tranquillisers.

> **Gems of Ancient Wisdom**
>
> *'Cast all your anxiety on him because he cares for you'* (1 Peter 5:7).

Spiritual therapy

(See also page 314).

Anxiety develops as **fear of the future**. Nobody knows what tomorrow will bring. Only God knows the future. This has helped many people to place their faith and hope in the Almighty who loves and protects those who accept him. Spiritual treatment has three facets:

- **Individual.** The person needs to work on his inner life, reflecting on the transcendence of existence, and contemplating a perspective that goes beyond here and now. This includes study of the destiny for the human family, and especially God's plan for eternal salvation, as explained in the Bible.

  This helps the person to acquire a long-term perspective that offers trust and the eventual triumph of good over evil. As an immediate emergency measure, spiritual therapy uses the repetition of powerful memory verses (a sample is offered in the Gems below). It also uses visualisation and meditation based on the **Bible promises**, for instance: 'A thousand may fall at your side, ten thousand at your right hand, but it will not come near you' (Psalm 91:7). These are repeated with a focused mind and fervour. This activity favours hope and dispels anxious thoughts.

- **Social.** The spiritual effect can be intensified with the **influence of fellow believers**. Worship in community, conversations about God's love and protection, giving and receiving spiritual advice... are some of the activities that strengthen spiritual development and enrich the sensation of serenity towards what is yet to come.

- **Divine.** The divine dimension encompasses the intimate and personal relationship between a person and God. Support is most clearly manifested in **prayer**. More than chanting, prayer consists of talking to God as to a friend and counsellor; talk about your fears, anxiety, doubts and problems; thank the Creator for all the good things in your life. A fully meaningful prayer life has helped many to take steps towards faith and trust, which are incompatible with anxiety and uncertainty.

Gems of Ancient Wisdom

'The LORD himself goes before you and will be with you; he will never leave you nor forsake you. Do not be afraid; do not be discouraged' (Deuteronomy 31:8).

'Have I not commanded you? Be strong and courageous. Do not be terrified; do not be discouraged, for the LORD your God will be with you wherever you go' (Joshua 1:9).

'When anxiety was great within me, your consolation brought joy to my soul' (Psalm 94:19).

'So do not fear, for I am with you; do not be dismayed, for I am your God. I will strengthen you and help you; I will uphold you with my righteous right hand' (Isaiah 41:10).

'Do not be anxious about anything, but in everything, by prayer and petition, with thanksgiving, present your requests to God' (Philippians 4:6).

Sayings of Jesus

'Therefore I tell you, do not worry about your life, what you will eat or drink; or about your body, what you will wear. Is it not life more important than food, and the body more important than clothes? Look at the birds of the air; they do not sow or reap or store away in barns, and yet your heavenly Father feeds them. Are you not much more valuable than they?' (Matthew 6:25-26).

TEST YOURSELF ::

In order to know your anxiety level, answer True (when you agree) or False (when you disagree), to the following statements:

Do I suffer from anxiety?	T	F
1. My own heartbeats bother me at times.		
2. When someone asks me to lend something, I have a hard time saying 'no.'		
3. I get nervous and irritated with unimportant things.		
4. It is very difficult for me to say 'no' to a salesperson.		
5. Sometimes I feel fear and apprehension for no apparent reason.		
6. I tend to turn down invitations to dates and meetings.		
7. I worry too much and that discourages me.		
8. I don't know how to say to a close friend that something he/she does bothers me.		
9. Many times I feel completely exhausted.		
10. It is very difficult for me to demand something or make claims.		
11. It is hard for me to make decisions.		
12. If I am not in agreement with my opponent, I tend to remain quiet.		
13. I always am afraid of something.		
14. I do not like to receive praise.		
15. I am almost always edgy.		
16. I have a hard time keeping a conversation with someone I disagree with.		
17. I often think that I will not be able to resolve my problems.		
18. If someone asks me a favour with insistence, I almost never say 'No.'		
19. I am always under pressure or tension.		
20. When I do not understand something, I have difficulties to ask in public.		

Interpretation:
If you answered T to 0-7 statements, you are out of danger from anxiety.
If you answered T to 8-13 statements, you have a tendency to anxiety. Study and practise the advice of this book. If your problem persists, consult your physician or psychologist.
If you answered T to more than 14 statements, you may be under the effect of anxiety. Seek professional help.

2.05
Depression

Depression is a modern plague in the context of mental health. It is the most common ailment in psychiatry and clinical psychology. And it is on the rise: it is reckoned that depression will become the second cause of illness and disability by the year 2020, just behind cardiovascular diseases (Riu, 2004).

With its corresponding variations, depression affects children, youth, adults, and the elderly; men and women; members of the working class as well as middle and upper classes; inhabitants of poor and wealthy regions of the world. WHO estimates that there are over 100 million depressed people worldwide.

Going through an upsetting experience or great worry or feeling stressed due to excess of work does not necessarily mean depression. However, those emotional ups and downs may be the preamble. It is necessary to be alert to avoid that these events become prolonged.

Depression has various **symptoms** and is not diagnosed until at least five are present and identified. However, the appearance of one should serve as a warning to take measures before the solution becomes more difficult.

Depression causes:

- **An intensely sad mood.** Sobbing and a sense of hopelessness are present, many times without knowing why.

- **Absence of pleasure in all activities.** There is no motivation to do anything. Not even favourite activities or being with most preferred people are welcome.

- **Loss of weight and appetite.** There is lack of desire to eat even the most delicious food. In some cases the patient experiences excessive appetite.

- **Sleep alterations.** Insomnia is most frequent, although depression can sometimes be accompanied by excessive, low-quality sleep.

- **Slow movement.** Walking, moving, and even talking turn into slow and infrequent tasks.

- **Fatigue or loss of energy.** Feelings of physical weakness are present. The countenance reveals dejection and lack of personal care becomes evident.

SUICIDE—A GREAT RISK OF DEPRESSION

According to WHO, one person commits suicide in the world every 40 seconds; and one attempts it every three seconds. Out of all patients diagnosed with depression, 15% die by suicide. Use these tips to help these people:

- **Pay attention.** When the person is willing to speak, listen to him/her and do not rush to offer counsel. Just listen to the disheartened, as it may help overcome depression.
- **Take certain alarm signs seriously.** Notes or conversations referring to death, changes in the diet or sleeping habits, alcohol or drug intake, returning loaned items... are signs of alarm.
- **Understand the person's mood.** Individuals contemplating suicide are extremely unhappy and desperate; they see themselves as helpless and hate themselves. It is necessary to comprehend this attitude in order to help.

- **Help the person to find the positive aspects of him/herself.** Talk of the positive sides of life, and the desirable features they possess.
- **Stay close to the person and always be available.** Loneliness is the main enemy for someone contemplating suicide. Maintain constant contact with him or her.
- **Remove objects that may lead to suicide.** Put aside guns and weapons, poisonous substances, ropes, drugs...
- **Speak directly about suicide.** Do not be afraid to talk about suicide, thoughts, impulses, and attempts whenever the affected person mentions it. Without sermonising, suggest hopeful attitudes as alternatives to suicide.

- **Negative feelings towards oneself.** There are thoughts of self-deprecation and lack of self-confidence.
- **Guilt feelings.** A sensation of guilt for unimportant things takes over and the person experiences a sense of failure.
- **Mental limitations.** The thinking process slows down and attention and concentration diminish.
- **Suicidal ideas or attempts.** Depressive people think of death as a way out. They may plan, attempt and even consummate suicide.

How to prevent depression

Try the following tips:

- **Seek sufficient social support.** Depression is not very common amid circles where there exist strong relational ties—marriage, family, work, friends.

It is, therefore, necessary to attain a happy family, be surrounded by good friends, and have a good professional environment, as all these are preventive measures against depression. The box below shows the importance of social support in order to psychologically face adversity.

RESEARCH RESULTS
Having good friends

A study (Nolen-Hoaksema and Morrow, 1991) conducted in San Francisco when the earthquake hit the city in 1989 clearly showed that, among those individuals who had a social support system to fight the earthquake, psychological sequels involved the lowest levels of depression and anxiety. On the other hand, those who isolated themselves to reflect over their unfortunate destiny experienced the highest levels. This was so not only during the few days following the earthquake but even seven weeks after the catastrophe.

If you have the habit of isolating yourself and thinking too much about your misfortunes, change your attitude lest you end up with depression. It is recommendable for you to have a friend or trusted person with whom you can share your sorrows.

- **Keep active.** It is amazing how a low mood can vary so quickly when one gets busy with some activity. To avoid depression, become active.

  It may seem difficult to go and visit a relative or run some errand, but only at the beginning. Once you start the activity, it will be easy to continue. Put your hands to work on tasks you enjoy and that are productive and edifying: tidy up your room, repair something at work, and make a few phone calls to show interest for others.

  If you can, practise a sport or aerobic exercise. Exercising is a source of health and good mood.

DEPRESSION AND DIET

The relationship between diet and depressive disorders has been intensely researched during the last few years. Through several studies (Christensen, 1993 and 1997; Christensen and Redig, 1993; Markus *et al.*, 1998; Young, 1993), it has become clear that the presence of **two nutrients** in the body in sufficient amount prevents depressive symptoms:

- **Tryptophan**, an essential amino acid to favour growth, is the precursor of serotonin and plays an important role in the relief of depressive symptoms.
- **Folate** (folacin), or folic acid, is a form of vitamin B and also affects mood positively.

As a preventive measure against depression, eat foods high in tryptophan every day such as all types of whole grains (bread, pasta, rice), legumes (beans, chickpeas, lentils, soya beans) and roots (potatoes, yams, beets, carrots…).

Foods high in folate are greens, beets, fruits (especially oranges and melons), and legumes (especially chickpeas, lentils, and mung beans).

BEWARE OF BLAMING PAST EVENTS FOR EVERYTHING OF THE PRESENT!

Past events are very important to explain the psychological world of the person, but they do not need to be a determinant of mental illness.

It is necessary to **accept the past** (which cannot be changed) and avoid the passivity of doing nothing to improve because 'after all, my past predestines me,' 'I am this way because of my troubled childhood,' or 'I have this problem because my parents didn't know how to raise me.' This attitude complicates the recovery process and blocks many sources of help and support.

OVERCOME DEPRESSION BY YOURSELF

Although depression generally requires medical and psychological intervention, self-help strategies are always beneficial to support treatment and prevention. These are some useful counsels:

- **Count on a friend or trusted acquaintance.** Look for someone who cares for and understands you in order to talk regularly. Ruminating about one's problems is the worst activity for the depressive.
- **Keep busy.** Go outside, breathe fresh air or practise a sport. Or stay home working on some do-it-yourself project. Activities will help keep your mind far from the thoughts that lead to depression.
- **Avoid alcohol.** It is a worldwide habit to drown one's sorrows in alcohol. But do not deceive yourself.

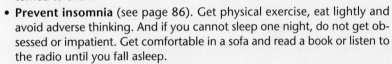

The substance may alleviate the symptoms during a few hours. But alcohol is a barrier that blocks psychological help, aside from the ruin it produces to physical health.

- **Keep a healthy diet.** Eat vegetables, fresh fruit, grains and legumes. If you are not used to these, it may be difficult at the beginning, but you will get accustomed to them.
- **Prevent insomnia** (see page 86). Get physical exercise, eat lightly and avoid adverse thinking. And if you cannot sleep one night, do not get obsessed or impatient. Get comfortable in a sofa and read a book or listen to the radio until you fall asleep.
- **Think positively** (see page 20). Focus on pleasant things and convince yourself that all misfortunes reach an end. Besides, there are many things for which you should be grateful in your life and those ought to be the target of your thoughts.
- **Take a hopeful outlook.** Hope (see page 64) is a human need. Without it, one falls easily into doubt, fear, and anxiety, factors linked to depression. Those with hope beyond life can maintain a relationship with a fatherly and caring God, which is a mighty source of help against depression.

Even what we eat may help (see the box 'Depression and diet' on the previous page).

- **Think correctly.** Depending on how people focus on either the dark or the bright side of things, they have more or less proneness to depression.

  Thinking is like any other habit and must be cultivated in order to avoid negative analyses of situations.

- **Look sanely at the past.** The past may be a source of depression but also the cause of emotional well-being. Instead of focusing on past adversities, enjoy thinking of happy events and stages.

  If there is a past trauma (sexual abuse, natural disaster, etc.) consult a psychologist or psychiatrist instead of falling into negativism and irresponsibility (see the box 'Beware...' on the previous page).

How to heal depression

The treatment of depression is carried out in a dual methodology: pharmacological and psychotherapeutic. In most cases, drug treatment is appropriate and prescribed by the family doctor or the psychiatrist. At the same time, psychological intervention is followed. This equips the person to overcome depression and to avoid relapse.

Medicines

Antidepressants are an effective source of relief for the psychological pain and the tendency to suicide so often experienced by depressive subjects. Drugs used for depression act upon the brain's chemistry in order to balance out the activity of the brain's neurotransmitters. They alleviate the symptoms and facilitate psychotherapy.

Sometimes, the patient has to be under several types of tablets until the right type is found and this may take weeks to determine effectiveness.

ANTIDEPRESSANTS: SHORTCOMINGS AND PROBLEMS

The antidepressants soothe the extremely unpleasant symptoms of depression. However, they *do not cure* the illness.

The removal of stressors, the change of attitude and behaviour by means of psychotherapy can cure the illness to the point of making medication unnecessary.

Patients under antidepressant drugs do not begin to feel better until two or three weeks into the treatment.

In addition, these are some of the **side effects**: problems with sexuality, cardiovascular alterations, drowsiness (or insomnia), blurred vision, nervousness, constipation, weight gain (or loss) and dryness of the mouth.

Also, antidepressants may produce side effects of variable magnitude (see the box on the left).

Daily routine

The preparation of an activity programme is one of the most common strategies used by psychologists. It is something like the patient's agenda for several weeks. Together with the patient and his/her family, the psychologist develops this detailed plan. When the activity programme is carried through, the patient spends the time positively and acquires new behavioural patterns to avoid relapse.

A good activity programme needs to maintain the following principles:

• Choose the **most pleasurable** activities and avoid hard tasks, especially in the beginning.

• Seek activities with a **social component**. For example, it is preferable to attend a friend's meeting than to go to the cinema.

• If possible, **do not break away from regular work**, but try to keep the employment or studies and at the same time reduce their length and intensity.

- In most cases, **manual activity** is desirable. For example, do-it-yourself tasks, sewing or gardening.

- Include **physical exercise when the patient's health allows**. The chemical and hormonal balance produced by medicine can also be attained or supplemented with sports and physical activity.

- The activity **agenda** should be as detailed as possible. (For example, outline what needs to be done between 8:00 and 8:30, 8:30 and 9:00, etc.).

Thinking style

Thoughts are receiving increasing attention in the treatment of depression. One of the most desirable goals is to help the person to see things in a correct and balanced way. Those suffering from depression tend to:

- Set **unrealistic** roles and expectations. A man gets depressed because at 50 years of age he has not become a famous businessman.

- **Magnify their personal faults** and reduce their achievements. A girl wins a literary contest at her school. When her friends congratulate her, she stresses the fact that there were few works submitted, or that they gave her the prize out of pity.

- **Compare themselves** with others and feel inferior. A woman attends a meeting with her fellow alumni at her former school and returns home depressed because she thinks that their achievements are much higher than hers.

Successful treatment of depression must include **thought restructuring** (see page 304) as depressive subjects tend towards negative thoughts about themselves, the environment and the future.

Therefore, avoid all thoughts of inferiority or self-pity. Think that much of success depends on what you set yourself to do. Think that you possess valuable personal qualities and abilities.

When you evaluate your context, do not focus on imperfections and dangers. Instead, gaze at the beautiful things of life and the enjoyable events. There are many good things to think about! And if there are negative aspects, do something to remedy them, not just moan over them.

And as far as the future is concerned, if anyone has the possibility of altering it, that would be yourself. Decide you are going to be happy and set out to do it. Repeat: 'I have decided to be happy!' and dismiss all adverse thoughts at their very roots.

Sayings of Jesus

'You will grieve, but your grief will turn to joy' (John 16:20).

Family support

Any professional treatment loses strength when the family does not provide support to the depressive person. It is of vital importance that if your spouse, child or family member suffers from depression, you take the challenge seriously and follow the advice outlined below:

- **Listen** attentively and with sympathy. This is, in itself, therapeutic.

- **Never nag** the person. Instead, treat him/her naturally and with calm.

- **Help** him/her to **keep busy**: walks, hobbies, small working projects...

- **Encourage** the person to keep **hope** and to think that he/she will overcome depression.

AN ANTIDEPRESSANT HERB

alternative option

The use of **St. John's Wort** (*Hypericum perforatum*) for the treatment of mild or moderate depression has scientific support (Gupta and Moller, 2003) and does not have side effects.

Herbal hypericum treatment (infusions or capsules) acts upon the central nervous system following an unidentified process to produce **beneficial effects on mild and moderate depression**. It should be noted that it does not produce improvement in severe depression.

Warning: It can be incompatible with other medicines (specifically with antidepressants) and the doctor should be consulted before using this natural remedy.

Gems of Ancient Wisdom

'My life is consumed by anguish and my years by groaning; my strength fails because of my affliction, and my bones grow weak. [...] But I trust in you, O LORD; I say, "You are my God"' (Psalm 31:10, 14).

'Why are you downcast, O my soul? Why so disturbed within me? Put your hope in God, for I will yet praise him, my Saviour and my God' (Psalm 42:11).

'The LORD is close to the broken-hearted and saves those who are crushed in spirit' (Psalm 34:18).

- **Help with the medical treatment** reminding him/her of taking the medication and avoid passing on doubts such as: 'What is the use of these tablets?' 'What is the point of going to the psychiatrist? You are not crazy!' If you have doubts about the treatment plan, talk to the doctor, not to the patient.

- **Prevent a calamity**, especially if the patient worsens and starts saying that life is not worth living, threatening to take his/her own life. Read the box on suicide (see page 103) and even consult the psychiatrist.

- **Watch** that he/she **eats enough** and does **not take alcohol**.

Do something for others

The depressive person tends to think that he/she already has enough with depression without thinking of helping others. However, there is something revitalising and therapeutic in doing things for others. Try and take care of a friend's child, do grocery shopping for an elderly lady, visit someone in hospital or do voluntary service. With this, you forget your own suffering and you realise that there are others in great need. Helping others is a way to help yourself.

Gaze at the future in hope

If you are experiencing depressive symptoms, you need to understand that the future is not at the mercy of circumstances and you have much to do with what will happen tomorrow. Flee from feelings of despair and inability.

Explain your failures realistically

Become consciously aware of your strengths and weaknesses and assess situations reasonably. For example, if you have not been successful in a job application, do not think that you are useless. Instead consider whether the process was too difficult or whether there were too many candidates. And for the next times, focus your attention on positions fit to your capacity with the competition of fewer applicants.

Gain control over your destiny

Gain control over your destiny. If the source of your problems is, for example, your family, do not think that the relationship will not ever be fixed. Instead, do something to improve your communication and put aside purely selfish aspirations. These are specific ways to make the future better.

Spiritual therapy

The first step to obtain a blessing out of spirituality is having faith (or belief) in God as someone willing to help, protect, support and favour those who so wish. This conviction brings about a relationship with Divinity that inspires inner peace. This is something like the feeling of a small child walking through a stony path holding the hand of her father—she is not afraid because of her strong hold on her father's hand. In similar manner, in life's walk, the believer realises that there are all sorts of dangers, but his/her faith in the Creator makes her look at the future with calm, because he/she has the certainty of the Heavenly Father's protection.

Specific ways to help include **prayer to God** as a friend with whom to share one's burdens. Also, the **reading of the Holy Scriptures** with their stories and inspiring messages that facilitate inner peace. The selection of key passages (like those of the Gems above) and their repetition and memorisation, in order to be able to retrieve them in moments of crisis, can also be a blessing. Lastly, the association with other believers who share these ideals can serve as a source of support for the better mental health of everyone.

2.06
Psychological traumas

Events of high emotional intensity, particularly if they are experienced in a **vulnerable moment of life**, may become traumatising. This is the case of insults, mocking a child, a scare in the darkness, chasing someone with snakes and spiders, slander, losing a parent at an early age, coercion for sexual advantage…

In the same way that a heavy physical accident leaves **permanent scars**, traumas may also leave marks for many years.

The most notable consequences are seen during the days and weeks following the experience. For example, dreams, flash memories, denial of facts, anxiety, and lack of attention and concentration.

In some cases, especially in children, the sequels may remain for years and become a barrier to lead a mentally healthy life. The box below outlines a few examples of long-term traumatic consequences.

Effects of past traumas

Past traumas may cause:
- **Inferiority feelings.** The ego receives a great part of the traumatic impact and the person loses self-assurance, showing feelings of insecurity and inferiority.
- **Difficulty to carry out normal tasks.** The affected person feels unable to reach simple objectives. For example, young women or girls who have been victims of sexual abuse may experience difficulty socially relating with males. Or the boy whose older brothers used to scare him with a spider may suffer from phobia for such invertebrates.

- **Paranoid tendencies.** Traumatised persons develop a lack of trust towards their surroundings and may interpret neutral behaviour in others as a coalition against them, thus considering themselves as victims of uncertain harassment and persecution.
- **Depression.** The traumatising event can be seen as a loss (e.g., loss of honour, loss of a dear one…), and every loss carries the risk of depressive symptoms.

How to overcome trauma

There are traumas that, due to their severity, require psychiatric intervention. Others, not so extreme in their consequence, tend to be barriers to leading a normal life. For these, the following pieces of advice are offered:

- **Accept the past and focus on the future.** The past cannot be changed and it is futile to attempt to blame events and persons that have had an adverse influence. If you get stuck in the past, you will not be able to look at the future with the necessary trust.

- **Verbalise the traumatic event.** Talking (or writing) about the event that produced the trauma in a relaxing and secure context is an extremely important step. Look for a person you can trust and confide what happened to you. It is also highly beneficial to get involved in **group counselling**. This entails people who went through the same experience.

- **Look for the positive side.** Disasters and calamities tend to draw survivors, families and communities together. Be thankful for the human togetherness caused by misfortune.

- **Resort to forgiveness and reconciliation.** Although difficult, it is possible to avoid holding grudges or resentment towards those who produced the trauma. This is an important step for the resolution of the past. It is not only applicable to others, but to oneself as well: self-forgiveness and self-reconciliation.

  But forgiveness does not always come easily, as our capacity to love (and forgiving is loving) is limited. Appeal to the source of forgiveness, a God of love who—according to the gospel—longs to make us his friends and can help us to overcome the incapacitating past.

RESEARCH RESULTS

It is healthy to write down traumatic experiences

At New York State University—Stoney Brook, **Melanie Greenberg and Arthur Stone** carried out an interesting experiment (Greenberg and Stone, 1992). Participants were 60 college students with past traumatic experiences. These were the steps followed:

1. Subjects were divided into groups: those having experienced a severe trauma, those under the effect of mild trauma, and those without trauma.
2. Some were asked to reveal their experience in writing, whereas others were not offered this opportunity so that they could serve as controls.
3. During the following months, health and illness signs were observed in all participants.

Results revealed that those with severe trauma who described their event in writing experienced the greatest physical health progress, much above and beyond those who had not written their traumatic experience.

Studies like this show that revealing the event around the trauma is not only good for the soul, but also for the body.

2.07
Stress

Very few escape from stress. It is part of our daily routine. Time and work pressure, relationship problems, noise, pollution, finances, insecurity… are some of the sources of stress.

(See also J. Melgosa, *Less Stress!*, Madrid, Spain: Editorial Safeliz, 2001).

The consequences of stress

Stress affects the physical body, the mind and emotions. It is not to be taken lightly, for its consequences are very painful and may become fatal.

On the other hand, in the right amount, stress is a **source of motivation** that must be taken advantage of. Stress mechanisms release necessary energy to face any emergency.

Elizabeth, a professional seamstress, knowing that she has to deliver her work on Friday, works intensely on Thursday. In fact, she accomplishes more work on Thursday than on Tuesday and Wednesday together. She concentrates well, works quickly and with acute skill, she forgets to eat, but does not experience weakness. On Friday, she delivers the dresses on time and enjoys the relaxation of her accomplished task. Stress has been useful

Organic effects of stress	Psychological effects of stress
Many organic diseases originate from mental states. Work and family pressure, financial problems, uncertainty about the future and other worries cause stress, and the following diseases may follow:	*We must add problems related to thought, emotions, and behaviour, also caused by excessive stress.*
• *Gastric ulcer* • *Irritable colon* • *Hypertension* • *Arteriosclerosis* • *Angina pectoris* • *Myocardial infarction*	*Thought processes:* • *Difficulty to think logically* • *Memory failure* • *Lack of concentration* • *Mistakes*
Stress can also be behind so-called psychosomatic reactions:	*Emotions:* • *Ongoing tension* • *Fear of disease* • *Impatience and irritability* • *Inferiority feelings*
• *Acne, hives, eczema* • *Backache, rheumatism* • *Asthma, allergy, bronchitis* • *Vaginismus, impotence* • *Obesity, hyperthyroidism* • *Migraine, anxiety* • *Conjunctivitis*	*Behaviour:* • *Decrease in verbal fluency* • *Risk of use of noxious substances* • *School/work absenteeism* • *Sleeping difficulties* • *Problems with relationships*

on this occasion. However, Elizabeth cannot constantly overuse this kind of energy. The worst effects of stress come when such situations prolong themselves (see the box below).

Stress and the immune system

When the limits of adequate stress have been surpassed, the body starts weakening and lowering its level of immunology, thus reducing the amount of protection against infections. In this way, people become more prone to contract all types of illnesses, including the common cold (see the table on the previous page and the box on the right).

THE DANGERS OF PROLONGED STRESS

Stress can be a useful source of energy, since it...
- activates the nervous system's alert mechanism;
- accelerates cardiac rhythm;
- raises blood pressure;
- releases hormones that favour achievement.

However, if a status of intense achievement based on stress and tension is maintained, effectiveness disappears. And when stress is prolonged a bit further, serious organic and mental disorders take over.

How to prevent stress

Good time management prevents stress; thus we need to know how to plan. Time is an asset given equally to everyone, and we make use of it according to our lifestyle. How can we use it harmoniously?

- **Be realistic.** There is a saying that goes, 'Don't bite off more than you can chew.' This warns against the attempt to do many things, as they will turn out wrong. It is necessary to establish realistic goals within the available time.

- **Establish priorities.** It would be easier for you to focus on the most important tasks if you know your priorities. This has a lot to do with your beliefs and values. What is the value you attach to money? Is your work important? How important are your family relationships? Do you consider it important to help others? Are there religious values in your life? Depending on your an-

RESEARCH RESULTS
Stress and defences

An experiment (Cohen, Tyrrell and Smith, 1991) carried out with 400 participants, all in a good state of health, measured their stress levels over 12 months. Subjects were administered a nasal spray containing five different types of common cold virus. On a daily basis, they were examined to assess the presence or absence of the virus in the respiratory pathways, as well as any possible cold symptoms. These were the results:
- Almost all participants carried the virus.
- Only one third contracted a cold.
- The greater the amount of stress, the higher the level of virus.
- The greater the amount of stress, the higher the number of symptoms.
- Those labelled as 'highly stressed' had double the probability of catching a cold.
- The effect of stress remained significant, even after eliminating important variables such as age, exercise, diet, and consumption of alcohol and tobacco.

swers, you will spend more or less time on each of those activities.

- **Seek variety.** It is not possible to find happiness through one single activity, as it will become obsessive and tedious. Work is important to attain income and personal satisfaction. Family and marital relationships are also ingredients for balance. Pastimes bring about much satisfaction and should supplement the usual occupation; for example, combining physical employment with a calm hobby.

- **Organise yourself.** Develop a list with all the things you plan to finish each day and week. Focus on them and do not get distracted with items that take your energy away from the desirable objectives. If you experience too much pressure, postpone some of the activities. If the task is too small, try adding to it.

- **Live a simple life.** All-absorbing pastimes, luxury holidays, expensive sports... can become a source of stress. They all require not only heavy financial expense but also an investment of time and energy. Try simple activities, such as taking a walk or reading a good book. Learn to find delight in simplicity, which leads to authentic happiness.

How to overcome stress

Stress treatment must be global or **holistic**. It should encompass all social contexts (work, family, friends…). In times of stress, choose the amount of work that you may reasonably carry out, but no more.

Take care of your social interactions. Forget about yourself and try to please others by displaying affection. Through kindness or a modest humanitarian contribution, help somebody, known or unknown. Their response can benefit you, as well.

Overcoming stress means tackling the various dimensions of existence: physical, mental and spiritual. Follow the counsel offered below.

Mental dimension

The most effective form of therapy for cases of stress is called cognitive psychotherapy. It consists of teaching individuals to govern their thoughts instead of allowing thoughts to govern them. How does one achieve this? Constantly practise the following exercises:

- **Forbid adverse thoughts** (see the box 'Watch out…!' on the adjoining page).

- **Choose positive or neutral topics and motives of thought.** For example, think about pleasant experiences from the past, people you admire, fun friends, or even scenes of a novel or exem-

self-help

PRACTISE TOTAL HEALTH

The best way to prevent stress is to lead a **healthy and balanced lifestyle,** both in mind and body. Maintaining good physical and mental health is neither difficult nor costly and it is helpful for everyone. Try the following healthy measures:

- **Food and diet.** The best foods are those close to their natural state. Whole grains, prepared in their simple form (such as rice) or in transformed state (such as bread or pasta) constitute the foundation of people's traditional diet. It is also necessary to use vegetables, fruits, legumes and nuts because of their nutritional and healing properties. Foods of animal origin, such as meat, fish, eggs, dairy products and their corresponding fats are not necessary for good nutrition and do carry risks.

- **Water.** Water is the best drink and the best means to renew organic fluids. It is recommendable to drink water abundantly (6-8 glasses outside of meals) every day. Other widely-used drinks such as sodas, beer or coffee are a burden to the human organism, which has to distil and process the nutritionally-empty ingredients until they are eliminated and stored in the form of useless energy.

- **Exercise.** All organs and systems contained in the human body are designed to be active. Therefore, you should exercise your muscles and bones to enjoy regeneration and well-being. Make efforts to practise a sport or *hobby* that brings you exercise. You may also walk regularly.

- **Rest.** Physical work must be followed by restoring rest. It is very important to get tired and to use the rest hours to sleep. Sleep 7 or 8 hours, as this is the amount needed by most adults. This is necessary to prevent stress. Without appropriate rest, it is not possible to face normal work tasks, and this will produce stress and anxiety.

- **Harmful substances.** Psychoactive substances (drugs, alcohol, tobacco, etc.) directly affect the central nervous system and, consequently, the mood and reasoning abilities. A prevention or healing plan against excessive stress must eliminate the use of substances that alter mental functions.

The practice of total health brings about organic well-being and mental health, necessary conditions to face life calmly and without stress.

plary film. Think of these things while carrying out routine tasks or to substitute adverse thoughts.

- **Use constructive worry.** Solutions to problems of stress come via thinking of answers, alternatives, ways out… and by avoiding falling into destructive worry, which is repetitive, recurrent and obsessive.

- **Reject irrational beliefs.** Negative ideas and beliefs about oneself or one's surroundings are illogical, ruin self-esteem and increase stress. For example: 'I am useless,' 'Nobody likes it when I am around,' 'Happiness is the luck of the draw and I didn't win.' These ideas must be rejected. When one is not able to do it by oneself, it is necessary to seek the help of a psychotherapist to talk about the matter and free oneself from such irrational beliefs.

Physical dimension

Physical exercise (see page 322) is the best remedy to fight stress. If your health permits, do heavy physical exercise (running, swimming, sports). If not, simply walk briskly every day.

Relaxation is another good remedy (page 40): put aside half an hour every day to lie down (not to sleep), tensing muscles one by one, inserting moments of relaxation between each tension.

Occasional **deep breathing** is also very useful to fight stress: breathe deeply, pressing on the belly (not thorax), and hold the air for a few seconds before breathing out.

Spiritual dimension

Peace of mind is incompatible with stress. A clear conscience and a serene mind may be attained through faith and prayer.

Jesus of Nazareth, after an exhausting day of preaching, walking and feeling the press of the multitudes, said to his disciples: 'Come with me by yourselves to a quiet place and get some rest' (Mark 6:31).

His method consisted of getting up very early in the morning, while it was still dark, and going to the wilderness to pray (see Mark 1:35).

The most meaningful meditation is based on the Bible. The method consists of reading a short Bible text (a couple of verses from Psalms or Proverbs) in an environment free from any distrac-

WATCH OUT FOR OBSESSIVE THOUGHTS!

Have you ever found yourself unable to quit thinking about something? Free yourself from such danger by following these steps (see also pages 146 and 306):

- Identify your anxious or distressing thoughts.
- At the first sign that those undesirable thoughts are approaching, say (or shout, if necessary): STOP!
- Distract yourself, concentrating on more edifying thoughts.

Always practise a **positive attitude** and keep your mind busy with pleasant and elevating thoughts. Remember that only when you make this technique part of your **automatic behaviour**, will you be able to 'wipe' from your mind undesirable thoughts in an instinctive and safe way.

Noise, that harsh nuisance

When it surpasses the risk threshold level (60 decibels), sound may become a notable stressing agent. If its volume increases, it can produce hearing lesions or even destroy auditory ability. Also, excess of noise may cause psychophysical alterations:

- Fatigue
- Irritability
- Insomnia
- Headaches
- Muscle tension

All these symptoms are linked to stress.

tion. Then one needs to concentrate intensely on the message, reflect on its meaning, feel the text's poetic strength, and imaginatively contemplate the message.

Do this during 15 or 20 minutes and finish with a prayer to God, thanking him for his message and asking him for strength to face the burdens produced by stress.

It is also useful to read the experience of a Bible character and try to find inspiration there (see the Biblical Example box on the following page).

TRANQUILLISERS' SHORTCOMINGS

The use of pharmacology (muscle relaxants and tranquillisers) is in many cases unnecessary. With the exception of specific pathologies requiring medical prescription, drugs do not surpass the symptomatic benefits of alternative non-chemical treatments. In addition, they carry the following side effects:

- Drowsiness
- Decrease in speed reaction
- Hypotension
- Exhaustion

Finally, many anti-stress medications are addictive, causing very unpleasant symptoms when their use is discontinued.

PLANTS TO CONTROL STRESS

There are medicinal plants known for their relaxing and tranquillising properties. Using them is safe, economic and effective. These are the most well known:

- Linden (*Tilia europaea*)
- Valerian (*Valeriana officinalis*)
- Passion Flower (*Passiflora incarnata*) and
- Hawthorn (*Crataegus monogyna*)

Water (hydrotherapy) also contains anti-stress properties. A 15-minute warm bath followed by a 30-second cold shower produces muscular relaxation and helps control stress. Sea water (thalassotherapy) and **sunbathing** tone the body and stimulate internal gland secretion and general metabolism.

Sayings of Jesus

'Come to me, all you who are weary and burdened, and I will give you rest' (Matthew 11:28).

BIBLICAL EXAMPLE

The story of Joseph

Joseph was a Hebrew who lived some two thousand years before Christ. He was born in a well-to-do family and showed superior intelligence and vision. Moved by irrational envy, his brothers sold him into slavery to citizens of a foreign nation. At his new destination, Joseph had to suffer silently and to adapt to conditions radically different from his own. Joseph lived through stressful experiences so intense that few human beings have ever experienced such levels. However, Joseph came out victorious, reaching his highest potential.

How was Joseph able to keep his mental health in spite of so much adversity? He practised an authentic faith in God during those painful decades. He asked his Creator for the necessary supernatural power to overcome so much oppression. He used prayer daily and kept in contact with God in moments of anguish as well as in times of relief. Above all, he maintained the living hope that pain would someday be removed and that his God, who loved him so much, held a good ending for him. The full account is recorded in the book of Genesis, chapters 37, and 39 to 50. (See also the Biblical Example box on page 237).

TEST YOURSELF ::

To see if your stress is high, answer YES or NO to the following questions:

Am I a victim of stress?	YES	NO
1. Do you seek nature in your free time?		
2. Do you use alcoholic drinks?		
3. Do you eat fruits and vegetables abundantly?		
4. Do you smoke?		
5. Do you exercise regularly?		
6. Do you take tranquillisers regularly?		
7. Do you live in a clean and orderly home?		
8. Do you live in a noisy neighbourhood?		
9. Do you enjoy a homey environment?		
10. Are there too many people around you?		
11. Have you a good appetite?		
12. Have you started to be forgetful?		
13. Do you have good digestions?		
14. Do you feel fatigued without apparent reason?		
15. Do you sleep well?		
16. Do you get easily irritated?		
17. Do you have a good relation with your superiors?		
18. Do you use a car as a means of work?		
19. Is your employment stable?		
20. Do you need to take work home?		
21. Do you get along well with peers and friends?		
22. Do you become very impatient when someone delays you?		
23. Do you know how to listen patiently?		
24. Do you speak too much?		
25. Do you feel comfortable with your sexual life?		
26. Do you try to do things better than others?		
27. Do you like the way you are?		
28. Are you a perfectionist?		
29. Do you have a good sense of humour?		
30. Does standing in a queue irritate you?		

Scoring:
Look at **odd** questions and add 1 point for each NO: . . . . · _____
Look at **even** questions and add 1 point for each YES: . . . . · _____
Ignore the **odd** 'YES' and the **even** NO.   **Total:** . . . . _____

Interpretation:

0-7 points	**8-13 points**	**More than 14 points**
You are well protected against stress and may even need a small alteration to bring excitement to your life.	You are in a middle range of stress. Things can go in one direction or the other and you would do well to take preventive measures.	This is a warning so that you examine your habits of life, your environment, your mental attitude and your relationships, and make plans to improve them.

Obsessions and compulsions

Certain persons suffer from absurd ideas or thoughts (**obsessions**) that annoy them and which they cannot reject. Such thoughts entice them to repetitive (**compulsive**) as well as absurd behaviour.

Obsessions and compulsions (sometimes referred to as 'oddities') almost always go together and are therefore known as **obsessive-compulsive disorder**, which is a serious and disabling illness.

These are the most common obsessive/compulsive themes:

- **Cleaning.** Cleaning and washing what it is already spotless.

- **Order and symmetry.** Putting everything away at the office or at home. This is done repeatedly following rigorous patterns of position.

- **Fear of illness.** Avoiding contact with persons and places for fear of acquiring a disease.

- **Hoarding.** Storing everything and not throwing anything away, even when the kept objects do not possess any material or sentimental value.

- **Fear of losing a dear one.** Constantly calling a friend or relative in fear that they may have had an accident or misfortune.

Obsessions are most often accompanied by an uncomfortable tension that lures the person to repetitive (or compulsive) behaviour to escape the tension.

Unfortunately, the discomfort does not go away and the individual feels the drive to repeat the action time and again. This diabolic cycle may lead the person to spend several hours devoted to something that should take only minutes.

MANAGING OBSESSIONS

Do not get alarmed by **obsessive-compulsive symptoms** that fall within the range of **normality**. In fact, they are a developmental step in the life of children. For example:

- Touching each and everyone of the light posts as one strolls the walkway.
- Following a very rigid ritual before going to bed.
- Avoiding stepping on the floor tile's joint lines.
- Counting objects insistently.
- Watching the same film again and again.
- Singing or humming the same refrain many times over the whole day.

These behaviours are not considered pathological and they disappear over time.

However, adults may experience much discomfort (and the corresponding barrier to lead a normal life) due to some obsessive-compulsive symptoms. The following behaviours are harmless in general but may indicate risk:

- perfectionist tendencies in everyday tasks
- extreme attitude towards personal hygiene
- stinginess and excessive saving
- total dedication to work, eliminating hobbies and pastimes
- excessive preoccupation for tidiness and cleanliness at home or work
- intolerance towards other family members who do not keep a scrupulous tidiness
- obsessive worry for not having locked the doors or turned taps and lights off

These symptoms may lead to **interpersonal problems,** as it is difficult to share one's life with those who display them. Carefully observe the aforementioned behaviours in order to modify them if necessary.

How to overcome obsessions and compulsions

As a means of prevention and treatment, try the following counsels:

- **Escape from stressful situations.** Many of these symptoms would never appear except in the presence of stressors that trigger the corresponding thought or behaviour. If you have this tendency, make sure you move away from the sources of excessive stress (see page 112).

- **Do not live by yourself.** Statistics show that these problems are much more frequent in those who live alone. Avoid this circumstance, especially if you are prone to obsessive-compulsive behaviour, as the mere presence of someone living with you is enough to reduce this strong tendency.

- **Keep busy.** Inactivity and the lack of responsibilities lead to obsessive-compulsive symptoms. Search for responsibilities connected to your work or with some altruistic task in order to free your life from this problem. (See also 'Occupational therapy' on page 324).

- **Talk about it.** Seek the company of someone who cares for you. Open up about your obsessions and compulsions. This is healing in itself. You may also seek professional counselling or join group therapy.

- **Practise relaxation.** Obsessions come in moments of tension and nervousness. Compulsions appear as a form of escape from tension, but this does not work. Learn and regularly practise relaxation (see page 40), as it is an effective way to overcome the problem. Even the way to eat is related to obsessions (see the Research Results box on the following page).

- **Trust in God.** Compulsions, as many other forms of addiction, are often beyond personal control. Therefore, when you feel unable to face the challenge by yourself, trust in an outside power: the loving God, the understanding Almighty who is willing to help you, if you ask in faith.

Clinical treatment

If your obsessive-compulsive tendency goes beyond light discomfort, you must take the matter seriously and seek professional advice to undergo the corresponding pharmacological and psychological treatment.

According to clinical research (Hohagen *et al.*, 1998; O'Connor *et al.*, 1999; Salaberria and Echeburua, 1998; Stravynski and Greenberg, 1998), **cognitive** strategies, especially **self-instruction** and **stopping thoughts**, are the most successful methods to treat obsessions and compulsions (see the box below and the adjoining page).

Lastly, it must be said that drugs prescribed to alleviate this disorder, although not able to eliminate it, help the patient to lower the impulse level and should be used under medical supervision.

According to recent studies (Goodman, 1999), the most recommendable drugs are the serotonin reuptake inhibitors, capable of reducing the neuronal activity causing obsessions and compulsions.

RESEARCH RESULTS

Nutrition and obsessions

A study published in the *British Journal of Clinical Psychology* (Rippere, 1983), refers to the case of a male with chronic obsessions who, for years, did not respond to either medication or psychological treatment. A cleansing diet was prescribed to compensate for the side effects of the drugs. As a result, the patient experienced a remarkable and lasting recovery from his symptoms.

What was in the diet? Just a high-protein, high-carbohydrate breakfast. The explanation of this effect has to do with preventing hypoglycaemia over the morning hours. In this case, it was concluded that symptoms appeared due to the absence of nutrients that are preventive of obsessive symptoms. This study recommends that this simple strategy be applied from the very beginning of any obsessive-compulsive treatment.

If you are prone to these behaviours, use **diet high in complex carbohydrates** (all types of grain and their derivatives). Begin your day with a good breakfast made up of soya milk, whole-grain bread, fruits and nuts.

self-help

SELF-INSTRUCTION

Cleaning is one of the most common obsessive behaviours, sometimes done out of fear of contaminating 'germs;' other times, engaged in for no apparent reason. If you have this problem or know someone who has it, this list may help:

1. **Identify your adverse thoughts.** Different thoughts affect different persons: 'Someone with HIV may have been here.' 'This has not been cleaned in months.' 'If I touch the toilet handle, I will get contaminated.'

2. **Transform them into reasonable and edifying thoughts.** For example: 'AIDS only is transmitted via sexual contact or open sores.' 'My immune system can fight dust and normal dirt.'

'I cannot live thinking of germs; I must get used to public places.'

3. **Think of something positive about yourself.** 'I have obtained a job by competition.' 'I am an organised person.' 'I have good health.' These thoughts promote greater personal security— a very necessary feature to overcome this problem.

4. **Visualise success.** Imagine yourself free from the burden of the cleaning compulsion. Look at yourself doing your work in peace, without tension or nervousness derived from the duty to clean everything conscientiously.

THOUGHT STOPPING

Obsessive thoughts are sometimes independent from compulsive behaviour; they always entail, nevertheless, the deep annoyance caused by the **fixed idea**. This is what Andrea experienced every time she saw a small baby. The fear of grabbing him and hitting him or throwing him against the floor overtook Andrea. She never acted on these thoughts or did anything like that, but the thoughts were extremely uncomfortable because every time she was among friends, relatives or neighbours with a little baby, she struggled. The following steps may be useful in cases like this.

1. **Discover the obsessive thought.** In Andrea's case, it was an impulse to hit an infant. Another could be a kind of inner voice insisting: 'Tidy up the room,' 'The books are not straight,' 'Your hands are full of germs,' etc.

2. **Identify the links that precede such thoughts.** There is always an idea, or clue in the surroundings, that occurs before the obsessive thought. It can be a message retrieved from memory, an odour, a word pronounced by someone else…

3. **Say: 'Stop!'** As soon as the first link (thought or word) appears, say immediately and decisively: 'Stop!' to avoid taking the step into the cascade of thoughts leading to the obsession.

4. **Consciously think about another topic.** Once the mental chain has been stopped, use an alternative image to distract yourself. To do this, you must have a motive of thought previously prepared for the occasion: 'that trip I went to,' 'that fabulous film,' 'my friend Samantha,' or any other agreeable and favourite theme that may free you from the obsessive thoughts.

<u>2.09</u>

Complexes

Many people suffer from the effect of a complex. Some offer an appearance of security and self-sufficiency. They present themselves as brilliant and work effectively and even look happy. However, they carry internal conflicts within themselves.

This may be due to an experience from early life. As a consequence, they manifest inhibitions, lack of adaptation, restlessness, pretentiousness, extreme jealousy, mental blocks, violence or remorse without apparent reason.

Complexes are **unconscious processes**. In other words, they are present in the mind, but they escape consciousness. The person thinks and acts without being able to explain what he/she is doing. While this makes help and support difficult, it is possible to provide adequate help. There are many kinds of complexes: Oedipus', Electra's, Cain's, castration complex, weaning complex… but above all, we find the most salient and common complexes: inferiority and guilt.

The inferiority complex

This is probably the most widespread complex of all. The expression 'complex' almost always refers to inferiority complex. This problem is now more relevant than ever before, due to the strength with which media make people feel inferior. The box below targets those affected by this problem.

self-help

HOW TO OVERCOME THE INFERIORITY COMPLEX

To overcome this complex, follow these steps:

- **Assess your surrounding in a critical manner.** Models (from publicity and public life) of relevance in society offer an image of perfection. Besides, our friends, neighbours, acquaintances, etc. tend to offer an image we perceive as superior to what they really are. Therefore, when those around you may seem full of virtue, think that, behind the outer image, there is plenty of imperfection.

- **Set up a realistic plan for improvement.** If you wish to be more organised, more outgoing or better skilled, think of the steps towards your improvement and follow them through. Do not compare yourself with others and do not get discouraged for not having reached the level of others. Focus on your own progress as you advance.

- **Escape from inferiority in connection with physical traits.** There are behavioural traits that can be modified, but not physical appearance. It is not possible to add centimetres to your height; neither is it possible to reduce the size of your nose if you don't like it, except through plastic surgery. Accept your physique and think that we all are beautiful because we are different, peculiar and unique.

- **Avoid alleged superiority.** A common reaction in those who intimately feel inferior is to project an image of grandeur and superiority. Do not fall into this tendency. Be natural and respect others. This will help you safeguard interpersonal relationships, which are a source of good self-esteem.

- **Compensate.** Improve the deficiencies you may have. If you are inhibited and unable to establish connections with the opposite sex, make efforts to be bolder and more talkative. If you suffer from obesity, go on a diet and engage in physical exercise. If you cannot do it by yourself, seek professional help or the support of a close friend. Another way to compensate for your weak areas is to emphasise the advantages you already possess. If you cannot excel in the intellectual realm, make up for it with manual or sports abilities.

- **Look for a good social support system.** It is very important to count on an environment with accepting people who are willing to support you. Perhaps your family and friends are the best people to do this. People near you must appreciate you, recognise your achievement and respect you as you are, without ridiculing your defects.

HOW TO FREE YOURSELF FROM A GUILT COMPLEX?

Try the following advice:

- **Undergo a realistic analysis.** If you cannot do it by yourself, find support in someone you trust with high moral standards.
- **Reflect on your ethical values.** Compare your values with your duties and commitment to them. If you feel guilty for something that is far from those fundamental values, perhaps you are being too strict with yourself.
- **Speak with those who are related to your guilt.** Guilt often originates in interpersonal relationships. Try to smooth those differences and ask for forgiveness when you have hurt someone.
- **Ask God for forgiveness.** Your conscience may torment you for some old event or past action. The involved person may even be deceased, but God promises salvation and also forgiveness for any offence for which you sincerely ask for forgiveness.

See also unit 3.08 (page 164), where advice is offered to confront feelings of guilt and false guilt. There you will also find a test to evaluate whether you have tendency to such guilt.

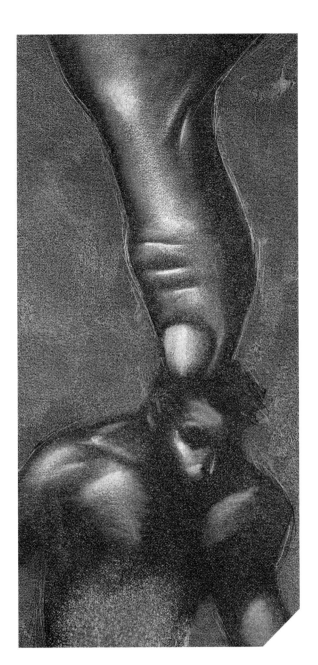

Sayings of Jesus

'The eye is the lamp of the body. If your eyes are good, your whole body will be full of light. But if your eyes are bad, your whole body will be full of darkness. If then the light within you is darkness, how great is that darkness!' (Matthew 6:22, 23).

The guilt complex

Unlike those experiencing guilt due to the transgression of an ethical or moral principle, there are people suffering from a false guilt complex who blame themselves excessively and who have difficulty forgiving themselves.

This sensation of false remorse is not linked to a specific act but is a generalised and imprecise fear, causing anguish.

(See the box on the top on this page).

2.10
Bulimia

There is an increasing number of girls who learn bulimic behaviour as they observe it or listen to it from their friends and end up practising it themselves. There may be, in fact, many more cases than those detected because the external appearance does not normally show (as happens with anorexia nervosa; see page 126), and the disorder goes without being diagnosed.

Although it is also present in males, the **typical profile** of a bulimic person is that of an **adolescent girl or** a **young woman** that:

- **Experiences uncontrollable desires to eat a lot at once.** During such binges, she tends to ingest highly caloric food: entrées,

deep-fried food, cream, cheese, cake, chocolate… feeling unable to stop until becoming full.

- **Uses inadequate behaviours to impede fattening.** The most common method (80%-90% of the times) is to induce vomiting after eating. Other methods are the use of an overdose of laxatives, diuretics, enemas, or excessive and compulsive physical exercise.

- **Assesses her weight and shape unrealistically.** For example, she may be slightly overweight and see herself as obese and deformed.

- **Suffers at least two episodes per week over a period of months.** Bulimic behaviour is not limited to sporadic occurrences, but is regular and prolonged.

How to prevent bulimia

The following tips target **two areas: internal** (targeted at thinking), and **external** (targeted to behaviour and to the environment where the person lives). They can also be useful to those suffering from bulimia.

Inner action (thoughts)

- **Do not undervalue yourself.** Be careful not to diminish yourself. Recognise your strengths and set moderate goals to improve your weaknesses. Think that others also have problems (you simply are unaware of them).

- **Do not blame yourself excessively.** Feeling guilty for having eaten too much is normal and you do not need to suffer from it. Just develop a rational plan to avoid behaviours that produce guilt, such as mentioned in the following point.

- **Decide your intake beforehand.** Before you start your meal, decide what you are going to eat and how much (seek a moderate and healthy diet). Set your mind to think that the food is limited and there is no more. In this way, you will be able to eat the right amount without recurring to vomiting (or another method of purging).

THE RISKS OF BULIMIA

Those affected by bulimia (90% are women) tend to be initiated into the practice by other bulimics who seem normal and well adjusted. However, bulimia (apart from being a mental disorder in itself) has serious complications:

- **Depression.** Among persons with bulimia, depression is much more common than in the general population.

- **Addiction.** Alcohol and amphetamine dependence are associated with bulimia.
- **Loss of dental enamel.** Due to frequent vomiting in bulimia, the enamel that covers the teeth deteriorates and caries develop.
- **Disrupted menstruation.** The menstrual period undergoes significant alterations due to an incorrect diet.

Outer action (behaviour and environment)

- **Seek good company.** Look for healthy people with whom you can associate. Avoid those who only value physical appearance and use inadequate slimming methods. It can be hard to change friendships, but you will be happy in the end.

- **Escape from highly stressful situations.** A binge episode followed by vomiting usually comes during moments of frustration or discouragement. Avoid these circumstances. Put order in your studies or work so that you are not subject to excessive tension.

- **Eat rationally.** Eating excessively will cause guilt and desire to induce vomiting. Try eating less amount more often to avoid feeling such a voracious hunger that causes you to lose self-control. Avoid fast food (so loaded with fat), sweets, ice cream, fizzy drinks and other empty-calorie foods. All this will help you enjoy healthy food, keep fit, and feel better about yourself.

How to treat bulimia

Clinical psychological treatment is the most adequate. The person learns to record her/his behaviour and to develop action plans, to improve her/his self-esteem, to talk about past conflicts, and to acquire good dietary habits.

The **family** also tends to attend a few sessions, as this enhances the chances of recovery. The table below shows an example of self-talk for a young lady with bulimia.

self-help

SELF-TALK TO FACE BULIMIA

Self-talk (see page 303) consists of substituting irrational and adverse thoughts with adaptive and useful ones in order to remind oneself on an ongoing basis as well as in moments of risk:

Adverse thoughts	Alternative thoughts
• *'I am ugly and obese'*	• *'I am sufficiently attractive'*
• *'Everything fattens me up'*	• *'Healthy food makes me feel good'*
• *'When I sit at the table, I cannot stop eating'*	• *'I am going to eat what I have chosen. I am in charge of my will'*
• *'I'll get fat if I do not vomit'*	• *'I have decided to quit the habit'*

By the use of imagination, the person learns to visualise the victory over bulimia via a rational diet. She also envisions the improvement of her health through a healthy lifestyle.

2.11

Anorexia

Anorexia cases are increasing and there is a great concern about this spreading disorder that affects adolescents and youth, especially females.

Although it also touches males, the **typical profile** of a person with anorexia is an **adolescent girl or young woman** who:

- **Is excessively slim** (below 85% of the normal weight) and refuses to attain adequate weight arguing that she is just right and that perhaps she could weigh a few less pounds to improve her looks.

- **Experiences an irrational fear of becoming fat.** This fear leads to strict diets or prolonged periods of fasting to lose weight (resulting in malnutrition which may even lead to death).

- **Perceives her own body incorrectly**, standing before the mirror and judging herself with excessive fat around the belly, hips and buttocks, when in reality she is emaciated.

- **Stops menstruating**, due to the lack of necessary nutrients to stimulate secretion of estrogens, which are the trigger of menstruation.

How to prevent anorexia

The frequency of eating disorders doubled between 1960 and 2000 (Daw, 2001). This facts shows that the phenomenon is basically socio-environmental, as genes cannot change in just two generations. It is therefore very important to work on the preventive side so that this problem stops growing and starts to decrease over the next generations. As anorexia begins in pre-adolescent and adolescent stages, the following counsel is especially for parents:

- **Watch out for media influence.** Advertising images as well as those depicted in films alter the concepts of beauty and desirability. Their specific emphasis has been that of extremely slim models. Take advantage of every occasion to explain to your children that what they see on television should not be a standard for behaviour or belief and it does not need to be accepted. Beauty is relative and there are many more important goals in life than being super-slim.

- **Do not place excessive demands upon your children.** Anorexia thrives in contexts where parents place a lot of expectations upon their

THE RISKS OF ANOREXIA

People suffering from anorexia (90% are women) start with an innocent slimming diet while they are still children. This is a very dangerous path with complications and adverse effects once the process ends up in anorexia:

- The **mortality rate** of eating disorders (anorexia included) is the highest of all mental illnesses.
- Ten percent of patients die of **starvation or suicide**.
- Women with anorexia, even those attaining recovery, have a **reduced chance to become mothers**.

- Anorexia tends to become complicated with other psychiatric syndromes such as **depression** and **obsessive-compulsive disorders**.
- **Social relations deteriorate** excessively and the patient loses sexual desire.
- The **age of onset** is **descending** alarmingly. Although the average is 16 years, it is frightening to see many cases of 7-, 8- and 9-year-old girls who begin dieting.

children. Encourage your children to make efforts, but do not push too hard, especially if they are submissive and wish to please their parents in everything. These children have the highest probability of becoming anorexic.

- **Emphasise character values.** Teach them the value of being honest, diligent, good hearted, organised… Play down the importance of physical attractiveness. After all, it can hardly be altered.

- **Promote self-esteem in youth.** Adolescents and pre-adolescents are very sensitive about what is said of them. This significantly affects their self-concept. Be careful how you talk to them and about them. Be positive in your remarks. Admonish their mistakes with love and never forget to praise their achievements and qualities when they deserve it.

- **Show them that one can eat well and not get fat.** Eating plenty of healthy food with moderate physical exercise does not make people fat. Teach your children from early life that they can enjoy simple and varied meals made up of legumes, vegetables, fruits, roots and grains (pasta, rice, bread) tastefully seasoned and beautifully presented. Fat, spice, dairies and sugar should be used in moderation. Your children will improve in health and in body shape and will end up enjoying natural foods.

How to treat anorexia

Diagnosed anorexia calls for **strict medical treatment** and, in many cases, hospitalisation. The health centre will establish a plan to gain weight (for instance, two pounds per week) in a safe and controlled environment.

At the same time, **clinical psychotherapy** is prescribed in order to help the young woman overcome the root of the problem and to gain autonomy. The **family** can contribute with a high level of support, encouraging the patient to follow the treatment and view the future with hope to successfully and comfortably reconstruct her life.

2.12
Panic attack

PANIC ATTACK SYMPTOMS

Not all symptoms appear together. Generally, four or five may coincide at a given time and that is sufficient for many to believe they are dying:

- Strong heart palpitation
- Cold sweat or fatigue
- Shaking
- Rapid breathing
- A feeling of choking
- Sensation of heart attack
- Nausea or abdominal pain
- Seasickness or fainting
- 'Out-of-self' sensation
- Fear of losing control or going crazy
- Fear of dying
- Lack of general sensitivity

Panic attack (or crisis) takes over unexpectedly, reaching its highest point in about ten minutes. Then the symptoms decrease progressively until they completely disappear.

In spite of the no-risk experience of panic attacks, the person suffers in the process because of the combination of symptoms experienced (see the box on the left).

It is important to know how to recognise these attacks and differentiate them from other disorders or pathologies. (See also the unit 'Anxiety' on page 96).

A panic attack causes feelings of horror and death. The heavy heart palpitations plus the chest pain (both are present in most cases) are interpreted by the patient as a heart attack.

This makes him go through a terrifying experience. Many times the panic attack is in the night.

The patient wakes up startled at what he perceives as alarming symptoms. His first reaction is to call a doctor or find a way to get to the hospital.

After the corresponding exam, the patient is assured that there is no cardiac risk.

The person accepts the fact, but, often times, he fears a new attack and cannot relax.

How to treat the panic disorder

This problem requires both psychiatric and psychological treatment. The psychiatrist usu- ally prescribes medicine to reduce the chance of a recurring attack.

At the same time, the psychologist designs a therapeutic plan to teach the patient to process his thoughts in a balanced manner.

Care is also placed on the environment so that it is favourable and free from stress. Long-term treatment may last for many months.

That is why it is necessary to be prepared for new panic attacks. That is the purpose of the box below.

self-help

TO FACE A PANIC ATTACK

One of the most important objectives for those suffering from panic attack is to face the moment when symptoms begin. A good preparation makes the attack less anxious and less painful. It also provides support for the prescribed treatment and leaves the patient with a feeling of control over the symptoms. If you suffer from panic attacks, bear in mind these tips:

Before...
- **Understand the symptoms.** Symptoms are anxiety manifestations without apparent reason. They are very uncomfortable, but involve no danger. They are organic reactions to defend the organism from a threat that is not real in the context of a panic crisis.
- **Avoid a catastrophic attitude.** Do not think that if another attack comes, it will be worse and that you will never get well. Think positively: 'I am under treatment and things will get better. If I have to experience another attack, I will be able to face it with fortitude for I now understand my problem better.'
- **Avoid stressful events.** Highly stressful and tense situations tend to trigger the panic attack. That is why your environment should be relatively free from stress.

During...
- **Breathing calms down the attack.** At the first sign of imminent attack, use breathing to fight the symp- toms. Slowly breathe in air through your nostrils and expand your belly as you take air. Breathe out very slowly.
- **Remember that nothing tragic is going to happen.** A panic attack does not end up in infarction, death, suffocation or madness. Understand that it is temporary and harmless, and you need to resist it until it passes.
- **Control your thoughts.** The moment of panic can become more distressing than necessary when the person despairs, lets go of control, and thinks of death or incapacitation.
- **Use self-instruction.** Repeat in your mind: 'This is the way it is. I must resist. It will soon go away. This is not dangerous. I have survived before. I will soon feel better.' If it is possible, retrieve some thought that may take your mind off the discomfort of the symptoms.

After...
- **Rejoice in your progress.** You have more control than you thought.
- **Do not worry.** Do things with plenty of calm and try by all means to remain relaxed.
- Put yourself in the hand of a **good mental health professional.**

2.13
Addictions

Happiness has been defined as the total absence of addictions. We are not just talking about addictions to **'hard' or 'illegal' drugs**. There are ordinary and regularly-used addictive substances such as **alcoholic beverages**, **cigarettes** or **coffee**. These are called **psychoactive** substances because they affect the mental function (see Escandón and Gálvez, 2005).

There are also **non-chemical addictions** and these are on the rise: gambling (see page 138), compulsive sex, pornography, and the Internet. There are even addictions to such common items as diet, medicines or physical exercise.

The **vicious cycle** of addiction is very dangerous, whether addiction is legal or illegal, chemical or non-chemical, harmful or harmless to health. All addictions deprive those involved of personal freedom. In addition, they involve serious risks:

- **Dependence.** Drugs or addictive behaviours produce a repetitive desire. And the more one satisfies the desire, the more it returns.

- **Tolerance.** The drug user needs an increased dose to reach effects of similar intensity as before.

- **Withdrawal symptoms.** They can be psychological, such as extreme restlessness at one's inability to obtain the drug or perform the conduct. They can also be physical since the organism is used to the substance and is not receiving it. Withdrawal symptoms include: insomnia, agitation, palpitation, sweating, nausea, vomiting…

- **Effects on the brain** (in chemical addictions). Drugs affect the central nervous system. When a chemical reaches the brain, several vital functions are altered and the person becomes unable to perform the simplest of tasks. When use is prolonged, the drug may cause permanent damage.

The first three risks listed above are not only present in chemical addictions, but also in behavioural addictions. A person addicted to pornography, for example, feels an extremely strong desire to repeat the behaviour. After some time, previous images are not sufficient, thus heavier and more

obscene ones are needed. And when images are unavailable, the person will experience strong tension and frustration.

How to prevent addiction

The majority of addictions, especially those to substances, begin in adolescence and early youth. Therefore, preventive efforts should be targeted at those ages. Since the first years of schooling, children ought to be instructed about drugs and their risks. School curricula need to make room for talks and seminars led by relevant persons (former drug addicts, physicians, lawyers, psychologists, police, social workers, etc.).

In terms of policy, all primary and secondary schools should declare themselves **drug-free zones**, taking necessary measures to avoid becoming drug traffic and initiation centres.

Parents of children and youth also have a responsibility to prevent and tackle the problem using strategies such as the following:

- Have a **clear position** on drugs and addictions.
- Help to build their children's **self-esteem in a healthy manner** (see page 28).
- Maintain a **safe and stable home**.
- Demonstrate **flexibility** in ideas and behaviours but within clear limits.
- Offer an **impeccable example** in all references to addictions.

Authorities also have an important role to play in training against addiction and for total health: attractive and suggestive programmes, use of warning labels (for example, labels on alcoholic beverages and tobacco), rules and regulations of distribution and sale, etc. It is particularly important to enforce the laws against substance trafficking in primary and secondary schools as well as any place frequented by children and youth.

Other addictions (work, sex, gambling...) can appear during adult age. It is important to remember that both chemical and non-chemical addictions carry a hidden **syndrome of anxiety**. For this reason, avoiding anxiety is a sure way to prevent an addiction (see page 96).

CO-DEPENDENCE

In order to support those using and abusing drugs, some initiate themselves into a dangerous path: a co-dependent relationship. This problem is common in the family of the drug addict.

Although with good intentions, the dear ones (mother, father, sibling) end up fighting the problem in the wrong way. They show blind love and yield to any request made by the addict. They invest a great deal of time, effort and emotional energy, but they end up being a barrier to recovery.

It is essential to seek **external professional help** to avoid this dangerous side effect.

How to overcome addictions

It is clear that addictions cannot be overcome alone. The affected person needs **social, professional and spiritual support**.

Therefore, the advice given below is targeted at the addict's family members or social support system:

- If there have been many attempts to abandon the addiction without success, put pressure on the addict to attend a **rehabilitation centre**.
- **Support the plan** developed by the centre or qualified professional. Trust the treatment and promote it for the wellness of the addict (your child, your spouse, your friend...).
- **Avoid overprotection.** This is a great temptation for the loved ones. But in these circumstances, it is necessary to remain firm in everything related to treatment.
- **Reward achievements**, as the drug addict needs external reinforcement to attain new goals. These may be sweets, films, outings, play, getting together with friends... according to taste and circumstances.
- Prepare a **relaxing, healthy and favourable environment** and try by all means to keep the affected person out of addiction-inviting environments: places, persons, objects, etc., as they can entice him/her to relapse (see the Research Results box on the following page).

Self-help groups (group therapy, see page 316) have proven to be excellent healing channels and ways to maintain sobriety. For example, Alcoholics Anonymous, Narcotics Anonymous, Gamblers Anonymous, Sexaholics Anonymous... enjoy a high success rate among participants. Involved individuals can fight with much more tenacity when joined together with others who have the same problem.

It must be recognised that the power of addiction is such that only with the help of supernatural power can many reach victory. The success of Alcoholics Anonymous is partly due to the human support provided by other ex-addicts and partly because of the divine help received by those who are willing to receive this power. See the 12-step plan of Alcoholics Anonymous in the adjoining page; notice that 7 of them clearly refer to a spiritual or moral component.

When victory has been attained, the fight is not over, as the risk of relapse is very high. Thus it is important to carefully plan the return to normality at...

- **Work.** The rehabilitated subject needs a new job with new companions and the firm decision to adapt and stick to the plan.

- **The social environment.** For a prolonged period of time, the person needs someone to continue to firmly watch the social context. Relationships must be with people who know how to enjoy life without substances or addictions, with simplicity and naturalness.

- **Free time.** Leisure time encompasses the highest risk of relapse. It should be planned carefully, including physical exercise, open-air activities, sports, etc. Bars, gambling parlours and other places where will power may weaken must be avoided.

- **Spiritual life.** The spiritual component is also important to return back to normal life. The addictive stage is now past and the person is to commence a new life. Guilt, a common feeling of ex-addicts, finds forgiveness from a caring and loving God. And as far as the future is concerned, God promises protection and continuous support. (See Escandón and Gálvez, 2005).

Gems of Ancient Wisdom

'So do not fear, for I am with you; do not be dismayed, for I am your God' (Isaiah 41:10).

RESEARCH RESULTS

Overcoming addictions by sensory control

Kenneth Perkins, from the University of Pittsburgh School of Medicine (USA), conducted an experiment (Perkins *et al.*, 2003) with 80 individuals from the university community.

They were invited to drink beer. In order to control the sensory effect, part of the group drank using a transparent glass, part using an opaque glass; some drank with a pin on their noses, and some without it. They were offered unlimited beer, and they were asked to assess the quality of the beverage. The

exact amount of beer taken was also measured and the findings show that participants with the blocked senses (vision and smell) drank significantly lower amounts than the others.

These findings confirm the important role that senses have upon substance consumption and how treatment may improve by controlling the sources of sensorial information, helping to avoid relapse.

The 12 steps

*Initially developed by **Alcoholics Anonymous**, these principles are also used successfully by those who try to abandon (or have already abandoned) gambling, food addiction or compulsive sex.*

We...

1. Admitted we were powerless over alcohol.
2. Came to believe that a Power greater than ourselves could restore us to sanity.
3. Made a decision to turn our will and our lives over to the care of God, as we understood Him.
4. Made a searching and fearless moral inventory of ourselves.
5. Admitted to God, to ourselves and to another human being the exact nature of our wrongs.
6. Were entirely ready to have God remove all these defects of character.
7. Humbly asked Him to remove our shortcomings.
8. Made a list of all persons we had harmed and became willing to make amends to them all.

9. Made direct amends to such people wherever possible, except when to do so would injure them or others.
10. Continued to take personal inventory and when we were wrong promptly admitted it.
11. Sought through prayer and meditation to improve our conscious contact with God, as we understood Him, praying only for knowledge of His will for us and the power to carry that out.
12. Having had a spiritual awakening as the result of these steps, we tried to carry this message to alcoholics, and to practise these principles in all our affairs.

Self-help groups have been gaining great success over the last decades. The principal foundations are: the belief in a loving God as the ultimate authority and source of power, total sobriety as the aim, commitment to help others who wish to abandon dependence, and confidentiality of participants.

self-help

TOBACCO ADDICTION

Tobacco use has declined in many countries, but it is increasing in others. As far as young people are concerned, cigarettes are popular. Nicotine has a highly addictive power and makes it difficult to abandon the habit. If you wish to quit smoking, try the following tips:

1. **Observe your habits.** There are invisible threads in your life. They tie you to objects and situations that invite you to smoke. Look for these circumstances and avoid them or get ready to fight them: when you go to bed, when you wake up, when you have a cup of coffee, meeting with your friends, sitting at your favourite armchair, finishing your meal…, flee from these situations.

2. **Look for new environments.** Change your schedule, your meetings, your settings. Do healthy activities in the open and in relaxing settings.

3. **Include friends and relatives.** Inform everybody that you have decided to quit smoking. They will surely support you. If possible, join someone who has also decided to quit the habit and get together to give and receive encouragement.

4. **Take care of your diet.** Detoxification must be accompanied by abundant fruits and vegetables. Drink water and citric juices. This will help you rid yourself of nicotine and reduce the craving for cigarettes.

5. **Do exercise.** Physical exercise will relax you from the tension caused by detoxification and will lead you to a state of well-being.

6. **Reward yourself.** Set up rewards for the end of those days of victory: invite yourself to a show, or buy an article of clothing with the money saved from cigarettes.

7. **Find support in the spiritual dimension.** Many addicts reject this aspect and do not attain success. Try praying to God as if you talked to a friend and ask him for strength to overcome the habit.

(See also the second chapter of Escandón and Gálvez, *Free from Addictions*, Safeliz, 2005, and *Free from Tobacco*, the DVD that comes with it).

DANGEROUS CAFFEINE

Many think that caffeine is far from being a drug, but the psychiatric handbook DSM-IV lists caffeine intoxication when the person takes 250 mg of caffeine in the same day. The effects are: nervousness, restlessness, insomnia, diuresis, excess of blood in the cheeks, muscle twitching, digestive problems, rambling flow of thought and speech, tachycardia and psychomotor agitation.

The following products contain variable amounts of caffeine:

Product	Caffeine
Cup of espresso	*100 mg*
Cup of instant coffee	*65 mg*
Can of caffeinated soft drink	*45 mg*
Tablet of analgesic	*50 mg*
Tablet of stimulant	*100-200 mg*
Slimming pill	*75-200 mg*
One-ounce chocolate bar	*29 mg*
Cup of cocoa (5 mg)	*5 mg*

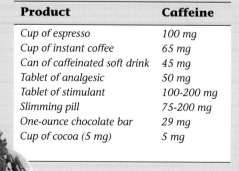

Addiction to sex

William is a married man with school-aged children. He is polite and well considered. He was addicted to pornography throughout years and did not want to accept it until his wife caught him and pressed him to seek help, since his behaviour significantly affected his family life and his marital relationship.

William was 'hooked' to porno magazines and his masturbatory behaviour made him not wish to have normal sexual relations with his wife. He rarely sought sexual encounters (since he was satiated by masturbation) and when he wanted sex, it was in such strange positions that his wife felt uncomfortable. Alleging excess of work, he spent hours on-line after everyone was in bed. Burdened with these activities, he devoted very little time to his children. In secret, he tried to quit the habit many times but without success, until he went to a sexologist, who established a treatment plan with the help of William's wife.

William's case is not extreme, but there are levels of sex addiction that encompass one or more of the following in an absorbent and compulsive way:

- telephone sex
- exhibitionism
- voyeurism
- prostitution
- paedophilia
- sadomasochism

Growing cybersex

Two unknown persons from distant places chat via the Internet and exchange a suggestive sexual comment. One or both reach sexual arousal and orgasm through masturbation.

Three percent of all Internet users end up addicted to cybersex. There are about equal numbers of men and women. Half of those practising Internet sex end up with telephone contact and between 15% and 30% make personal contact.

This habit is putting family and marital relationships in jeopardy (Smith Bailey, 2003)

TO IDENTIFY SEXUAL ADDICTION

If you observe in yourself, your partner, or any friend or family member two or three of the following behaviours, there may be a case of sex addiction. You should talk to him/her in a calm manner, offering to help and without accusations. He/she:

1. Insists on staying at the computer or TV when there is no one in the house or everybody is in bed.
2. Keeps a briefcase, backpack, drawer, or cupboard under key, and nobody in the family has access to it.
3. Looks at someone of the opposite sex for a long time as they pass by.
4. Receives credit card charges that are not explained.
5. Arrives very late from the workplace or is absent, blaming travelling or work.
6. When on-line and someone approaches, he/she quickly changes the screen.
7. Does not have sex with his/her partner or asks for unusual ways to have it.
8. Shows emotional distance with spouse.
9. Seems to be distracted and absent even in the most intimate moments.
10. Shows mood changes and unkind or threatening behaviours.

How to overcome sex addiction

The psychological process is very similar to any other addiction and much of the advice for substance dependence is also valid for sex addiction:

1. The first stage is to **admit the problem** and show willingness to correct the conduct.

2. **Seek support in someone else.** The best person is the spouse (under the guidance of an expert). And if this is not possible, a friend or close relative can help.

3. Keep oneself **under surveillance.** For example, do not stay alone for long and follow through with prescribed activities.

4. Keep **absolute sex sobriety**: Sex only with partner.

5. Use **structured mechanisms of help**: Block certain Internet sites, limit the time at the computer.

6. **Plan leisure activities.** They are best in the open air and at places away from the usual ones.

7. This tendency may be rooted in sexual abuse or a troubled childhood. In these cases, rehabilitation plans should be accompanied by **formal psychotherapy** to explore past events and eliminate conflicts.

8. **To the support person:** Use a compassionate style and deal with the addict as an ill person who needs recovery; he/she has to accept responsibility. Once accepted and applied, it is not advisable to scold or criticise excessively for unacceptable behaviours. He/She needs understanding, sympathy, and support.

Gems of Ancient Wisdom

'Who has woe? Who has sorrow? Who has strife? Who has complaints? Who has needless bruises? Who has bloodshot eyes? Those who linger over wine, who go to sample bowls of mixed wine' (Proverbs 23:29-30).

'For the lips of an adulteress drip honey, and her speech is smoother than oil; but in the end she is bitter as gall, sharp as a double-edged sword' (Proverbs 5:3-4).

TEST YOURSELF ::

Answer YES or NO to the following questions to find out whether you are alcoholic:

Am I alcoholic?	YES	NO
1. Do you feel a strong urge to drink after having lived unpleasant moments (family row, financial problem, difficulties at work)?		
2. Can you now take a greater amount of alcohol than when you began drinking?		
3. Have you noticed that, moments after having drunk, you cannot remember details of what happened before?		
4. Do you worry about running out of drinks?		
5. Do you sometimes feel guilty for having drunk too much?		
6. Do you sometimes drink in hiding?		
7. Are you bothered if someone close to you warns you to be careful with your drinks?		
8. Do you feel that it becomes almost impossible to stop drinking once you start?		
9. Do you remember having shown aggression under the influence of alcohol?		
10. Have you tried many times to reduce or quit drinking without success?		
11. Do you now have more financial and work issues than before due to alcohol use?		
12. Do you get discouraged thinking how unpleasant it is to drink without being able to quit?		
13. Do you often feel that others look down on you?		
14. Do you feel better when you have a drink in the morning?		
15. Have you lived inebriation episodes lasting several days?		
16. Do you now notice less resistance to alcoholic beverages than in the past?		
17. Do you feel sick or nauseated after not having drunk for a few days?		
18. Have you seen images or visions that, in reality, did not exist?		
19. Have you heard unpleasant voices/shouts and, later on, realised that they were all a product of your imagination?		
20. Have you felt depressed under the effects of alcohol to the point of thinking of suicide?		
21. Have you experienced panic after having drunk?		

Scoring:
1 point for each YES from the 1-7 block:. . . . . _____
2 points for each YES from the 8-14 block:. . . . . _____
3 points for each YES from the 15-21 block: . . . . _____
Total:. . . . . _____

Interpretation:

1-7 points:	8-14 points:	15-24 points:	More than 24 points:
You are at the alcoholism threshold. The easiest option is to give up drinking now in order to avoid it in the future.	You are an alcoholic in a lesser degree. Decide to quit and talk to a friend or a dear one so that you may successfully abandon the habit.	You are alcoholic and you will find it difficult to free yourself from it. You need help. Seek detoxification treatment or ask someone to look for it. Outpatient treatment may be sufficient, but you may need to be admitted to hospital.	You are suffering chronic alcoholism and your life may be in danger. Your heart, liver, and brain may have already been significantly damaged. You need urgent psychiatric and hospital treatment.

2.14
Pathological gambling

There are many pastimes that do not create addiction, but gambling is one of the most dangerous, as it is easy to fall into the net of this habit. Pathological gambling transforms the person into someone irrational and impulsive where gambling is concerned. The problem does not only touch the individual, his judgement, and his behaviour. It also affects family, personal, and work relationships.

The potential pathological gambler starts gambling in an innocent way. Sometimes he wins something; other times he loses. But then he ends up becoming obsessed with the idea that a big stroke of luck will happen any time soon. This attitude leads him to:

- Lose all available money.
- Borrow from family and friends.
- Ask for cash advances at work.
- Lie to prevent his intentions being discovered.
- Apply for bank loans or even to illegal money lenders.

- Steal to pursue gambling or betting.

When displaying this conduct, the individual does not have any bad intention, but, step by step, he progressively sinks into difficulties.

Some use gambling as a **means of evasion** from problems or stressful situations. Sometimes, the behaviour appears after the loss of a dear one, separation, or divorce.

TEST YOURSELF ::

Am I a pathological gambler?	YES	NO
1. Are your thoughts absorbed by gambling? (For example, your thoughts are constantly on the next venture).		
2. Do you feel the desire to bet a greater amount next time?		
3. Have you attempted—without success—to stop gambling?		
4. Have your failures to quit gambling caused you to feel irritated?		
5. Have you used gambling to improve your mood? (For example, when you felt sad, guilty or gloomy.)		
6. After having lost, have you felt the drive to gamble further to get even?		
7. Have you lied to your family, boss, or therapist to conceal the extent of your gambling?		
8. Have you ended up committing fraud to raise funds for gambling?		
9. Have you failed your subjects or lost your employment because of gambling?		
10. Do you depend on others to face the financial trouble caused by gambling?		

If you have answered positively to five (or more) questions, you may consider yourself a pathological gambler. Seek help, as it will be very difficult to solve your problem alone.

How to overcome pathological gambling

Gambling can be likened to a drug without the chemistry. Thus, solutions to pathological gambling are very similar to detoxification treatments:

- **Stop gambling.** To break completely away from gambling, it is necessary to quit once and for all. It is useless to reduce the betting or leave the door open to gamble 'once in a while.'

- **Develop a healthy self-esteem** (see page 28). Many gamblers feel inferior and want to win a lot of money as compensation. However, self-esteem is not fed with money, but with the conviction that personal value lies in what one is, not what one has.

- **Carry out activities to fill the spot** (see page 324). Compulsive gamblers invest hours each day preoccupied with raising the money and planning for the next game or bet. This time must be filled with healthy activities, such as those conducted outdoors or by keeping busy through reading and cultural/spiritual activities.

- **Seek the support of others.** Pathological gamblers very rarely attain victory over their habit by themselves. It is necessary to speak about the problem with a close person or psychotherapist. Together with your confidant, develop a plan to pay off your debts and look forward to a hopeful future. Self-help groups, such as Gamblers Anonymous, can become very valuable in the 'detoxification' process.

- **Change your lifestyle.** Freedom from gambling requires a radical change of lifestyle. It is imperative to find new friendships, frequent different places and change pastime habits.

- **Find support in divine power.** As with any other addiction, it is necessary to trust in a supernatural and omnipotent power in order to leave the pathology behind. Abandoning oneself to that power of the Eternal God through prayer, private and corporate worship, and the reading of Holy Scriptures are basic steps that help one to obtain benefit from that infallible force.

RESEARCH RESULTS

High correlation between drugs and gambling

In a study (Spunt, 2002) on addiction, there were 462 drug dependants as participants, all following methadone treatment to achieve rehabilitation. Twenty-one percent were or had been gamblers, an extremely high proportion as compared with the general population.

Substances most commonly associated with gambling are **heroin, cocaine** and **alcohol**. It is not a surprise that casinos serve free alcoholic beverages and many gamblers use cocaine to remain alert at the games.

For complete recovery, we recommend **complete abstinence** from both psychoactive substances and gambling.

Gems of Ancient Wisdom

'Do not wear yourself out to get rich; have the wisdom to show restraint' (Proverbs 23:4).

2.15

Dyslexia

Dyslexia is a **serious** learning and performing **difficulty** related to **reading** and **writing**. It is generally identified during the first years of schooling when a child seems unable to learn to read at the pace of others.

As reading and writing are necessary academic tools, the problem is reflected in all school subjects.

Diagnosis

These are the general characteristics of dyslexia:

- Dyslexics **substitute, reverse, and omit letters and syllables** when reading. They also read and write very slowly and their comprehension is poor.
- Dyslexics show problems of laterality. In other words, they **confuse right from left**.
- Dyslexics **tend to lack motivation** for school tasks.
- The problem has **neurological foundations**. Children (and untreated adults) perceive visual or auditory symbols with small errors and 'translate' wrongly when they write or say the symbol.

- Dyslexia **runs in families**. It is more common between first-degree relatives than between subjects without relationship.

- The **environment** affects its development. Reading difficulties increase or decrease depending on the emotional tone of the family or the school.

- Dyslexia is **not related to intellectual ability**. In fact, many dyslexic children have a privileged intelligence, sometimes not obvious because it is not translated into good reading and writing.

- It is **relatively common**, especially among males. Depending on the definition applied and of the interest to identify it, it varies from 1 to 5% of the general school population. Six or seven out of 10 cases are males.

- It has a **good prognosis**. If identified before 8 to 10 years of age and properly treated, there is an 80% chance of correction and a notable improvement in any case.

PRACTICAL CASE

Rick's dyslexia

In his second year of primary education, Rick was behind in his learning of reading and writing, especially in comparison to other boys and girls of his age. He could not read many simple words; he read others but he took a long time.

In addition, he wrote very poorly. Very often he copied letters in an inverted way (for example 'b' instead of 'd') even when he had the letters in front of him.

He pronounced some words at the level of a 4 year-old child. For example, he said 'pasketti' instead of 'spaghetti,' and similar words. Rick would get very confused and

be unable to say: 'Peter Piper picked a peck of pickled peppers.' When he was asked to correct his pronunciation, he would say it incorrectly again. His parents thought he was dyslexic, but they were not sure.

A good diagnosis was needed, so his parents took him to a psychologist who performed mental, verbal, numeric, graphic and dexterity tests.

He also talked extensively with Rick, observing his spoken language and his idea of time and space. In addition, he assessed Rick's general behaviour. Lastly, he gathered information from the teachers, which was very useful to make the diagnosis.

TREATING DYSLEXIA

The first step is to be aware that dyslexia is a **learning disorder** and has no relationship with intellectual ability. Many parents think that their dyslexic child is a bit 'thick' due to the observed learning difficulty. But the truth is that there is no relationship between one and the other. And with a good strategy, dyslexia can be overcome.

The solution requires effort, as it takes perseverance, time and method. The child must be taught to organise space, reduce anxiety, regain the lost self-confidence, be methodical in the learning exercises, coor-dinate the muscles well and develop the affective balance. The help of a professional is necessary.

In any case, exercises within the following **areas** are to be done in order to overcome dyslexia:

- General mental activity
- Reading, spelling and grammar
- Drawing and visual perception (colours, sizes, shapes, structures, etc.)
- Handling, classification, and orientation
- Psychomotor activities (body balance, well controlled movement, ball games, etc.)

Specific exercises

Dyslexia has a variety of causes—from a problem of neurological development to emotional trouble. Hence the treatment is also varied.

The following are a number of psychomotor exercises that will help the child to coordinate mind and muscle. They are good to prevent dyslexia.

- **Walk on a plank** or line of bricks on the floor. Through this game, the child stimulates psychomotor skills that are necessary in writing.
- **Play ball** with hands, feet or head: Throw penalty kicks, throw from hand to hand, throw at a target.
- **Fit shapes** into spaces, since one of the problems of dyslexics is time-space coordination.
- Practise **visual perception** of colours, sizes and shapes.
  - Play with **dough or clay**. Shaping figures trains the hands and develops spatial abilities.
  - Cut out using **scissors**. Similar to the above exercise but with added precision.
- Using a pencil, **follow a set of pre-drawn lines** (they can be drawings or words).

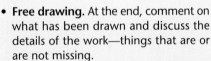

- **Free drawing.** At the end, comment on what has been drawn and discuss the details of the work—things that are or are not missing.
- **Crawl within hoops** as if in a tunnel. The whole body is involved in this exercise. If the time factor is added (go through all hoops in a limited time), depending on the child's circumstances, the exercise is more complete.
- Work **puzzles** appropriate for his/her age and circumstances.
- Learn **songs** that have easy rhyming.
- Do **crosswords** with letter tiles. Form words with tiles.
- Perform basic **rhythm exercises**.
- Practise specific **written** exercises. There are quality, commercial methods available to help correct defects. However, that is not all. It is necessary to practise exercises, as indicated here, to tackle the problem in a global manner.

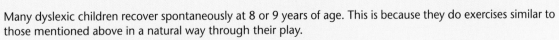

Many dyslexic children recover spontaneously at 8 or 9 years of age. This is because they do exercises similar to those mentioned above in a natural way through their play.

Treatment is simple, but it requires constancy. It is important to be systematic.

Lastly, we must say that it is important that the family support the child, not only in the follow up of exercises, but also through emotional support, which is necessary for full recovery.

Chapter Summary

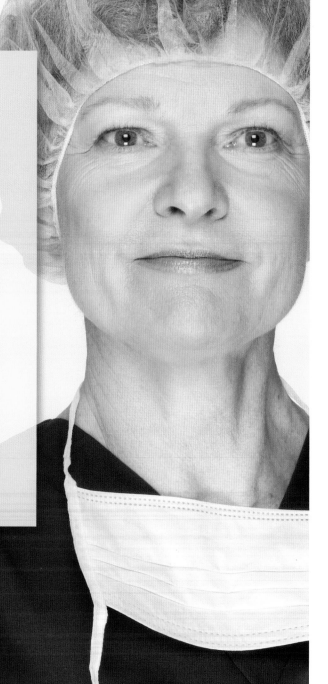

Self-centred problems (II)

3

Janet, a 34-year-old nurse, had an impeccable professional background and a strange personality. Her colleagues avoided her instinctively because she only knew how to talk about herself.

She boasted about how physicians asked advice from her and of the numerous famous hospitals that would like to have her as an employee. These jobs had not materialised because, according to her, some of her jealous peers had interfered. While talking about these things, Janet displayed an air of arrogance that made her intolerable to be around.

Recently, Janet attended an international professional meeting to present a paper. Upon her return, she reported that she was received with warm acclamation and that after the end of her presentation, several editors approached her requesting permission to publish her work in the most prestigious medical journals. In her briefcase, Janet had the notes from the conference and photographs where she appeared with notable persons. When she found someone willing to listen, she opened the briefcase and began praising herself.

This is an obvious case of narcissism.

Chapter Highlights

- Just **becoming conscious** of these thoughts and their effects is a ***big step*** towards modifying or eliminating and substituting them with more edifying and positive thoughts.

- Feelings of **inferiority and low self-esteem** are very common among adolescents. Parents, teachers and adults in general need to be careful and avoid expressing negative sentiments about a young person's abilities and achievements.

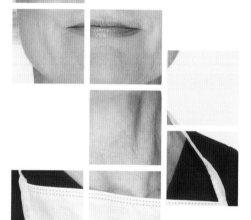

  - It is absolutely necessary to **live in a consistent way** with noble principles. This is better than dogmatism, which attempts to impose itself by force.

  - Identity does not always develop adequately and a person may adhere to an identity different from his/her own. A **balanced identity** involves an adjustment between self-image, real identity and ideal identity.

  - A real sense of guilt is a symptom of an awakened conscience (something very desirable), which works as **self-censorship** and prevents immoralities and crimes. However, not all consciences are healthy.

  - The traditional idea of the elderly person who waits for the day of death is one of the past. Today, retirement years are full of **activities and opportunities**.

- In some cases, **peculiar ways of being and thinking** weaken defences and lead to illness. These are psychosomatic diseases, organic ailments but with psychological or emotional origin.

More problems with oneself

This chapter continues to deal with problems centred around oneself. We start by remembering and emphasising how important it is to have an appropriate mental attitude, free from **automatic thoughts** (unit 3.01) that harass us, causing our internal conflicts to grow.

This attitude is useful, for example, when facing **incapacitating fears** (unit 3.02), which may not always reach the dimension of phobia but can make one's life bitter and prevent freedom. It is also useful to fight affective problems derived from excessive **mood fluctuation** (unit 3.03).

According to many experts, **adolescence** (unit 3.04) is a stage of life characterised by its turbulence. Adolescents must face challenges in school, peer pressure, sexuality, drugs, delinquency, issues of self-esteem, of family relationships, and must decide the choice of values and principles for the rest of their lives. All these tasks appear simultaneously at an age of immaturity and often produce crises. Young men and women need proper preparation to face these multiple difficulties.

It is a challenge to live in a generation where **values and ideologies** are in crisis (unit 3.05) and special care must be taken not to lose those ideas and basic principles, or we will find ourselves without guidance or direction in life.

The rest of the chapter covers a series of relevant problems, such as **general identity** (unit 3.06), **identity and sexual orientation** (unit 3.07), **guilt** (3.08), **memory** (3.09), personal **insecurity** (3.10), **narcissism** (3.11), **superstitions** (3.12), **retirement age** (including Alzheimer's disease; 3.13), **psychosomatic disorders** (3.14), **consumerism** (3.15), **chronic fatigue** (3.16), **covetousness** (3.17) and **perfectionism** (3.18).

For all these, primary help strategies are suggested that can soothe the effects of these problems. The units present the reader with the correct attitude and proper skills to fight these disorders and help those close to them to do the same.

3.01

Automatic thought control

Automatic thoughts are brief, quiet, repetitive messages told to oneself that appear in certain situations (see examples in the table on the adjoining page).

These thoughts are so **deeply rooted** and are so frequent that we hardly realise their presence within us. They may be positive or negative and they appear suddenly, with neither reflection nor analysis. They exert a very powerful influence.

Automatic thoughts are especially bad for pessimists. For them, thoughts appear in a negative and absolute manner: 'This will last forever,' 'There is no solution to this problem,' 'This is sure to break,' 'All the blame is mine alone,' 'It is too late.'

How do automatic thoughts remain for so many years? Their constant presence becomes part of our daily thoughts and they stay with us unconsciously. For this reason, they tend to be difficult to uproot, but it is possible to defeat them.

Just becoming **conscious** of these thoughts and their effects is a **big step** towards modifying or eliminating and substituting them with more edifying and positive thoughts. Follow the steps presented in this unit carefully until you take control of your automatic thinking, developing positive thoughts and rejecting negative ones.

Catch your automatic thoughts

It may seem difficult to identify your automatic thinking, as it often remains in hiding. However, it is possible to recognise these thoughts if you carefully observe the mental process.

An effective way to identify them is to stop your activity and ask **these questions**: What has gone through my head in the last 15 minutes? What images and memories have I held?

Another way to find those thoughts is to focus on your **emotionally-intense moments**: Meeting up with an old friend, passing by someone you dislike, talking to your boss about a raise in salary, visiting someone you have problems with... Remain attentive to what goes through your mind automatically and capture those thoughts.

Typical examples of automatic thoughts

Negative automatic thoughts lead to low personal performance, decline of interpersonal relationships, low self-esteem, and hopelessness.

Situation	Automatic thought
My husband fixes himself a sandwich and does not offer one to me	*'He doesn't love me'*
The neighbour greets me and smiles	*'She is a phoney, she is mocking me'*
My friend tells me she cannot do the favour I asked of her	*'She hates me'*
I prepare conscientiously for my examination	*'I am going to fail'*
The result of the interview was not good	*'I am good for nothing...'*
There is a dog tied up that appears tame	*'It is going to bite me'*
I pass by someone who made fun of me many months ago	*'How stupid and disgusting!'*

Analyse them

At times, these thoughts could be realistic and useful. But usually they are almost always exaggerated and will adversely affect your behaviour. Ask yourself: 'Is it realistic to think that I always fail?' 'Does he really hate me?' 'Does it make sense to remain fearful throughout this situation?' Be fair and honest with your assessment. Consult with someone you trust or go to the psychologist. Such persons can help you discern and be objective. In your analysis, remember the following:

- Do not believe everything that goes through your head.
- Nobody knows others' intentions and your assessment is only a guess.
- Statements such as *'never'*, *'always'*, *'everybody'*, *'nobody'* go along well with false or exaggerated thoughts.
- Many automatic thoughts are about oneself. Watch out that they do not become too pessimistic or negative.
- Thoughts of depressive people tend to be self-demeaning, negative towards the environment and hopeless towards the future.
- Thoughts of anxious people tend to be apprehensive, threatening and marked by danger.

Design your thoughts

Automatic thoughts strongly **affect our beliefs and behaviour**. If you want to have a handle on your own emotions, you must choose the thoughts you wish to engage in.

Make a **list** of thoughts and study them. Set aside the negative ideas and exchange them for positive, edifying, and motivating thoughts to carry with you; for example: 'If I am patient, I can attain it,' 'Deep down, his intentions are not bad,' 'I have done this well other times; it should turn out okay' 'I am going to display kindness,' 'Being a pessimist, will not get me anywhere,' 'I am going to have a good day.'

Certain negative thoughts may seem very resistant to change. Be patient and persevere, because they can change if you wish.

Gems of Ancient Wisdom

'For as he thinks in his heart, so is he' (Proverbs 23:7, Amplified Bible).

How to face a variety of fears

It is normal to be afraid of situations that really pose danger: travelling by ship in the middle of a troubled sea, for example, or walking across a frail hanging bridge above a deep gorge are natural fears. Feeling frightened when surrounded by thugs in the darkness is a useful mechanism of survival.

However, there are people who experience an **irrational and persistent fear of situations with minimal risk**. They become preoccupied in order to avoid the source of fear, and if they are forced to confront it, they experience tremors, sweating, nausea and strong stomach pain. Below we offer advice on how to face three typical situations of irrational fear: fear of flying, fear of doctors and fear of people.

Overcoming the fear of flying

Those who do not use aeroplanes as a means of transportation do not need to worry about flying. But for those who are afraid but need to fly, they must do something to overcome such fear.

The following three-step plan has been used successfully by airlines with their clients.

1. **Information.** The first step is to explain how planes work, why they fly, their possible risks and how to face them. Instructors present statistics of aeroplane accidents compared with other means of transportation and they demonstrate that air transportation is safest.

2. **Approximation.** The patient visits the airport and takes part in a simulated flight. This provides the experience of identical sensations to a real flight. The person is exposed to vibrations, turbulence, tilts… Anticipation of anxiety disappears when the patient approaches the source of fear and nothing happens.

3. **Confrontation.** As the patient is exposed to the source of fear, the fearful behaviour weakens and the patient can now fly. At the beginning, he/she may be tense but convinced that a flight is not as bad as anticipated. As flights are added, patients continue to gain confidence.

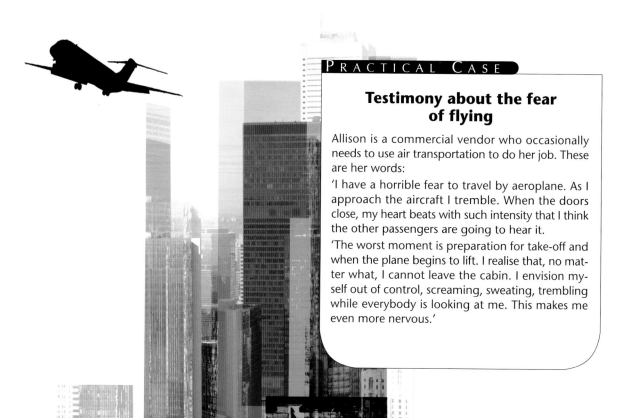

PRACTICAL CASE

Testimony about the fear of flying

Allison is a commercial vendor who occasionally needs to use air transportation to do her job. These are her words:

'I have a horrible fear to travel by aeroplane. As I approach the aircraft I tremble. When the doors close, my heart beats with such intensity that I think the other passengers are going to hear it.

'The worst moment is preparation for take-off and when the plane begins to lift. I realise that, no matter what, I cannot leave the cabin. I envision myself out of control, screaming, sweating, trembling while everybody is looking at me. This makes me even more nervous.'

Overcome the fear of medical settings

Certain people become sick at the sight of blood, syringes, or open sores. Others experience these symptoms simply by walking into hospital, the surgery, or any place frequented by doctors. Try the following tips, or share them with someone with this problem:

- **Mental training** towards the phobic object. Imagine the dental clinic that causes you so much anxiety; picture the dentist, remember the smell of anaesthesia... Revive these images in your memory. Do this only briefly at first, extending the time dedicated to the imagination as you progress.

- **Practise relaxation** while thinking of the phobic object/situation. Learn how to relax (see page 40); then imagine the clinic, hospital, doctors, etc. You will notice that the level of anxiety is relatively low, as relaxation and anxiety are incompatible.

- **Observe the behaviour of others who do not feel fear.** Accompany a friend to the doctor's office and notice how people go in without anxiety or fear.

- **Confront the source of fear.** As a final step, and after having rehearsed sufficiently, go to the dentist that you fear so much. Put all the steps together in order to achieve relaxation and maintain it once you are in the clinic. Positive thinking, breathing, and relaxation techniques will help you maintain a state of relative calm.

- **Find support** in someone else. It is a good thing to carry out the therapy with someone else at your side who, through physical contact, soothing voice and other instructions, can help you to avoid panic. In difficult cases, a psychologist should be sought in order to apply therapies, such as systematic desensitisation, with guarantee of success.

How to overcome social fears

Fear to attend a public function, to meet new persons, work in teams or address an audience (albeit small) is a relatively common problem that needs to be tackled. If you have this tendency, follow these tips:

- **Set up moderate aims:** say 'hello,' talk about the weather or something trivial in a group. Try to smile while you talk—smiling helps to relax.

- Do not wait for someone to come to talk to you. Instead, go and **start the conversation**.

- **Ask questions** and give others the opportunity to tell their experience; then you may share something of yourself.

- **Use sincere prais**e towards others. Comment on their achievement, personality or appearance. This will help you to be accepted and welcome.

- Before and during the encounters, **give yourself positive instructions**: 'It is easy,' 'I can do it,' 'Have courage!', 'Go for it!', 'It is going well,' 'I am moving forward.'

SOCIAL FEARS MUST BE TREATED

Leaving social fears untreated can cause two potential negative outcomes:

1. **They tend to get worse.** The problem feeds itself, reaching the dimension of a full social phobia (see page 94). The inhibited person avoids social situations. Thus he/she lacks practice in relating to people.

   The next attempt brings about poorer results. The person doubts him/herself and becomes more fearful. Statistics show that 50 to 70% of patients with social phobia suffer depressive episodes (Lucribier and Weillier, 1997; Stein *et al.*, 1999).

2. **They contribute to the risk of alcohol use and abuse.** A peculiar risk is that the affected person tends to resort to alcoholic beverages (Lepine and Pelissolo, 1998) in order to 'get a boost' in their interpersonal relationships. This complicates the syndrome in the medium and long term.

3.03
Mood management

Seasonal affective disorder

Seasonal affective disorder (SAD) is a **form of depression linked to the winter season**. Symptoms remain latent during spring and summer and gain severity with the reduction of daylight and the increase of night hours. The **absence of natural light** seems to be the determinant factor. For this reason the illness is endemic in countries far away from the equator, such as Iceland, Norway, Denmark, Sweden, Finland, Australia and New Zealand. The affected person feels sad, very tired and discouraged, suffers lack of appetite, sleeping difficulties and can have thoughts of suicide. The frequency of suicide increases during the months of January and February (July-August in the southern hemisphere), the months with fewer hours of daily sunlight.

Treatment for this peculiar disorder (apart from regular drugs) consists of exposing the patient to a **lighted box** with light similar to sunlight, but without damaging the eyes. One hour with the luminous box in the morning and one in the afternoon during winter days suffice for the symptoms to be significantly alleviated.

In any case, the general advice for depression (see page 102) is also valid to this seasonal syndrome:

- Remember the good things from the past.
- Look at the bright side of events.
- Keep yourself busy.
- Be in contact with nature.
- Seek the company of healthy people.
- Carry out some altruistic work.
- Look at the future with hope.

Boredom and apathy

There are many more activities and pastimes these days than ever before. However, apathy and boredom are increasing. Many suffer from lack of motivation, interest, or energy. They have lost the **ability to use their time creatively** or to take advantage of available energy.

But these feelings can be prevented (see the box on the adjoining page).

HOW TO PREVENT BOREDOM AND APATHY

These feelings obstruct personal development and can be prevented with simple steps and plans, such as:

- **Escape from routine.** Bring change to your daily life by introducing innovations and modifying your normal behaviours: go home using a different form of transport, call a friend that you have not seen in years, surprise your spouse by taking him/her to a show.
- **Plan for the future.** Develop specific plans and goals and take the first steps towards their accomplishment. There is nothing like becoming excited about the future.
- **Learn to enjoy simple things.** The spark of life is not found in great and impressive events but in the delight for simple things: the reading of a book during a peaceful evening, a relaxing conversation with an old friend, or an ordinary picnic. These may bring unspoken joy to the human soul.
- **Help someone in need.** Supporting a humanitarian programme will bring a special spark to your life and will help you forget your problems of motivation, helping you to experience happiness as you observe joy in others.
- **Reflect on the purpose of life.** Focus on fundamental questions: Why am I here? What is the purpose of my life? What is truly important? Finding answers to these questions is linked to the achievement of a full and stimulating life.

Irresponsibility

Irresponsibility is a problem with **negative effects on mood**. It touches many life dimensions and poses a barrier to carry out the most basic tasks.

These are the areas affected by this problem:

- **Household** and personal items, which suffer deterioration.

- **Personal habits** with random sleeping and meal schedules, as well as procrastinating with uncomfortable tasks.
- **Work achievement**, as the person does not contribute to the team, delays his/her tasks and does not honour promises.
- **Finances**, as the person delays or fails to make payments, borrows money and spends without thinking about priorities.
- **Relationships**, since lack of responsibility causes family and friends to question this lifestyle. It brings endless conflict to relationships.

Facing irresponsible behaviour is not easy, as these habits are very deeply rooted. However, with determination and family support, the person can change. The following recommendations may be useful to initiate the change:

- **Enjoy a tidy environment.** Devote one day to bring order and cleanliness to your house or room and enjoy the new environment. Realise how easy it is to maintain it daily, instead of spending an entire day or two to organise everything.
- **Carry out the unpleasant tasks first.** It will be very difficult for you to complete difficult tasks if you delay them. Do first what you like least. Then relish the easy and enjoyable tasks.
- **Do not leave your job until you have another one.** Even if you do not like your current employment, do not resign until you have another job. Impulsively quitting a job will leave you unemployed and without income.
- **Develop a budget.** Include a list of unavoidable fixed expenses (house payments, installments, utilities, food, etc.). Money allocated to those items is untouchable. If additional money is available, you can consider other expenditures.
- **When you wish to spend, think twice.** When you see something you like, ask yourself: Is it necessary? Is it urgent? Often, by deferring a purchase, you will realise that after a few days the item is no longer attractive.

3.04
Problems of adolescence

The stage of adolescence tends to be **the most difficult** one throughout the life cycle. Many boys and girls of this age seem to cause problems in the family, school and community. And, above all, they suffer from those problems.

At the same time, adolescents possess highly positive traits which, properly channelled, are of benefit to everyone. Seven common problems are reviewed in this unit. Any of them may appear around or after the age of 11 or 12 and we suggest a number of ways in which adults support adolescents.

Self-esteem

Feelings of inferiority (see page 122) and low self-esteem (page 28) are very common among adolescents, especially girls. The consequences are low academic achievement, mood disturbances, relational difficulties and an inability to carry out tasks and responsibilities.

Parents, teachers and adults in general need to be careful and avoid expressing negative sentiments about a young person's abilities and achievements. On the other hand, positive comments, offered casually and indirectly, will have a positive influence on adolescents.

Family interaction

Family dynamics usually change in a radical way when children reach puberty and adolescence. At this time, parents should change their method for guiding their children. The authoritarian style that may have worked during childhood will fail in adolescence. Now it is time to suggest, consult and offer understanding. Dictating to teenagers may cause rebellion and undesirable results. We must state, however, that adolescents should be expected, through tact and care, to respect those aspects that parents consider fundamental.

Academic achievement

Many youth of this age go through some social or emotional crisis that causes school achievement to decrease. Parents should try to be near the adolescent in order to offer **support** during times of discouragement, disappointment, or when certain events interfere with the adolescent's studies. With patience and perseverance, they must remind their children that school tasks should have priority.

It also helps to be in permanent contact with the teachers of the adolescent. As school content becomes more complex at this stage,

---

RESEARCH RESULTS

Unhappy babies, conflictive adolescents...

A study (Hay *et al.*, 2003) conducted at the University of Cardiff, UK, followed 132 families residing in the south of London for 12 years. They were administered a series of questionnaires and a clinical interview to find out the extent of depressive problems and their effect upon family life.

One of the most amazing findings was that the babies of mothers who had experienced **post-partum depression** during the first three months following delivery had four times more probability to display violent episodes at age 11 than those children of mothers who had not suffered from postpartum depression.

These results may be interpreted in various ways, but they clearly point at the necessity to pay due attention, and give **love and care to infants from the first few days** after birth in order to avoid problems in adolescence.

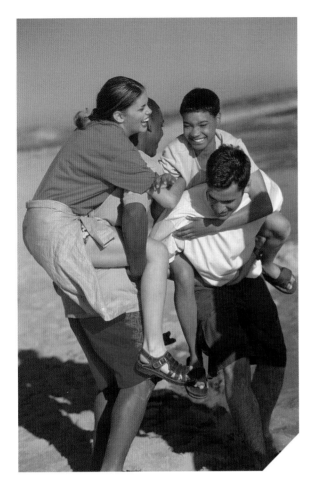

the influence they receive will be beneficial for their development.

The use of substances

In almost all social contexts, adolescence is a time when there is high risk of initiation into smoking, alcohol, drugs, and non-chemical addictions (gambling or Internet sex).

In order to escape from these threats, young people need to feel good about themselves (not inferior and desirous of being like those using drugs…) and should be surrounded by a group of friends and peers who offer **healthy and fun alternatives**. Parents need to make sure that children receive enough social and affective support, time, dedication and love.

Sexuality

Adolescence brings hormonal and affective changes with subsequent sexual awakening. Throughout previous years, young men and women should have already had a good education in this area, which explained its implications, responsibilities and principles. In order to prevent sexually transmitted diseases and because of the maturity required to enjoy sexual interaction, it is recommendable that the young person **postpone sex** until such a time when there is maturity in the context of a stable relationship with lasting commitment.

Values and principles

Adolescence is a crossroads where young people ask themselves many fundamental questions about what is ethical, right and lasting. Parents need to insist, in a gentle and persistent manner, on values of utmost importance.

However, adolescents tend to look at other adult friends in order to learn from them. Their words and their conduct can be more important than those of the young person's own parents. Values observed during the adolescent years may be adopted for the rest of life. It is the responsibility of the **adult world** to offer a **good example** that young people may imitate.

(See also the next unit).

adolescents must also learn study methods and personal organisation. A warning: If your son or daughter experiences a decline in achievement, do not show anger. It is very important to keep an optimal relationship; the storm will pass in the large majority of cases.

Peers and their influence

The peer group becomes a source of great influence during puberty and adolescence. There is no need to fear this influence. On the contrary, this influence may offer affective balance to adolescents. The peer group is the place where they feel accepted and where they feel free to speak of things important to them.

The main problem is whether peer **values** and principles are clearly **antisocial** or immoral. If this is the case, parents should act quickly and guide their children to alternative social circles where

3.05
Crisis of values and ideologies

It is rare today to find people of any age with **clear and firm ideals** who are able to submit their desires and personal impulses to such values. In spite of the increasing evidence that money, popularity and possessions are not linked to happiness, most people's behaviour is targeted at obtaining and preserving material goods. It is so much so that ethical principles, values and ideals succumb to them. The following are evidence of such tendencies:

- A **growing corruption** on the part of **politicians**, who should be unblemished examples of behaviour to all citizens.

- The **violation of sports rules and codes** on the part of athletes, who should be models of discipline for children, youth and adults.

- The use of **violence** and aggression, either by the ordinary delinquent who is driven by selfishness to break the law or by political systems that attempt to impose their ideologies by force.

- The **use of the legal system to achieve selfish goals** that do not correspond to the spirit and essence of the law.

- The violation of basic ecological principles through **unlimited and indiscriminate use of natural resources**; this is done out of simple convenience and personal interest without thinking of contemporary or future generations;

BEWARE OF MEDIA INFORMATION

Media messages come to us offering an image of impressive authority and balanced judgment. However, a careful analysis of the news will often show that the ultimate goal is to emphasise a **disturbing or** perhaps **minuscule aspect of reality**. It is therefore important to view information critically. Think that:

- Information does not have to be true just because it is presented with an impeccable image, using brilliant technology or elegant print.
- Information providers have their bias as well as their professional and personal interests.
- News agencies compete to present their work and often engage in exaggerations and bias in order to sell their report.

- The public prefer (for whatever reason) bad news to good news; and reporters wish to please the public.

In general, beware of the media. Even if they are truthful, they are only presenting a small portion of reality. Reality contains much more than what is reported. Search for additional information. **Independently research something you are interested** in and you will learn many things the news does not tell.

- The **rejection of values**, principles and ideas on the part of education systems that leave them out of the curricula, thereby depriving children of guidance towards high aims.

- The ubiquitous **fraud in business transactions**, at the personal and enterprise levels.

- The use of extremely powerful tools, such as **television** or the **Internet**, to spread ideas that entice people to violence, free sex, the deterioration of family and couples, and the undermining of values.

- The **lack of respect** and consideration towards other human beings, evidenced by street attacks, domestic violence, mobbing and other forms of invasion of individual rights.

How to preserve values and ideologies

The answer is deep **reflection** on what principles we wish to use as guidelines for our lives.

Once clarified, it is good to express them in the family and among friends with kindness, respect and conviction.

Besides, it is absolutely necessary to live in a consistent way with these principles. This is better than dogmatism, which attempts to impose itself by force.

A fundamental task for adults is to transmit those values to the next generation.

The box below suggests a few ideas on how to equip children and adolescents with the ideological apparatus to guide them throughout life.

self-help

HOW TO TRANSMIT VALUES TO THE YOUNGER GENERATION

To school-aged children...
- Provide time for value transmission.
- Present alternatives and debate with them the pros and cons.
- State your own decision and invite the child to do the same.
- Show your ideals through your behaviour and invite the child to do the same.
- Debate real ideas to affirm values. Dialogue about these questions:
  - ✔ Can lies be justified under certain circumstances?
  - ✔ What would a world without cars be like?
  - ✔ What would happen if nobody used animals as food?
  - ✔ And if nobody would pay taxes?
  - ✔ Is violence sometimes good?

To adolescents...
- Be tolerant and flexible. Listen and listen again; do not sermonise.
- Preach with your example.
- Remember their normal desire for ideological independence.
- Bear in mind that the adolescent is growing intellectually and requires depth.
- Do not become alarmed if he or she adopts an extreme position, as it will weaken with time.
- Show your disagreements with great respect and consideration.

3.06
Identity problems

Identity takes shape throughout the growth years and settles towards the end of adolescence, although the development process continues throughout the entire life cycle. Identity helps people see themselves as individuals, holders of unique attributes, traits and qualities.

The results of a defective identity

Unfortunately, identity does not always develop adequately and a person may adhere to an identity different from his/her own. A few of these false identities are described below.

Dependent personality

The dependent person has very little self-confidence and needs others even for tasks of little relevance. Extreme cases need constant care and experience the following:

This person...

- has difficulties making decisions (even unimportant ones) without the support of another. This is due to lack of self-confidence.
- needs help from other people in order to assume any important responsibility.
- does not express disagreement for fear of rejection.
- is willing to do anything in order to receive approval.
- resists being left alone for fear of not being able to care for himself or herself.
- urgently looks for another person to depend upon when the primary relationship ends.
- worries unnecessarily about being abandoned by the dear one.

Sexual identity disorder

The individual strongly identifies with the opposite sex and longs to be part of that gender community (see page 162). In addition, this person feels a strong opposition towards his/her own anatomic gender. In childhood, boys reject clothes and activities typically associated with males and seek to have the female equivalent. Girls resist wearing

Towards a congruent identity

Incongruent self

Congruent self

Identity includes three components:
- perceived identity (self-image)
- ideal identity (desirable goal)
- real identity

The greater the congruence among the three, the more authentic is the personal identity. But if there is a significant incongruence, there will be a high risk of anomalous identity and emotional imbalance. Everyone needs to perceive themselves in a true and balanced manner and set attainable goals to mark their direction.

dresses, long hair, and playing with dolls; instead, they seek the appearance and pastimes of boys. Adults try to live as if they were members of the opposite sex and, through hormonal or surgical treatments, change their resemblance to that of the opposite sex.

Age crises

Other times, identity is shaken during certain stages of the life cycle when it is especially vulnerable. **Adolescence** is a high-risk period. This is the case with Victoria, a 20-year-old female from a well-to-do family who is 'searching for herself.' In a brief period of time, she has had several 'dubious' (according to her parents) boyfriends, and she has changed her academic course twice, from social work to stock exchange investor.

Middle age may also be a susceptible time for an identity crisis. Jack, at age 55, should be making plans for his retirement. However, he has resigned from his job as an economist and is now an interior decorator. He says this is a way of letting his creativity out. He is thinking about leaving his wife for a much younger woman. He admits that he is going through a perplexing crisis. It is likely that Jack returns to his job and to his

wife, but, for the time being, he is searching for his temporarily-displaced identity.

How to prevent defective identity

It is possible in many cases to avoid identity deviation. The following tips are tested to prevent anomalous identity and can positively influence mental health generally:

- **Enhance self-confidence.** 'I do not know enough... I'm immature... Others know more...' are typical thoughts in those prone to suffer from defective identity, especially at the time of making a decision or beginning a project. Reject those negative thoughts and substitute them with more positive ones. See unit 1.04 on self-esteem (page 28) and follow the advice to enhance it.

- **Set your own objective.** Avoid following blindly what others do, thinking that they know better. Set your own realistic aims and make efforts to follow the pathway towards them. When you have clear goals, you will realise how your motivation grows. You will move away from the risk of diluting your own identity within that of others.

- **Establish a solid set of values.** Without an internal point of reference, it is easy to fall into accommodating behaviour. When one possesses firm principles capable of leading behaviour, personal identity is affirmed and self-doubt vanishes.

- **Prevent a possible developmental crisis.** As mentioned before, there are life stages, especially menopause/climacteric, that lend themselves to identity crises. Establishing a healthy identity in early adulthood can help to avoid 'crazy behaviour' during this stage of life. Parents and other adults can help younger ones

to establish a healthy identity early on (see the box below).

How to attain a stable identity

The information presented in the chart on the previous page shows how a balanced identity involves an adjustment between self-image, real identity and ideal identity. The congruence does not have to be perfect; in fact, it is never perfect.

However, it should allow the person to maintain balance, set positive relationships and successfully engage in daily responsibilities. The following suggestions will help the reader to establish and affirm a balanced identity:

self-help

ENHANCE YOUR CHILDREN'S IDENTITY

If you are a mother or father of adolescents or have influence over them, it is possible for you to positively support the task of identity formation. Try this advice with care, patience, and tenacity:

- **Accept them unconditionally.** Many identity problems come as a result of adult rejection. This happens often to disobedient or lonely youth. Try by all means to separate the person from the action. Demonstrate affection and acceptance towards the young person, even if their behaviours seem unacceptable.

- **Help them compensate for their shortcomings.** There is no perfect or absolutely imperfect human being. Adolescents have their strengths and their weaknesses. Openly recognise their accomplishments in order to nourish their self-image while giving them a hand in their school tasks and duties.

- **Assign responsibilities.** Some parents do not do this because they want to remove stress

from their child's life, or simply wish not to bother them. However, all children and youth can take up some responsibilities. By asking them to do house chores, you enhance their self-discipline and improve their self-concept.

- **Avoid overprotection.** Many counsellors have confirmed that people with identity problems come from families where they have been overprotected. Within the confines of safety, you should allow youth to experience the consequences of their own actions, as they acquire greater autonomy every day.

- **Do not be authoritarian or indifferent.** These are dangerous extremes with adolescents. Instead, try to invest time, giving them opportunities for dialogue. Show interest in their problems, knowing that they are often unwilling to talk, but being aware that at other times they are. Maintain links with them. Otherwise, they will end up believing that they are of no value.

1. **Know yourself.** We can only identify ourselves when we know ourselves. This implies the honest evaluation of our traits, capabilities and achievements (both positive and negative). Thus we can acquire a reasonable self-image that reflects reality. Aside from our own perception, other persons also influence the formation of our self-image. Therefore, we need to remain open to the impressions of others, especially from those who respect and appreciate us.

2. **Practise good interpersonal relations.** Pathological identity cases (with the exception of those suffering from cranial trauma) reveal that those losing identity have lived anomalous social situations. Highly satisfactory interpersonal relationships produce an adjusted identity.

3. **Affirm yourself in your own worth.** Those with low self-esteem or feelings of inferiority need to recognise that they possess positive traits. Everybody has valuable characteristics. On the other hand, one's identity should be realistic, also recognising areas for improvement.

4. **Find support in your group identity.** Belonging to an ethnic or religious group can be a source of great support towards building one's identity. And when the group is a minority, the strength becomes even greater. It is therefore necessary for individuals to nurture their worth as group members. This will bring about a healthy love for self and will complete their personal identity. Those who believe in the inspiration of the Bible will find evidence that God offers a privileged identity when they choose to become His children (see the Gems below).

SUCCESSFUL RELATIONSHIPS DEPEND ON YOU

Some people apply wrong relational methods and end up in a cycle that makes a solution increasingly difficult.

William's case illustrates this problem. His distance, arrogance, and critical stance make him detestable. As a result, he ends up isolated and without friends. This leads him to an erroneous identity—that of a victim, hated and persecuted by everybody. Convinced of this situation, he behaves suspiciously, using verbal aggression against others. Seeing this attitude, people around him affirm their disdain.

Try to be cordial; listen to others, show interest in them, have a good sense of humour, and give a hand to others in their practical needs. Your self-image will become more balanced.

Gems of Ancient Wisdom

'Fear not, for I have redeemed you; I have summoned you by name; you are mine' (Isaiah 43:1).

'But you are a chosen people, a royal priesthood, a holy nation, a people belonging to God' (1 Peter 2:9).

3.07

Homosexuality and change of sex

When someone feels sexual or romantic attraction towards persons of the same sex (instead of the opposite sex), they are said to have homosexual tendencies. Being homosexual (also referred to as 'gay' for males and 'lesbian' for females) seems more common today than in past times. This is probably due to the fact that society views sexual orientation more flexibly today, showing less condemnation towards those displaying this tendency. We cannot forget, however, that this was frequent practice in pre-Christian Greek and Roman cultures.

Except for a few cases where genetic alterations cause a clear and marked predisposition to live as the opposite sex, homosexuality normally develops as a result of environmental effects and **personal choice**. For this reason there are ways to prevent and correct homosexuality as well as help those who are unsatisfied with this tendency and who wish to adhere to their biological sex. Of course, offering this advice does not imply lack of respect for homosexuals who prefer to continue with their tendency.

Prevention of homosexuality

Consider the following tips to avoid future homosexuality:

- **Help children to develop trust in the adult world.** Give all the love and affective support you can to your children from birth. Never reject them even though their behaviours may be frustrating at times. Children need to develop trust in adults. Otherwise, they may suffer emotional problems as well as homosexual tendencies.

- **Make sure your children are exposed to both genders.** Parents are the best models to them in terms of gender. Life and behaviour shown by the father are example to boys and those of the mother to girls. If one of the parents is not able to live together in the family, it is advisable to offer the child frequent opportunities to relate with the same-sex parent. In this way, children reinforce their natural sexual identity.

- **Never treat a child as if he/she was the opposite sex.** Although you may have wished to have a girl, treat your boy as a male (or your daughter as a female). Treating the child as belonging to the opposite sex is a common cause of homosexuality.

- **At all cost, avoid incest or sexual abuse.** Take all necessary precautions to avoid incestuous sexual contact within the family or social sphere. For example, girls who have been victims of incest/abuse develop repulsion towards males and find attraction in females.

- **Do not reproach a boy because he is sensitive,** intuitive, artistic, or because he has 'effeminate' manners. This does not mean he is a homosexual. If you rebuke him too much, he will end up believing this is so.

- **Reasonably promote pride in being a man or a woman.** It is common, especially during adolescence, for boys and girls to be at the crossroads of sexual identity. They are uncertain of their gender preference. Adolescents need affirmation and support to feel satisfied with their own sexual orientation.

- **Help young adults clarify their sexual identity before entrance into college.** College and university is a crucial time because 'liberalism' favours stretching boundaries. Young people entering adulthood must have clear and determined ideas of their identity as male or female. In this way, when they are invited to try different options, they will be able to refuse without difficulty.

Correction of homosexuality

If you have homosexual tendencies and wish to overcome them, try the following advice:

- **Make a firm decision to change.** The removal of undesirable homosexual tendencies is a matter of personal will. If possible, nourish this desire of change with the help of a close friend, a family member or a psychologist.

- **Avoid the environments inviting to homosexuality.** The old habits, company, places frequented by homosexuals, etc. are contexts that make change extremely difficult. Without rejecting homosexual friends and companions as persons, focus on heterosexual settings and seek the company of those in such locations.

- **Focus on the virtues and attractiveness of the opposite sex.** If you are a man, think of the positive traits of the female sex (physical, social, emotional…). If you are a woman, think of the desirable aspects of masculinity, avoiding stereotypes ('All men are the same,' 'All are selfish…').

- **Improve self-esteem.** Work on your self-concept. Being homosexual carries inner messages such as 'different,' 'inferior,' 'unable,' and 'inadequate.' Flee from these thoughts and reinforce your strengths.

Homosexuality and the Bible

Due to the increasing acceptance of homosexuality in cultures of Christian influence, there have been a number of misunderstandings. Setting aside the positions of different denominations, it is true that the Bible, common source to all of them, rejects homosexual practices. This is found both in the Old and the New Testaments (Genesis 19:1-29; Leviticus 18:22; 20:13; Romans 1:24-27; 1 Corinthians 6:9; 1 Timothy 1:8-10; etc.).

But this should not be understood, biblically speaking, as an open door to condemn homosexual persons. Besides, thanks to divine power, there is a way out of any undesirable tendency discouraged by the Creator (be it homosexuality or any other): 'I can do all things in Christ who strengthens me' (Philippians 4:13, compare with Romans 7:24-25).

- **Deal with the past with serenity and never as a pre-determinant of your present.** We all have a past that is partly sweet and partly sour. Focus on the pleasant events and put the undesirable past aside.

- **Have trust in the future.** Try to look at your future with the certainty that your decisions carry more weight than your entire past and that you have control, mastery and choice within yourself. Therefore, you do not need to be moved by compulsions, habits or impulses.

- **Seek the help of a specialised psychologist** with ample experience in the treatment of homosexuality. This professional can help you understand your present behaviour through the experiences of the past and can help you to correct undesirable tendencies.

Change of sex

This is an option that attracts those who are dissatisfied with their apparent biological sex. Individuals submitting themselves to sex change through hormonal treatment or surgical intervention are called **transsexuals**.

Transformation occurs via **plastic surgery** to the genitalia. Facial plastic surgery is also used in order to make the face look like that of the desirable gender.

Men undergo castration and artificial vulva implant. In the case of women, a synthetic penis is implanted and/or their breasts are surgically re-

Change of sex and self-esteem

One of the main arguments for the change of sex is to overcome the low self-esteem (see page 28) derived from an unacceptable body, a body that does not fit the subject's sexual **self-identity** ('mental sex'). (See Medline, 2006).

In addition, many transsexuals point out that there is a **physical cause** of their identity problems. There are studies that seem to affirm this. One of them (Zhou *et al.*, 1995) shows that there are neurochemical and structural similarities between the transsexual person's brain and the average individual of the gender they identify with. Accordingly, these persons would feel in their brain, which is the master organ, that they are members of one sex, while the body would feel as that of the opposite sex.

However, it does not seem like a change of sex, apart from other risks, can guarantee victory over this identity problem (see the box on the adjoining page).

moved. The surgeon takes some of the nerve terminals in the area and connects them to the new organs. This allows transsexuals to receive sensations similar to those in natural sexuality.

However, the majority of transsexuals do not experience orgasm, do not possess the new sexual function and, of course, are unable to perform the reproductive role. The change has to do with external looks.

Hormonal treatment consists of hormonal injections to the circulatory system in order to stimulate the development of secondary sex characteristics: breasts, hips, voice, hair, etc. For example, the administration of estrogens in men will cause the development of fat tissue in their chest and hips resembling a woman's figure.

Likewise, when androgens are given to a woman, her voice will turn deep and facial hair may appear.

The benefits sought by transsexuals are related to their **subjective perception**: they feel more satisfaction with a body that fits the gender with which they mentally identify. In other words, they seek to overcome their identity problem (see page 156).

This new appearance will make a transsexual fit better in certain social contexts (for example, showing nudity in a group of nudists). However, the change of sex entails **clear drawbacks**, as is shown in the box below.

PHYSICAL AND PSYCHOLOGICAL PROBLEMS

Hormonal or surgical treatments may produce a general feeling of well-being in transsexuals. They might feel more like a woman or a man. However, apart from the very high cost of these interventions, there are significant risks. These are the most notable:

- **Surgical complications.** Nerve terminals in the genital area may suffer permanent damage. Also there is the risk of bone infections in the facial bones (when face surgery is performed) and damage to the larynx (when change of voice surgery is applied).
- **Pain and general discomfort due to hormonal treatment.** This can include prolonged discomfort and specific symptoms such as venous thrombosis, cardiovascular disease, breast carcinoma, and uterus carcinoma.
- **Regret.** There is a high proportion (more than half) of transsexuals that regret having taken the step. This can end in major depression due to the fact that often results are not what people

expected (and previous identity problems prevail after the intervention).
- **Suicide.** Several studies show that suicide rates increase among those subjects that have submitted themselves to change of sex.

Due to all of the above, it may be more sensible to follow the advice given elsewhere in this book to solve identity crises (see page 156) and problems of self-esteem (page 28).

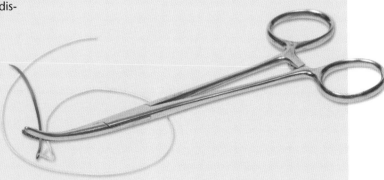

3.08
Guilt feelings

Many live with an unfounded or false feeling of guilt. This brings conflict to their lives along with the following tendencies:

- Feelings of inferiority (see page 122)
- Perfectionism (page 192)
- Constant self-blame
- Fear of failure (with the consequent hypervigilant state)
- Being too demanding of others

On the other hand, a feeling of guilt is a **useful resource** that encourages considerate and positive behaviour and favours healthy interactions. A real sense of guilt is a symptom of an awakened conscience (something very desirable), which works as self-censorship and prevents immoralities and crimes. However, not all consciences are healthy (see the box below).

How to face a sense of guilt

If guilt is **justified**, there is no other option but to rectify behaviour, obtain pardon and try to restore any damage incurred. Mary hurt her work companion greatly by initiating slander and ruining her reputation. This caused Mary a deep sense of guilt. She could not free herself from her burden until she went to her friend, admitted her fault, asked for forgiveness and talked to the other persons to rectify all the false statements made.

As far as **unfounded** or disproportionate guilt is concerned, the process is more complex and requires several strategies:

- **Avoid approaches that are too strict.** A family or social circle that is too demanding or too threatening contributes to a narrow conscience with the subsequent risk of unfounded guilt.
- **Thought control.** It is necessary to instruct oneself with messages such as: 'I have done what I could,' 'Perfection does not exist in this world,' 'Mistakes are chances to learn.'
- **Unload oneself.** Talking about guilt feelings with a trusted friend helps to organise one's own thoughts and ideas. And it is especially useful to unload the built-up tension created by guilt.
- **Practise forgiveness.** To forgive others helps one to forgive himself or herself, which is the ultimate goal to experience freedom from guilt.
- **Seek God.** God is willing to forgive even the greatest evil, including what humans are not willing to forgive: 'Though your sins are like scarlet, they shall be as white as snow; though they are red as crimson, they shall be like wool' (Isaiah 1:18).

WHEN CONSCIENCE DEGENERATES...

Consciences do not always provide a wise standard of conduct. Some are too narrow while others are too wide.

Those with a strict conscience expect similar standards in others. And those with more lenient ones often see everything as being good.

It is therefore necessary to compare one's conscience with **external and transcendent standards**; with ethical principles of transcendental validity. This is why the apostle Paul warned his disciple Timothy of some people, 'whose consciences have been seared as with a hot iron' who would command others to do absurd things (see 1 Timothy 4:2, 3).

These seared consciences are insensitive. They become useless due to repeated transgressions and cannot be trusted as a valid guide for conduct.

Gems of Ancient Wisdom

'Blessed are they whose transgressions are forgiven, whose sins are covered' (Romans 4:7).

Healthy in the right measure

The longitudinal study (Kochanska *et al.*, 2002) carried out by **Grazyna Kochanska** and her associates found that guilt feelings in the proper amount help children to abide by the rules and to respect others. One hundred and six preschool boys and girls participated in this study. They were observed in the laboratory at ages 2, 3, 4 and 5. In order to find out the degree of guilt feelings, researchers made children believe that they had broken a highly valuable object. Behaviour was observed and input was taken from their mothers as well as the children themselves. These are the most relevant results:

- Girls showed greater guilt feelings than boys.
- Preschoolers from assertive families showed lower levels of guilt.
- Guilt rates at 2 years of age were related to moral autonomy at age 5.
- Children with a sense of guilt violated fewer rules than children without guilt.
- A proper amount of guilt helps prevent bad behaviour.

TEST YOURSELF ::

There is a close relationship between guilt and certain behaviours. The following questions depict conducts associated with guilt:

Do I blame myself too much?	YES	NO
1. Did you grow up in a strict environment?		
2. Is it difficult for you to forgive your own mistakes?		
3. Is it difficult for you to forgive those who offend you?		
4. Do you live in constant fear of breaking any rule, regulation, or principle?		
5. Do you become alarmed at any sign of bad news?		
6. Are you frequently afraid when you think of the future?		
7. Do you feel very uncomfortable when something does not work out perfectly?		
8. Does it bother you excessively when others are not punctual?		
9. Do you often suffer from feelings of inferiority?		
10. Do you become easily angry with yourself and others?		
11. Do you worry too much about what others may think of you?		
12. Do you imagine God constantly angry at your sins and imperfections?		

If you have answered YES to more than three questions, you are prone to a false sense of guilt and should find solutions. Start with the advice of this page. If insufficient, look for help.

3.09
Improving your memory

Memory is essential to survival. The usefulness of memory does not only reach to remembering the name and phone number of a friend.

It also has much to do with sensations, emotions and life experiences that cause certain moods.

Without memory we would not be able to learn, since taking a single step in any area of learning requires one to remember the previous steps.

Without memory we could not talk or walk, chew, read, write or ride a bicycle.

Someone with Alzheimer's disease (see page 178), for example, who still has much memory intact, runs the constant risk of getting lost, not recognising certain persons and being without direction.

How to maximise memory

Some people seem to have a remarkable memory, while others possess one that is less powerful.

Nevertheless, everyone can use **mnemonic principles** to help memory. The most effective are described below.

- **Use and repetition.** Memory content used regularly is never forgotten. It is therefore important that you use and rehearse behaviours, ideas, tasks, verbal information… that are important to you.
  Repetition is a good way to store content in the long-term memory. Whenever you wish to memorise words or numbers, you only need to repeat them (or have someone repeat them) hundreds of times. The hammering effect of the sound causes retention. Although tedious, it is an effective method.

- **Verbal association.** When you need to learn new words, associate them to familiar words and establish a common tie between them, be it by sound or by meaning. If you need to remember the female name 'Joy' in the long term, you can imagine that particular woman expressing joy and happiness. Or you can associate this woman with another Joy you knew from before and put the two together in your imagination. This is an effective

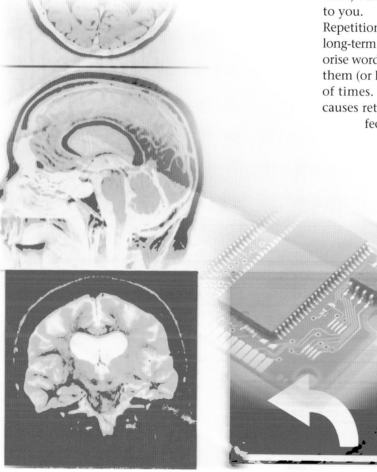

MEMORY AND STUDY

The **growth years**—childhood and adolescence—provide the best time period to store content for life. At later stages, many other memories will be stored, but not with the same intensity of the younger years. This is the time when basic school content is stored. Take advantage of these years to memorise and learn material. Many of them will remain with you for the rest of your life and will be the foundation for future learning:

- **Organise content.** Memory storage follows order and logic. Things cannot be stored blindly. Prepare all study material in an orderly and organised manner following a coherent system. If history, use a chronological approach. If chemistry, classify by substances… Place in your mind the material to memorise as if you were putting clothes away in a drawer or wardrobe.

- **Prepare environmental conditions.** You cannot study if it is too cold or excessively hot. Study with plenty of light at a time of day when you are not tired. Have all materials on hand as to avoid interruptions. Put aside a sufficient portion of time and prevent disruptions (for instance, disconnect the phone).

- **Distribute study sessions over time.** With some exceptions, it is more effective to study over short and frequent periods than in a sit-down stretch of several hours. Memorise content within the study period and return to them later. This practice moves information from short-term to long-term memory storage.

- **Personalise the information.** Content in any subject should have personal meaning, apart from the details offered by the teacher or textbook. If it is a geometry lesson, apply these principles to your house measurements or the shape of your furniture. If it is a lesson of contemporary history, try to make contact with someone who lived at that time or visit a museum with relevant objects. These connections will anchor the material in your mind for the rest of your life.

- **Exercise memory.** There are activities in the school curriculum that can be useful for generally exercising memory capacity: puzzles, crossword puzzles, letter puzzles… It is also useful to do mental math exercises: do not take a written list when you go shopping, but memorise the list of items. Mentally keep adding your expenditures and estimate your total.

method used widely in school settings to learn foreign language vocabulary, names of countries, cities, rivers, and so on.

- **Imagery.** The effectiveness of imagery methods surpasses any other. Because memory is especially impressionable to visual contents, using this method helps to ensure that they are retained for a very long time. In order to encode for lasting retention, try to form strange, illogical, funny and very colourful images.

If you need to remember to buy onions, eggs, tomatoes and a tin of condensed milk, for example, make a visual image combining them in a strange way. For example, visualise an onion growing branches that bear tomatoes and eggs; coat everything with very sticky condensed milk and observe the picture for a long time. It will be difficult for you to forget such a combination.

- **Action.** Physical movement favours retention of content. This method is called **kinaesthetics**. So, if you need to memorise a list of words in a foreign language or of kings in a dynasty, jump or leap when saying each word. Children benefit from this type of learning and results may be outstanding from very early in life. Poetry and music are within this category and are of great support to memorisation.

- **Emotions.** Memory content encoded under highly emotional conditions is recorded permanently. The more intense the emotion, the more lasting the memory will be. Following this principle, seek contexts and situations within a new and pleasant context to favour learning and teaching. We remember for longer periods, for example, events that happened in unfamiliar places, far from our home or in a romantic place shared with a dear person. Hence the importance of creating a memorable environment in which to remember special events; in this way, things will be long remembered.

ALCOHOL AND MEMORY

'It was a wonderful party, we all ended up drunk and I don't know how or why I woke up half-naked at one of the benches in the park.'

This is the statement of a young man who went to the discotheque and drank too much.

Alcohol produces a type of **amnesia** upon most recently experienced events. Few events happening around the inebriated person are actually recorded in the person's memory, and that accounts for the unawareness of what he/she did, said, saw, heard or felt. It is as if the episode was never lived.

Apart from the many adverse effects on a variety of organs, alcohol radically affects memory.

Alcoholics, who are subject to its effects during several hours each day, live obliviously to what is happening around them.

This condition may produce many complications and even tragedies in the life of people who drink.

Sayings of Jesus

'Do this in remembrance of me' (Luke 22:19).

Gems of Ancient Wisdom

'These commandments that I give you today are to be upon your hearts. Impress them on your children. Talk about them when you sit at home and when you walk along the road, when you lie down and when you get up. Tie them as symbols on your hands and bind them on your foreheads. Write them on the doorframes of your houses and on your gates' (Deuteronomy 6:6-9).

NATURAL REMEDIES FOR A GOOD MEMORY

Over recent years, natural herbs that prevent memory loss have grown in popularity. Here are some examples:

Ginkgo (*Ginkgo biloba*). The leaves of this plant, originally from the Far East, have been utilised from ancient times to generally improve blood circulation, especially in the brain. Due to its dilating effect upon brain arteries, ginkgo helps with intellectual functions and the preservation of memory.

Rosemary (*Rosmarinus officinalis*). This medicinal plant is known in some places as the 'memory herb.' An infusion from Rosemary leaves is an excellent tonic that facilitates circulation, especially in the brain, thus producing memory enhancement.

Sage (*Salvia officinalis*). In certain locations this plant is known as a longevity enhancer, capable of improving memory in the elderly. Sage has anti-oxidant qualities that help slow down aging symptoms, including loss of memory. This is why sage extract is utilised for the treatment of Alzheimer's disease and dementia.

3.10
Insecurity

Insecurity is characterised by a **weak and suggestible ego**. This makes a person unable to perform tasks for fear of failure.

However, insecurity has nothing to do with inability. Many individuals of the past who possessed great talents were, deep down, extremely insecure. Such is the case of philosopher **Rousseau** or novelist **Dostoevsky**.

Movie director and scriptwriter **Woody Allen** often depicts the image of the insecure subject in his movies: fragile, undecided, eaten up by his doubts, aware of his own weakness but fun after all.

Unfortunately, those who experience insecurity do not enjoy it as mere spectators watching a Woody Allen movie. They live in a constant state of doubt and uneasiness because they must bear the consequences of this uncomfortable state (see the box below).

How to overcome insecurity

Insecurity may be eliminated by experiencing **success and triumph**.

However, this requires a strong initial motivation that only comes with a nourished self-esteem (see next page Self-help box and unit 1.04, page 28) mixed with assertiveness.

It is also useful to:

- seek social relationships;
- aim at emotional independence from others;
- become conscious of one's rights;
- practise self-discipline, effort and sense of duty;
- trust in God.

The effects of insecurity

An insecure person tends to be caught up in the following adverse effects:

- **Lack of achievement.** These persons do not perform well at work; not because of lack of ability, but because they do not possess the necessary self-confidence.
- **Emotional dependence.** Such people need permanent support from others. This fact makes them unable to function, and they can do little by themselves.
- **Weak ego.** Behind a normal appearance (sometimes arrogant), the person hides feelings of inferiority and is very sensitive to oth-

ers' actions and comments in reference to him/herself.

- **Avoidance behaviour.** When looking at the task to be done, insecure individuals feel inclined to avoid it, as it suggests trouble.
- **Tendency to timidity and loneliness.** The person remains quiet or isolated. He/she does this to avoid others discovering his/her 'inability.'
- **Proneness to guilt.** He or she experiences remorse for something uncertain. This constitutes a significant barrier to perform any task or function.

SELF-ESTEEM AND INSECURITY

Most times, insecurity is linked to low self-esteem. Those who undervalue themselves perform tasks at an inferior level. When they see the low level of their output, this confirms their beliefs and tendency to failure. Self-assurance is a good emotional habit that can reinforce self-esteem and self-identity.

In the following example, two employees were laid off due to retrenching. Both held a similar position, and had the same age and experience. However, their attitude and reactions to being laid off were different:

Employee A– Laid off	Employee B – Laid off
• *'I am useless'*	• *'The company is in crisis'*
• *'I don't know how to maintain relationships'*	• *'The situation is difficult'*
• *'I have been a bad worker'*	• *'They laid off many'*
• *'Everybody is better than me'*	• *'Only those with seniority were kept'*
• *'I will not find another job, and if I do, they will make me redundant'*	• *'I am going to work hard until I find another job'*

The fundamental difference between the two is that A attributes failure **to himself**, whereas B relates it to **external circumstances**, while recognising the need to do something to improve his situation.

If you have the tendency to devalue yourself and to feel insecure, try this:

- Focus your thoughts on your **positive traits**.
- Do **not** be too **hard on yourself** in your inner dialogue.
- Encourage yourself by reviewing your own past victories and triumphs.
- **Trust** that the **present and the future** will be **good**.
- List your **praiseworthy characteristics**; if you do not find enough, ask a close friend to share the good things he/she sees in you.
- **Do not blame yourself** for all failures; and do not diminish deserved merit for your victories.
- **Practise this attitude** and enjoy self-confidence and a balanced self-esteem.

Sayings of Jesus

'For I will give you words and wisdom that none of your adversaries will be able to resist or contradict' (Luke 21:15).

3.11
Narcissism

Narcissists love themselves excessively, and they often focus on a specific aspect of themselves. Sometimes it is their physical attractiveness; other times their personality traits, or their personal skills. The narcissist may also love the entirety of his/her attributes. More than flashy, the narcissistic is **egomaniacal**.

These are the features of the narcissist (although all do not normally appear together, 5 or 6 will be present at the same time):

- Disproportionate sensation of grandeur and arrogance.
- Excessive need of admiration.
- Inability to understand the feelings of others.
- Obsession for power, success, great achievements, immense wealth or exquisite beauty.
- Feeling of superiority and the impression that others do not understand him/her.
- Impression that one is the holder of special privileges that make him/her deserve exceptional treatment.
- Desire to exploit others.
- Covert jealousy towards others.
- Belief that others envy him/her.

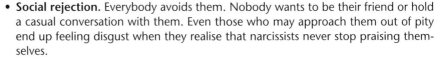
The effects of narcissism

Narcissists suffer the following as a result of their disorders:

- **Social rejection.** Everybody avoids them. Nobody wants to be their friend or hold a casual conversation with them. Even those who may approach them out of pity end up feeling disgust when they realise that narcissists never stop praising themselves.
- **Poor achievement.** Whether it be in their studies, trade or profession, narcissists do not achieve much, since their time and effort are spent building up themselves, not on actual accomplishments. When they do try to reach a goal, fear of failure leads to doubt and inability.
- **Emotional problems.** Behind the narcissistic personality is a fragile individual, insecure, lonely and determined to hide his/her vulnerability. Depression can occur when they realise that they are not what they would like to appear to be.

How to overcome narcissism

If you have narcissistic tendencies, it is imperative that you change your behavioural direction. In this way, you will avoid many interpersonal problems; nurture self-assurance, mental balance and inner peace.

Sometimes, narcissism is rooted in deep problems of the past or in a **traumatic experience** that caused a strong impression, hurting the 'ego.' If this is your case, you need to visit a good psychotherapist to obtain professional help.

Whatever the cause, and whether or not professional help is sought, your own personal desire to change will be beneficial. Try the following advice:

- **Be aware of your situation.** Perhaps you do not realise it, but if you observe your own behaviour and others' reactions, you will soon see the anomalies. Accept reality as a challenge that will give you the determination to change.

- **Help someone every day.** Offer to give a hand to a peer, invite a friend for a drink, or just use words of praise for others. Opening to others helps you to understand their needs as well as your own. You will soon see that your help brings satisfaction to others and to yourself.

- **Try to forget about yourself.** When interacting with people, focus on listening, ask questions and show interest in them. You will see how they soon change their attitude and their rejection turns into warmth and kindness. It is the only way to make friends.

NARCISSISM, A COVERT INFERIORITY COMPLEX

Narcissism is really a **compensatory reaction** of **minimal self-esteem** in hiding.

If you encounter a narcissist, **do not hate him**. On the contrary, offer your sincere and friendly hand to help him. He needs it.

Of course, not all narcissists wish to be helped, but you can give it a try.

- **Assume a global vision of your environment.** Think that great things can only be accomplished in teams. Likewise, the pain of others can only be soothed through community support. If you have the opportunity, one of the best strategies is to become involved, together with other volunteers, in humanitarian tasks serving the needy.

Gems of Ancient Wisdom

'Do not think of yourself more highly than you ought, but rather think of yourself with sober judgment, in accordance with the measure of faith God has given you' (Romans 12:3).

'Live in harmony with one another. Do not be proud, but be willing to associate with people of low position' (Romans 12:16).

3.12
Superstition

Superstition is the **irrational belief** that certain objects or situations may provide safety or misfortune. There are those who believe that it is bad luck to walk under a ladder; others attribute misfortune to a black cat or spilled salt. Still others will avoid any activity that falls on Friday the 13th. As far as good fate is concerned, some knock on wood to avoid calamities, others carry a good-luck charm or wear a talisman around their neck for extra protection.

Superstitious beliefs seem harmless, but they have their **drawbacks**:

- **They add an unnecessary burden**, as there is no evidence whatsoever that they work, for better or for worse.

- **They interfere with goal attainment.** For example, superstitious people are forced to cancel or postpone an important trip if Friday the 13th is the only possible day to travel; or they may be unable to accept a hotel reservation because it is on the 13th floor (or 4th according to Japanese tradition).

- **They can cause anxiety.** An example is when the good-luck charm is not available. For example, 'If I forget my amulet, I am in trouble.' Or, 'What might happen if I discover in the middle of the night that my room is not on the 14th floor, but that the label was changed and I am actually on the 13th floor?'

- **They complicate other disorders.** There are people with phobia to travel by air who use these methods. When they realise that these methods do not work and finally go to the psychologist, they find that their problem has got worse and they have been suffering unnecessarily.

Superstitious person profile

A typical superstitious subject tends to:
- **Be uneducated.** Although there are exceptions, people without causal understanding explain events without logic and find refuge in superstition.
- **Have an insecure personality.** Those without personal self-confidence do not see themselves in charge of their destiny and may find support in superstition.
- **Be emotional, not cerebral.** Excessively emotional personalities tend to explain everything in magical and mysterious terms, thus being more inclined to superstition.

- **Have a certain neurotic component.** Although not in extreme, superstitious people are prone to emotional turmoil, psychological ups and downs, anxiety and panic.

Furthermore, superstition is frequent in cultures where, as a tradition, these phenomena are part of everyday life. It is also relatively common in high-risk professions such as bullfighting or sports.

How to overcome superstition

If you wish to free yourself from superstition:

- **Use objective data.** Examine statistical information (just as insurance companies do in order to discover the true risk).

- **Apply external, rational strategies.** In order to avoid an accident, do not trust a good-luck charm, but engage in preventive measures. Have the engine checked; listen to the meteorological report; check traffic density. In this way you will be able to plan a safe trip.

- **Apply personal rational strategies.** To get a good mark in your examination, it is better to prepare yourself conscientiously. Study well and use reliable comprehension and memorisation techniques.

- **Test superstition.** Eliminate superstition and observe the results. Once you discover the lack of relationship between superstition and results, you will want to free yourself from such an unnecessary burden.

- **Substitute superstition by faith.** Believing in God's authority and love for people is an optimal source of personal safety (see the Self-help box on this page). And if things take the wrong turn, it is not because God is at fault, but because of the presence of evil. The Bible teaches us that evil will be eliminated and that good will prevail.

RELIGION AND SUPERSTITION

Said **Voltaire**, 'superstition is to religion as astrology to astronomy: the crazy daughter of a prudent mother.'

Religious faith may be used as support in the middle of doubt. God promises: *'And surely I am with you always, to the very end of the age'* (Matthew 28:20).

This statement comes from the Creator and Sustainer of the universe and it is worth accepting. Reflect on these words, try to pray to God and share your anxieties and doubts; trust that he, and not superstition, will lead you to a positive result in all aspects of your life.

BIBLICAL EXAMPLE

Apostle Paul's speech in Athens

The book of Acts describes the apostle Paul in Athens debating theological matters with Jews, Christians, Stoics and Epicureans. Probed by the latter, the apostle, in the midst of the Areopagus, addressed Athenians. In his speech, he called them 'superstitious' (other versions say 'very religious'), since a nearby altar showed that they worshipped *'an unknown God'* just to be safe. On this occasion, Paul encourages them to put nonsense aside and seek 'the God who made the world and everything in it, [since he] is the Lord of heaven and earth and does not live in temples built by hands. And he is not served by human hands, as if he needed anything, because he himself gives all men life and breath and everything else' (see Acts 17:16-25).

3.13
Problems of retirement age

A new concept

The traditional idea of the elderly person who waits for the day of death is one of the past. Today, retirement years are full of activities and opportunities.

The senior citizen stage is often one of ambitious plans. Many anxiously wait for the moment when they can retire so they can carry out projects that are difficult to accomplish now.

However, with age, there are also health risks and other problems that require preparation. They are the object of this unit.

Keep fit

If one aims at well-being and longevity, it is of utmost importance that the elderly maintain a moderate plan of physical exercise, adequate to their age. This can be attained by keeping **active** during the retirement years. Read the following advice and try to put it into practice.

Home accident prevention

Older persons experience a decrease in their reaction speed and sense perception. This increases the probability of home accidents. The large majority of domestic accidents could be avoided by following these simple tips:

In the kitchen...

- keep frequently used utensils within easy reach.
- immediately clean up water or liquid that has spilled onto the floor.
- cook on a low flame. It is healthier and prevents fires.
- keep clothes and kitchen towels away from the stove.
- leave enough counter surface free upon which to rest a boiling pot.
- if you use gas, ask that the gas company perform regular checks.
- when you have finished, take a final look to ensure that everything is off.

Gems of Ancient Wisdom

'Surely goodness and love will follow me all the days of my life, and I will dwell in the house of the LORD for ever' (Psalm 23:6).

'Though you have made me see troubles, many and bitter, you will restore my life again; from the depths of the earth you will again bring me up. You will increase my honour and comfort me once again' (Psalm 71:20).

Prejudice towards the elderly shortens their lives

Our attitude towards the elderly may shorten or lengthen their lives. This is important to family, friends, neighbours, health professionals, media... A joke where the elderly are humiliated or indirect remarks ('Less memory every day!') affect the elderly person's self-concept and may shorten his/her life.

In a longitudinal study (Levy *et al.*, 2002) led by **Beca Levy**, of Yale University (USA), 660 subjects participated, all older than 50. The study found that participants with a highly positive self-perception lived an average of 7.5 years longer than those perceiving themselves as inferior. It was also evident that the first group had better memory and personal balance than the latter. It is everybody's responsibility to affirm and reinforce the self-concept of the elderly.

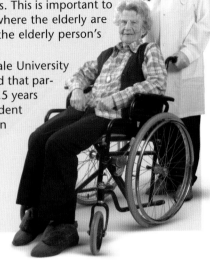

In the bathroom...

- place a rubber suction mat on the shower or bathtub floor.
- install safety handles in the shower or bathtub.
- avoid loose carpets where you may trip and fall.
- do not lock yourself in the bathroom.
- do not set the water heater at a very high temperature.
- if any plug sparks or is loose, have it repaired immediately. The bathroom is a zone of high-risk for electrocution.

In the bedroom...

- install a light switch that you can reach from the bed.
- ensure that the bed is the right height—not too low, not too high.
- check that lamp and phone cables run along the wall and not on the floor.
- keep heaters away from curtains and bedspreads.
- never smoke in bed.
- avoid the use of electric blankets and pillows.
- keep a phone near your bed. Many emergency calls are made from the bedroom and this connection may save your life.

How to support retirees

Family, friends and neighbours can help seniors, making sure that the right safety measures are in place. With the right measures in place, the elderly can maintain a good measure of **autonomy and responsibility**. The secret is not in doing everything for the retiree so he or she is left idle. Rather, the retiree should be entrusted with areas of responsibility and care in order to provide motivation. This will help the person continue to feel useful and to live a meaningful life.

The attitude towards retirement age is important, as well as the opinion that we all have of the elderly. Our feelings towards them are noticeable and affect their mental and physical health. In fact, it may influence their longevity (see the box on the top of this page).

Sayings of Jesus

'Come to me, all you who are weary and burdened, and I will give you rest' (Matthew 11:28).

The cognitive function

Mental capacity in old age tends to decrease when not used. We must insist on the adaptive ability of the brain and its functions.

When **mental activity** is **regularly** exercised, the brain maintains its functions and neurons remain alive.

Exploration of new areas of knowledge as well as projects requiring thought enlarges the number of neuronal connections. This is necessary to maintain mental capacity in good condition during advanced age.

Nevertheless, diseases such as Alzheimer's do affect the elderly (see the box below).

LEAD AN ACTIVE LIFE

- Do home improvement work or gardening.
- Do not be reticent to run errands and go out. You will improve your health.
- Use the stairs, not the lift, but hold tightly onto the handle.
- Use comfortable and safe rubber-soled shoes.
- Carry out your tasks during daylight and sleep at night.
- Put aside quiet time every day in order to meditate, pray, or listen to relaxing music.

Alzheimer's disease

Alzheimer's disease, normally associated to old age but often latent during previous years, increasingly affects more persons and their respective families, who suffer from the results that the disease has upon the patient. Alzheimer's patients follow a **degenerative process of mental deterioration**. It starts with forgetting the names of known people and ends up with the loss of short-term memory, loss of speech and the inability for personal care. The disease is not limited to the cognitive function; it can also carry hostility, aggression, disorientation, anxiety and depression.

Research continues in order to find an appropriate treatment. For the time being, there are drugs that stop (or slow down) the process of neuronal death, but they cannot reverse the process. The most effective action is to prepare **people to live with the Alzheimer's patient**. These are a few useful tips:

- Calmly speak to the patient and do not despair because he/she does not use logic.
- When the patient becomes obsessed with an idea or behaviour, try and distract his/her attention with something else instead of giving explanations or orders.
- The house may be classified with colours in order to avoid confusion for the patient.
- Encourage safe activities that were liked by the patient in the past.
- Offer opportunities for the patient to talk about the remote past.
- When there are fears, reasoning and explanations do not work. The source of fear must be removed and the patient distracted.
- Lock doors to avoid the patient leaving and getting lost.
- Place on the patient some identifying label in case he/she gets lost.

RESEARCH RESULTS

Hormonal therapy may aggravate Alzheimer's symptoms

An experimental study (Marriott *et al.*, 2002) by **Lisa Marriott** and her team of researchers showed the risk of using post-menopausal hormonal therapy in Alzheimer's patients. The interaction of hormone replacement and the disease makes the memory loss more acute.

The study was carried out with female rats whose ovaries were removed in order to produce the genetic alteration resembling women's menopause. They were administered estrogens to resemble post-menopausal hormonal treatment and a neuronal inflammation (typical in Alzheimer's) was induced.

The result was remarkable: The removal of the ovaries did not affect the solution of maze problems at all. But when the hormone was administered (even in small amounts), neuronal inflammation appeared and the rats could not solve the problems due to the loss of short-term memory.

Although this is an animal experiment, it would be useful to consider alternative therapies for menopausal disorders among those patients under the effect of Alzheimer's.

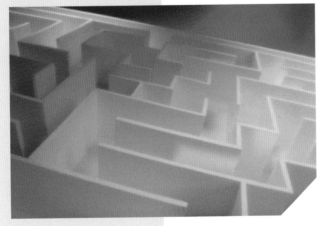

The importance of faith

It is especially hard to face the approaching end of our days without faith. A biological analysis of life and death is incomplete. Although possessing satisfactions, human existence is full of suffering and injustice. What we see must be part of a greater picture, of a global, durable and eternal existence.

In order to face death with integrity and dignity, we need to believe in something beyond this reality. It is necessary to believe that God exists and that he wishes our eternal salvation.

But the very divine nature is such that he cannot impose salvation. This act must be strictly **voluntary and free**.

Scripture explains how salvation can be accepted and how one can face death and the afterlife with assurance. It also explains how happiness can be reached in this present life and how inevitable suffering may become lighter if human beings associate with their Creator.

Gems of Ancient Wisdom

'Even when I am old and grey, do not forsake me, O God, till I declare your power to the next generation, your might to all who are to come (Psalm 71:18).

3.14

Psychosomatic disorders

Certain illnesses seem to be caused by organic or hereditary weakness. But there are others that are intimately related to mind and personality. In these cases, **peculiar ways of being and thinking** weaken defences and lead to illness. These are psychosomatic diseases, ailments that affect organs but have a psychological or emotional origin.

Medical science identifies a long list of diseases encompassing all the systems in the human body that fall into this category. Consequently, health education, preventive medicine, psychological intervention, and the treatment of patients rather than disease are key to face these ailments today.

As a sample of the many psychosomatic illnesses in existence, some of the most common are included below with corresponding advice on how to deal with them.

Acne

Common or youth acne appears frequently during the adolescent stage when **hormonal activity** is **intense**. It causes skin blemishes (pimples and blackheads) on the face, forehead and neck. Of course, this disturbs young people a great deal. They feel ashamed and anxious. These worries negatively affect the course and healing of acne.

What to do

Learn to **appreciate your values and qualities**. Put aside complexes and insecurities. Be courteous, kind, and willing to help others in order to forget your own problems. Think of acne as something common and transitory. Keep your skin clean, washing it with mild soap three or four times a day. Eat less sugar and fat. If your case is severe, go to the doctor, who can provide medicine that will help

BIBLICAL EXAMPLE

Death by psychosomatic reaction

Before becoming king of Israel, David was persecuted by his predecessor, Saul. He was forced to live for years as a fugitive, holed up in caves and mountains together with a small army of loyal soldiers.

On one occasion, his soldiers went to Nabal, a wealthy farmer, to ask for supplies. They had maintained a good relationship with Nabal's shepherds and had protected them from danger and harassment on many occasions. Unfortunately, Nabal refused to provide the needed supplies. When David found out, he prepared his men to annihilate all the males in Nabal's household and estate. Abigail, Nabal's wife, intercepted the army with her kindness and submission, providing them with an abundance of food. Given her attitude, David reversed his intention.

Once the danger was past, Abigail informed Nabal of all that had happened. The news left Nabal in such a state of illness that he died ten days later.

(The complete story is found in the Bible, 1 Samuel, chapter 25).

PSYCHOSOMATIC PERSONALITIES

There are traits that favour psychosomatic disorders. For example, a person with **Type A personality** is typically tense, frustrated, hostile, lives in a rush and arrives late; this individual gets consumed when he has to wait, does several things at the same time and cannot stay still. He becomes easily irritated and is abrupt and inconsiderate of others. Type A is a candidate for heart attack. A variety of traits relate to different psychosomatic diseases:

low self-esteem $\longrightarrow$ respiratory disorders
anxious and nervous personality $\longrightarrow$ ulcerous colitis
pessimism and apprehension $\longrightarrow$ gastroduodenal ulcer
perfectionism $\longrightarrow$ migraine
emotional conflicts $\longrightarrow$ hypertension
co-dependence $\longrightarrow$ respiratory allergies

Although the above relationships are not mathematically correlated, if you have any of the traits mentioned, try to keep them under control, diminishing strong tendencies. Seek the company of balanced people and escape from extremes in your behaviour and thought.

the acne to heal and prevent the formation of permanent scars.

Herpes

This is a skin manifestation caused by the *Herpes* virus and produces blisters on the lips, tongue, palate, and nose. In addition, the virus may cause fever, chills, sore throat, gum sensitivity, and general irritability.

The course of this infection lasts between one and two weeks. Then the symptoms disappear, but not the virus. When the person is under excessive stress or goes through adverse psychological experiences, symptoms reappear.

What to do

Above all, you need to **slow down**. Take on responsibilities but without burdening yourself excessively. Learn to say no and, apart from your work and duties, seek relaxing activities as entertainment. Be thankful for people and circumstances around you.

Physical exercise is always a good anti-stress measure. If possible, practise it regularly and moderately.

Asthma

Asthma is manifested in breathing difficulties caused by inflammation of the respiratory pathways. Often this is caused by the presence of an amino acid called histamine in the lungs and bronchi. Emotional states complicate symptoms, thus worsening the condition.

What to do

Asthma requires **medical treatment**, since a severe attack could be fatal. Symptomatic treatment consists of expectorants/bronchodilators, anti-allergy injections, and steroids. In addition, persons suffering from asthma may learn good behavioural habits that can help to prevent the crisis. It is known that worry and anxiety aggravate symptoms.

Learn to enjoy the here and now. Give consideration to the pleasant things of the past and forget the unpleasant ones. As far as the future is concerned, much depends on the present.

Do your best throughout the day, maintain a peaceful conscience and trust in a happy future.

Stomach ulcer

A gastric ulcer is a sore appearing in the digestive lining. This happens when the lining weakens and does not resist the presence of gastric fluid.

The most susceptible areas are the upper part of the small intestine (duodenum ulcer) and the stomach itself (gastric ulcer). The term gastrointestinal ulcer refers to both and includes the majority of **stress**-related ulcers.

What to do

Gastrointestinal ulcers can be treated with drugs designed to control the production of gastric acid and to protect the stomach lining.

In addition, **foods** should be used that naturally protect the stomach membrane. These are a few examples:

- **Cabbage, cauliflower and broccoli.** These vegetables exert an anti-inflammatory and scar-forming effect on the

PRACTICAL CASE

Tom's changing ulcer

Lynn Gillis, Professor of Psychiatry at the University of Cape Town, South Africa, cites the amazing case of Tom, a lab assistant with a fistula in the abdominal wall that allowed the stomach lining to be observed with the naked eye.

When Tom was afraid or felt sad, the stomach membrane turned pale and secretions decreased to minimum levels. When he experienced anxiety, hostility or resentment, the lining became swollen and reddish. When emotions prolonged themselves, occasional bleeding could be observed. Over time, a major bleeding ulcer was formed with the consequent risk of perforation.

The case shows the course followed by most ulcers: **stress and negative emotions** initiate **stomach irritation.** These irritations form small ulcers. The sores on the membrane permit gastric fluids to touch inner tissue and the patient complains of acidity. Small ulcers cluster together to form a bigger ulcer that bleeds into the stomach. Finally, the ulcer may become chronic and even pierce the stomach wall.

membrane. Their healing action is greater when they are eaten raw, chopped or shredded in salads or liquefied.

- **Potato.** This tuber acts as an antacid over the digestive tract, apart from softening the tissue. The best way to eat it is boiled, baked or in puree. It can also be liquefied.

- **Oats.** Taken regularly, oats are an excellent anti-inflammatory and scar-forming agent over the stomach lining. They not only prevent ulcer development, but also encourage total healing.

- **Fibre.** The absence of fibre in contemporary diet has caused an increase in gastric ulcers in many communities. It is therefore necessary to seek high-fibre food: whole grains (bread, rice), vegetables, fruits, and beans.

Nevertheless, if stress continues to be present, ulcers re-open and new ones appear. Hence the importance of **psychological treatment** for the prevention and healing of this problem, through activities, habits and behaviours such as those contained in this advice:

- Accept sufficient (but not too much) work and responsibility.

- Separate work from leisure and respect both.

- Organise your tasks in order to avoid unnecessary stress.

- View the future positively and with hope; after all, nobody knows the future and it is therefore best to approach it with optimism (see page 48).

- Nourish your family and social relationships; they can provide great emotional support.

- Follow the advice given in unit 2.7 (page 112) to prevent and overcome stress.

Enuresis

At about 3 to 4 years of age, most children have learned to control their sphincters. However, 7% reach the age of 5 and still have not attained the skill, continuing to wet the bed (or their clothes).

The disorder affects many more boys than girls. 'Accidents' occur twice (sometimes more) a week. This produces family tension.

The problem sometimes appears again two or three years after full toilet training. In such cases, the origin is almost always psychosomatic.

Common **precipitating events** are: the birth of a sibling, moving house, admission to hospital between ages 2 and 4, beginning to go to school, and family separation or death.

What to do

It is necessary to tackle the problem from several fronts:

- **A good family environment.** Ensure that there is peace and harmony at home. If there is a baby, do not forget to pay attention to the child suffering from enuresis. Nourish his self-esteem; make him feel good about his achievements and himself. Do not ridicule him or embarrass him.

- **Avoid changes.** Routine is highly desirable for children and especially to those suffering from enuresis. Avoid trips, unnecessary movement, and schedule alteration, etc. Send him to bed at a prudent hour and do not give him fluids 2-3 hours before sleeping.

continued on page 185

SUPER-EMOTIONS

In the same way that negative emotions adversely affect health, positive emotions bring about a state of well-being. Affection, tenderness, sympathy, peace, optimism and joy are examples among a long list.

There are in addition three emotions that, because of their soothing effect upon the organism, could be called super-emotions. They have also been called **virtues**. They are really **mental attitudes** of primordial importance for mental and physical health: faith, hope and charity (or love).

Faith

According to the Bible, faith is the substance of things hoped for, the evidence of things not seen. There are needs, hopes, and desires that are not met from the human perspective (this is strongly experienced by those who live under some form of dependence). In these cases, faith means becoming aware of a power outside oneself that is capable of responding to our needs. The sick person who has faith in the Supreme Being who can heal is much closer to health than the patient who has no faith.

Hope

Doctors know that the restoration of health to the sick closely depends on seeing health as a reality. Consequently, hope is a decisive factor in the prevention and healing of psychosomatic diseases.

Norman Cousins, a journalist who was diagnosed with an incurable disease of the organic tissues, was supposed to die in short order. The probability of healing was about 1 in 500. However, Norman did not give up. He concentrated on hope and trusted that he would return to normal life. During weeks, he kept a positive mental attitude, good sense of humour and the conviction that he had a long life ahead. Physicians observed a spectacular shift in the course of his ailment and they attributed the change to his hope and desire to live. His attitude affected his immune system, defending his organism from the pathology.

Through hope, Norman Cousins saved his life and began to share this concept in his teaching at the University of California School of Medicine. (See also page 311).

Love

Feelings of love, sympathy, care, and tenderness towards others bring about well-being to those practising them. Seemingly insurmountable problems have found solution by loving, forgiving, accepting and welcoming even those who have perpetrated evil upon us. This attitude contains extraordinary therapeutic power.

continued from page 183

- **Conditioning.** There is a device ('**Pee-Pee Stop**') that, when applied to the urethra, wakes the child at the first sign of urine. This unpleasant experience helps the organism to self-correct. Rewards, such as sweets, toys, small gifts, or words of praise, can also be used when the child shows control.

- **Drugs.** Imipramine (Tofranil®) and other pharmacological products have been successfully used in the treatment of enuresis together with psychological strategies.

Encopresis

Encopresis (soiling) is the inability to retain feces. It is not very frequent (1% of children between 5 and 12), but it is an obvious problem. As with enuresis, it is more common in boys than in girls. Those suffering from this disorder are victims of high levels of tension within the family, and may be the object of hatred and scorn at school, which further aggravates the problem. Anger, anxiety and fear also exacerbate the symptom.

What to do

Try the following tips with your son or daughter:

- **Avoid family stress.** Try by all means not to dramatise the situation. Do not tell him off or humiliate him. Limit yourself to saying that this is not acceptable and that it needs to be solved. Arrange circumstances so that the child has a sense of control over his environment: give him tasks and responsibilities.

- **Avoid embarrassing situations.** If the accident occurs during the day, it can become very embarrassing, for example, in school. Speak to the teacher about the problem and make arrangements including additional underwear, in case of need.

- **Toilet at fixed intervals.** Placing the child on the toilet at fixed intervals, for example 20 minutes in the morning and 20 minutes in the evening, can help him to acquire the habit.

- **Self-esteem and anxiety treatment.** These are frequently psychosomatic causes of encopresis. Consult the corresponding units to face these problems (pages 28 and 96).

- **Enrich your diet.** Contemporary diet omits fibre, consisting of highly processed foods. Eliminate sweets and add fruits, vegetables and whole grains (through bread or rice) to his diet.

Consumerism (compulsive shopping)

Do an increase and concentration of goods mean **greater happiness**?

The answer is *no*. A survey of young people from rich countries today shows that, when compared with their grandparents, who did not possess the same ability to spend, they are slightly less happy.

What do we gain by controlling consumerism?

These are the advantages of self-control:

- **Greater reserves.** Natural resources are not infinite and we should preserve them for future generations.

- **A better environment.** Waste can be reduced by means of moderate consumption of goods; this leads to a cleaner environment.

- **Greater personal autonomy.** With moderate use of resources, it is not necessary to use credit or pay interest. In this way, debt can be reduced or eliminated. As a result, people can become free from financial dependence.

- **Greater enjoyment of simple things.** Less consumption prepares us to enjoy simplicity. Even with scarcity, people are able to enjoy life.

Strategies to avoid consumerism

These are the avoidance strategies:

- **Choose a simple lifestyle.** This is the key to avoid consumerism. Seek simple activities and learn to find delight in them.

- **Set up priorities.** If you value your profession or your children's studies… focus on them and do not respond to the call of publicity.

- **Assess your real needs.** Perform an objective analysis of what you really need and make plans to limit yourself to these things. If in doubt, ask yourself, 'Do I really need it?'

- **Buy less.** Many purchased goods are never used. Decide to reduce your expenses. Before spending, think twice.

Advertising, the behaviour of others, the availability of goods, and opulence are the main reasons for consumerism being much greater today than two or three generations ago, especially in the wealthy regions of the world.

If we divide the world into five equal parts, we find that the top fifth consume 64% of everything produced, while the inhabitants of the bottom fifth use up only 2%. Such disparity requires consideration.

RESEARCH RESULTS

Poverty-materialism relationship

A study (Kasser *et al.*, 1995) designed to investigate the relationship between early life experiences and materialistic attitudes found the following: Children whose childhood was marred by poverty and whose mothers did not supply enough loving care and attention showed a significantly higher materialistic attitude in adolescence than other adolescents who, in the early years, enjoyed sufficient economic means together with the appropriate maternal emotional support.

The result can be interpreted saying that those subjects were compensating for their early privation by displaying a desire for money and material goods. In any event, these results call for due attention when it comes to providing emotional support to children.

self-help

PROTECT YOUR CHILDREN FROM PUBLICITY

The advertising sector has a special interest in reaching children. This makes the child a consumerist and sets the foundation to re-affirm this attitude in the future. Consider the following preventive measures:

1. **Limit the amount of TV** watched by your children and establish agreements with them in order to take breaks during commercials.

2. **Apply Internet filters**, since this medium contains large amounts of aggressive advertising.

3. **Discuss commercials with your children**, explaining how they often include false information. Help them to be wise consumers.

4. **Observe whether the school makes excessive use of advertising** and demand of the principal adequate restrictions.

5. **Dispose of unwanted advertisements** instead of leaving them around the house.

6. When shopping with your children, **frequent businesses** that do **not** display **excessive publicity targeted at minors**.

7. **Suggest that criticism of advertising be a part of the school curriculum** and get involved to petition authorities for greater control on advertising to children.

- **Think of others and share.** Acquire goods that can help others and share them. This will help you gain perspective and attain greater self-control, apart from helping others.

- **Try to avoid purchasing brand names.** Assess the quality and the cost, rather than the brand. Famous brand names are expensive and lead to ostentation, which is the enemy of simplicity, a necessary virtue when avoiding consumerism.

- **Postpone unnecessary purchases.** Leave for next week (or month) that product you may not need. The desire to buy it may vanish over time.

- **Reduce the use of credit cards.** It is easy to buy without money, and it is easy to fall into the trap of buying superfluous items with credit. Some people help themselves by leaving their credit cards at home when they shop, except in a case of absolute necessity.

Sayings of Jesus

'Watch out! Be on your guard against all kinds of greed; a man's life does not consist in the abundance of his possessions' (Luke 12:15).

3.16
Tiredness and chronic fatigue

A growing problem

It is increasingly common to find people complaining that they are always tired. They get up fatigued and suffer from sore muscles, headaches, etc.

However, they are not tired because they have accomplished many things. In fact, often these people suffer from low production. This may be due to temporary circumstances that produce tiredness. If so, the symptoms will go away in a few days. However, when tiredness continues for months, the problem becomes chronic fatigue.

How to face chronic fatigue

Follow these tips:

- **Get physical exercise.** Moderate and progressive physical exercise is good to correct the chronic fatigue symptoms. It is only normal that your own fatigue takes away your motivation. But you need to make an initial effort and you will end up enjoying the benefits of exercise.

TEST YOURSELF ::

'Do I have simple fatigue or chronic fatigue?' 'Are my symptoms serious?' Many people ask themselves these questions. If you answer positively to one or more of the following questions, you should consult your physician and change your lifestyle.

Do I suffer from chronic fatigue syndrome?	YES	NO
1. Do you feel excessively tired even when your duties are not intense and has this fatigue been present for more than six months?		
2. Do you accomplish only half of what you used to accomplish due to fatigue?		
3. For over six months, have you had four or more persistent and recurrent symptoms such as those listed below? • Sore throat • Sensitivity or pain in the neck or underarms • Sore muscles or backache • Sore joints without swelling • Headache • Problems with memory, attention and concentration • Insomnia		

Even when your fatigue is simple and does not meet the above criteria, the advice offered on these pages can be useful to overcome tiredness.

- **Verbalise your feeling.** Seek support in your family and friends, and talk about your frustration, anger, or sadness. This will cause the symptoms to remit and you will feel in a better mood.

- **Practise breathing and relaxation exercises.** Breathe deeply 15 or 20 times a day, at various moments throughout the day. Learn how to achieve progressive relaxation in a regular way.

- **Reinforce your diet.** Eat food high in magnesium (soya beans, leeks, cashew nuts, coconut and melon) and potassium (cauliflower, pumpkin, yam, peanuts, chestnuts, cherries, peaches, papayas, bananas and grapefruit). Make sure you get enough vitamin B by eating a variety of fruits, vegetables and grains. If you have a few extra pounds (kilos), shed them by reducing your calorie intake and using foods in as natural a state as possible.

- **Profit from botanic medicine.** Products such as Ginseng root, St. John's Wort or liquorice root have highly beneficial effects upon fatigue.

- **Reduce stress.** Approach work, relationships, finances, etc. calmly. Do not try to do too many things and forbid adverse or catastrophic thinking.

- **Consult your doctor.** Chronic fatigue is a medical condition and requires the attention of health professionals with possible pharmacological treatment: anxiety medicine, antidepressants, hydrocortisone…

RESEARCH RESULTS

Exercise improves attention in chronic fatigue patients

A team of researchers from the University of Western Australia carried out an experiment (Wallman *et al.*, 2003) with 61 patients diagnosed with chronic fatigue syndrome. Due to the incidence of attention failure in cases of chronic fatigue (it appears in 85% of all patients), this research proposed to study the effect of physical exercise (see page 322) and relaxation therapy upon attention capacity.

Patients were randomly assigned to two groups to follow either a physical exercise plan or a relaxation therapy plan. Using psychological tests, the researchers verified that participants had comparable levels of initial attention/concentration. After the treatment, tests were administered again and it was observed that the group following a gradual plan of physical exercise had a higher level of attention/concentration. This experiment confirms the efficacy of physical exercise to improve the symptoms of chronic fatigue, especially to correct decreased attention capabilities.

Gems of Ancient Wisdom

'Ask for the ancient paths, ask where the good way is, and walk in it, and you will find rest' (Jeremiah 6:16).

MAYBE NO ONE BELIEVES YOU

Chronic fatigue syndrome normally starts with flu-like symptoms. The patient goes to the doctor, who prescribes ordinary antibiotics, performs routine checks and concludes that there is no pathology. The patient is left without a specific answer and continues to complain of the ailment.

According to a study developed in the UK (Raine *et al.*, 2004), family practitioners tend to stereotype patients with chronic fatigue syndrome as individuals with apprehensive personality who like to play the role of a patient.

Do not give up and talk openly with your doctor. Seek further information and try and find a self-help group.

3.17
Psychology of greed

Greed is a marked **desire to possess something that belongs to someone else.** This impulse may become pathological enough to cause dangerous behaviours (see the list in the following paragraphs). Greed is an irrational process, very different from the noble action of wishing to reach legitimate goals.

Advertising often takes advantage of this human inclination and utilises it to introduce attractive, powerful, and immensely happy models in possession of the advertised product, thus making it desirable to the observer. But greed goes beyond disproportionate consumption. It touches interpersonal relationships and mental health itself. These are some of the **consequences** of greed:

- **Limits personal autonomy**, as greed, especially when intense, reduces the subject's freedom. All his/her energy is utilised to obtain the coveted object.
- **Reduces objectivity** and rationality.
- **Increases the risk of getting into debt**, as greed is not patient and pushes the person to borrow money in order to obtain the desired object.

- **Leads to unethical behaviour.** When someone harbours greedy feelings, he/she may engage in acts of fraud, stealing, and unfaithfulness.
- **Damages interpersonal relationships** between the person possessing the coveted good and any individual who may come in between.
- **Is insatiable**, as, once the coveted object is obtained, the impulse does not stop, but changes its focus onto a different object.
- **Produces depressive symptoms:** insomnia, pessimism, bad temper, loss of appetite... (see the box below).

How to avoid and overcome greed

1. **Practise contentment.** Look at the good things you already have and express gratitude for your possessions without focusing on what others have. This is perhaps the most powerful tool against greed. **Dennis Marquardt** wrote: 'Contentment eliminates greed the same way that greed eliminates contentment.'

2. **Review your value scale and set up goals.** Free yourself from adverse emotions, examine what

---

BIBLICAL EXAMPLE

David and Bathsheba

David, king of Israel, had many wives and concubines. But one day he saw a beautiful woman taking a bath on her house terrace. He inquired about her and learned that she was the wife of one of his soldiers who was at that moment engaged in a military campaign. Instead of putting aside his greed, he permitted it to grow. He ordered for her to be brought to his palace and he slept with her. When he discovered that she was pregnant, David designed a plan for her husband to die in the front line, making it appear as a wartime casualty.

But God disapproved of his behaviour and told David so. David repented and God forgave him. However, the king had to bear the consequences of his wrong behaviour.

The complete story is in 2 Samuel, chapters 11 and 12.

Greed is the threshold of avarice

Leo Tolstoy, in his tale 'How much land does a man need?', tells the story of Pahom, the hero who was offered farming land as a gift. He was offered as much as he could encompass with his plough in one day from sunrise to sunset. With balanced intention, Pahom begins his work, attempting to cover a moderate amount of land.

But as the day grows, greed grows within him. The hero moves forward farther and farther. But he reaches a point when it is virtually impossible to return before sunset. Then he decides to make a superhuman effort to enclose the land, but the effort kills him.

Finally, the landowner sadly provides twenty square feet of land in which to bury Pahom.

is truly important to you and set up goals and objectives to guide you. Seek to attain your aims rather than looking at the possessions of others.

3. **Avoid comparisons.** Do not become obsessed, comparing your life to that of others. Rather, concentrate on your own life and abilities. Then move on towards what is valuable and transcendent to you.

4. **Practise altruism.** Sharing what you have is a very powerful weapon against greed. It is a hard step for those with selfish tendencies, but you must try it and observe the results. Pay attention to someone with a specific need and try to meet that need. You will find out that greedy thoughts weaken or completely disappear.

5. **Use self-instruction and thought-stopping techniques** (see pages 303 and 306). Greed begins by observing others but grows with thought.

You can, at will, deviate, channel, transform, reject or harbour that line of thought. Choose alternative and edifying thoughts and nip greed at the first sight of it.

6. **Ask God for just enough.** If you are a believer, pray to God thanking him for what you have and for what you legitimately long for. If you do not believe, try and pray anyway. Use the prayer registered in Proverbs 30:8-9: 'Give me neither poverty nor riches, but give me only my daily bread. Otherwise, I may have too much and disown you and say, "Who is the LORD?" Or I may become poor and steal, and so dishonour the name of my God.'

Gems of Ancient Wisdom

'Such is the end of all who go after ill-gotten gain; it takes away the lives of those who get it' (Proverbs 1:19).

'All day long he craves for more, but the righteous give without sparing' (Proverbs 21:26).

3.18

Perfectionism

Perfectionists tend to be capable people but they impose upon themselves (and often upon others) very high standards. Perfectionists are unable to set up priorities because, **in their mind, everything is important** and must be done with exacting precision. At the same time, the difficult-to-reach high aims cause the corresponding feeling of failure and frustration.

There are **two kinds** of perfectionism—**incapacitating** and **adaptive.** The first one carries with it several complications and is a barrier to the attainment of goals (see the box on the right). Adaptive perfectionism is less problematic because the person uses this natural tendency to do things thoroughly, and to advance personally or professionally. However, even adaptive perfectionism has its risks, as it can be seen in the box below.

How to prevent and overcome perfectionism

People prone to perfectionism must set up **aims above and beyond their duties.** In this way, they may preserve their mental health:

- **Eliminate fear of failure.** It is important to understand that there is no merit to obtaining one hundred per cent of victories. The normal human being needs to experience both victory and occasional failure or error.

- **Eliminate fear of rejection or disapproval.** Believing that one needs continual acceptance by and approval of others is one of the most dangerous and irrational thoughts.

- **Eliminate the 'all or nothing' idea.** Being close to the maximum goal is an important achievement and does not constitute failure.

PERFECTIONISM CAN BECOME A VICIOUS CYCLE

The perfectionists:
1. Set up unrealistic goals.
2. Are unable to attain the goals because they are very difficult.
3. Fail, causing effectiveness and productivity to decrease.
4. Condemn themselves for the failure.
5. Set up new (unrealistic) aims with the purpose of reaching them this time.

And then the cycle repeats. The perfectionist needs to be aware of this danger and should try to vary his/her attitude following the advice offered in this unit.

(RESEARCH RESULTS)

Perfectionism, a barrier in social relations

Golan Shahar, of the University of Yale (USA) together with his associates, carried out a study (Shahar *et al.,* 2004) with 144 depressive patients who completed a 15-week psychotherapeutic treatment. They were administered several perfectionism-related psychological tests.

One of the clearest findings of this study was that subjects identified as perfectionists experienced **significant difficulties** in their **social and interpersonal relations**. These problems encompassed not only family, friends and work but also the therapeutic dimension (relationship with the psychologist).

These people were not able to establish an adequate therapeutic relationship as compared with the non-perfectionist patients.

- **Eliminate the excess of rules.** Even though our lives are to be guided by important principles, it is not good to live by an endless list of regulations and standards.

It is possible to overcome perfectionism. The main step is to understand the serious drawbacks of this attitude, since many do not see any problem with being a perfectionist. It is therefore essential that the person realise that although perfectionism can lead to achievements, it often prevents action.

Once the problem has been accepted, perfectionists should fight self-destructive thoughts and substitute them with adaptive ideas.

Avoid these ideas	Replace them with these thoughts
'I must reach the absolute top'	*'I will do as well as I can within the existing limits'*
'I am worthless unless I reach perfection'	*'Even though I may not reach perfection, I am a person of value'*
'My goal is to win and to attain perfection'	*'I am going to enjoy and gain experience in the process'*
'A mistake is a catastrophe'	*'One can learn a lot from mistakes'*
'I have to be better than So-and-so'	*'I will do my best and will not compare myself with others'*
'I do not have time for myself as I need to do everything with exactness'	*'I am going to put time aside for a relaxing hobby'*

TEST YOURSELF ::

There are certain traits of the perfectionist personality. The following questions highlight these typical signs. To see if you have perfectionist tendencies, answer YES or NO to these questions:

Am I a perfectionist?	YES	NO
1. When you make a mistake, does it come back to mind once and again, and is it difficult for you to put it aside?		
2. Do you feel very uncomfortable making a mistake in the presence of others?		
3. Are you very demanding with other people?		
4. Do you spend much more time than others to complete your tasks?		
5. Do you consider all your tasks important and have difficulty setting priorities?		
6. At the time of submitting work, do you wish to have extra time to do it even better?		
7. Do you often compare yourself to others, wishing to outperform them?		
8. Do you prefer to leave a task undone rather than doing it less than perfectly?		
9. Are you ashamed of asking questions for fear that others may think you are ignorant?		
10. Do you tend to focus on the small mistakes of others?		
11. Do you feel an extra push to do things perfectly when you are alone?		
12. Once your work is finished, do you feel the desire to review it again to ensure that everything is well done?		

If you have answered YES to more than 5 questions, seriously consider relaxing your self-demands and your expectations of others. Look at things more realistically and convince yourself that happiness does not depend on a perfect product, but on perceiving things in an acceptable and satisfactory way.

Chapter Summary

My problems
with other people

4

Alfred rarely goes out. A shy man, he becomes fearful when facing anyone. He never had a girlfriend; he cannot buy his own clothes. His mother complains when she has the chance: 'At age 30, he could become more assertive and face life. He gets nervous in front of everybody; and if someone contradicts him, he agrees to avoid confrontation.'

Alfred would like to be more assertive and talkative, but just thinking about it makes him so nervous that he looks for refuge at work, at home, watching TV and reading novels. His difficulty to relate to women bothers him a great deal. When talking to young ladies, he feels uncomfortable, sweaty, and nervous, and he blushes during any conversation.

Encouraged by his boss, Alfred is going to a psychologist who has helped him feel better about himself. In the session he learns ways to talk to people and he practises his speeches. Outside of counselling, he studies DVDs, reads brochures and applies the learned skills in real life. Alfred is beginning to see improvement as he begins to solve his problem.

Chapter Highlights

- In the past, it was thought to be beneficial to vent one's anger much as one releases the valve on a pressure cooker. Today it is clear that the **risks** are greater than any small achievement that may be obtained through **bad manners**.

- Shyness has a strong **hereditary** component, especially if the shyness is very extreme. Nevertheless, the tendency may be modified when circumstances demand it or when there is a strong determination.

- To combat workplace harassment, **assertiveness** is absolutely necessary. Being assertive means being able to communicate one's position and feelings expressively, directly, honestly and with dignity.

- Prevention of marital violence should occur from **several fronts**: the victim, the perpetrator who wishes to recover, and friends and family of the couple.

- Many people find themselves in **competitive situations**, fighting others in order to reach a goal, seeking a reward or gaining authority over others. Competitive contexts have some advantages (all questionable) and also disadvantages.

- There are persons who do not mind being alone. They engage in occasional social contacts and enjoy the independence and freedom of being alone. However, loneliness is a **source of pain and imbalance** to many.

Direct barriers to healthy human relations

Social relations have a lot to do with people's **mental health**. In fact, life's satisfactions are most enjoyed together with other persons. At the same time, the most complex problems are usually rooted in **interactions with others**. Learning how to solve these problems is a valuable investment towards happiness and mental health.

Anger and aggression (unit 4.01) are adverse manifestations for everyone implied. They cause very serious consequences and it is useful to know how to avoid them. Another barrier to overcome is **shyness** (unit 4.02), as it causes dissatisfaction to the shy person, prevents the establishment of desirable interactions and damages work relationships.

Even though some maintain that true love includes **jealousy** (unit 4.03), the truth is that a jealous attitude hurts the couple's relationship and destroys the love that may exist. It is therefore crucial to know how to overcome jealousy. Avoiding **hatred** (unit 4.04) is another great challenge in order to improve relations. The effects and risks of hatred are so negative that it is necessary to remove it from our lives.

More often than we wish, we find bad interpersonal relationships: **Mobbing** (unit 4.05) and **sexual harassment** (unit 4.06) in the work environment, **physical and/or psychological abuse** among married and other couples (unit 4.07), as well as relationships where the victim ends up identifying him/herself with the perpetrator by a process called **Stockholm syndrome** (unit 4.08). In all these harmful situations, people need to understand their role and how to prevent and overcome these circumstances, as the consequences of remaining in such relationships may be psychologically devastating.

Instead of being a source of closeness and enjoyment, sexual relations are sometimes a source of pain, suffering and anguish. **Sexual desire disorders** (unit 4.09), together with other dysfunctions and anomalies, should be understood in order to avoid them and to restore authentic sexuality.

Sometimes, human groups enter into the dynamics of **competition** (unit 4.10) producing stress, pain to the majority, absence of ethics and deterioration of teamwork. It is therefore imperative that one explore cooperative projects where steps followed are debated, tasks are fairly and effectively distributed, and more positive targets than crude competition are established.

Another problem causing deterioration of human relationships is stealing, not out of necessity, but due to mental and behavioural issues. This is **kleptomania** (unit 4.11), a type of shoplifting by impulse. Any person suffering from this tendency or living through a situation like this needs to learn how to successfully face the problem.

Individuals suffering from **affective loneliness** (unit 4.12) may be surrounded by people, even under the same roof, without having their social needs met. In order to obtain benefit from the positive influence of others' company, it is necessary to learn simple yet sometimes difficult steps to resolve the problem.

Envy (unit 4.13) is one of the strongest emotions against personal happiness and social relations. Envious people must admit their problem and take the corresponding steps to get rid of this burden, which carries consequences, not only in the emotional dimension, but also in behaviours that may destroy good relationships.

Lastly, **multicultural and multiracial groups** must successfully face the inevitable issues of racism and xenophobia (unit 4.14). In a world of increasingly mixed communities, it is urgent to understand and practise integration, and introduce the necessary peace, love and understanding. This will favour the interaction of people coming from diverse backgrounds and cultures.

4.01
Anger and aggression

Anger, rage and aggression offer very little benefit. However, many lose control of these strong tendencies.

As a result, they are forced to pay the price with their own physical and mental health, as well as their relationships.

Rage and anger sometimes appear, and although one should not submit to them, they may occasionally occur.

But when they become regular, they ruin families as well as social and work relationships. Physical aggression is **unacceptable** in every human group and must be prevented.

How to avoid anger and aggression

Bursts of anger and aggression can be governed by everyone. It is necessary to observe oneself and adopt simple habits of peace and calm. Practise the following tips:

- **Consider the true extent of the situation.** Simple observation will tell you that the real reason for anger is some small thing. Ask yourself: Is this so important as to explain my anger? What will happen if things do not work out my way? Is it worth wasting so much adrenaline? Will I have to repent for having lost my temper?

- **Breathe deeply and calm yourself.** Deep breathing relaxes. Use this technique slowly and deeply when you feel rage setting in. Instruct yourself: 'Calm down, Frank, nothing is going to happen... Control yourself; this will pass.'

- **Distract yourself.** Thinking about what irritates you is adding fuel to the fire. Take your mind far away from the topic of rage. 'Trick' yourself

EFFECTS OF RAGE ON THE ENRAGED

In the past, it was thought to be beneficial to vent one's anger much as one releases the valve on a pressure cooker. Today it is clear that the risks are greater than any small achievement that may be obtained through bad manners. Compared with the person of peaceful habits, those who often get angry:

- Have four times more likelihood of suffering from **coronary disease**.
- Are at higher risk from **dying young**.
- Experience **guilt feelings** after their rage attack.
- Feel isolated from **family and friends** who **avoid them** because of their bad temper.

- Have a **more conflictive marital relationship**.
- Are more likely to **use psychoactive substances** (tobacco, alcohol, drugs...).
- Run higher risk to **overeat** and be overweight.

Before displaying anger, think twice, as it is possible to stop the process and prevent greater problems.

as when distracting a child with funny or trivial thoughts. Think about something else; go for a walk until anger weakens.

- **Try an assertive solution.** Avoid messages said to others, such as: 'You are selfish,' 'You always do this to me,' 'You never care about what I think...' Prepare assertive responses: 'I would like you to try doing it differently,' 'This attitude makes me feel very sad,' 'Maybe we can do this or that... I can help in this way.'

- **Do not look at the opponent as an enemy.** When someone irritates you with their words or behaviour, do not think that they are provoking you. Think of other reasons and circumstances to explain the behaviour. And if the person really is being mean, think that he is very unlucky and should be pitied for such conduct.

- **Practise forgiveness.** Forgiving does not mean losing the battle. An old Castilian proverb says: 'Forgive the offender, and you will be conqueror.' Forgiving will not only bring serenity to you, but it will also benefit the other person who may end respecting you for your nobility and graciousness.

TEST YOURSELF ::

To know whether you are inclined to anger, answer YES or NO to these questions:

Am I prone to anger?	YES	NO
1. Is it very hard for you to forget the bad things others did to you?		
2. When you disagree with your friends, do you end up in a heated argument?		
3. When you think of your opponent, do you suffer strong palpitations?		
4. Does it bother you when you have to queue up?		
5. Do you get upset at yourself whenever you cannot control your emotions?		
6. Do you get irritated when others are not punctual or do not do a thorough job?		
7. Whenever you are angry, do you normally feel that you don't remember anything you said?		
8. Have you observed adverse relational consequences due to your bad temper?		
9. After a show of bad temper, do you experience a strong desire to eat, smoke or drink alcohol to compensate for the distress?		
10. Have you ever been angry to the point of hitting someone or something?		

Interpretation:
- If you have answered YES to 8 or more questions, seek help as soon as possible to be able to control your temper. Your interpersonal, family and work relationships may be in danger.
- If you have answered YES to 4-7 questions, this is a warning that you are not far from danger. You must develop patience and tolerance; you need to learn to live amidst diversity, remain calm, yield and observe others to learn how to reach goals through the use of good manners.
- If you have answered YES to 3 questions or less, you are on the safe side as far as anger and rage are concerned. Stay in the zone, as you are a person who is difficult to upset.

Gems of Ancient Wisdom

'In your anger do not sin: Do not let the sun go down while you are still angry' (Ephesians 4:26).

Sayings of Jesus

'Put your sword back in its place, Jesus said to him, for all who draw the sword will die by the sword' (Matthew 26:52).

4.02
Shyness

Shyness is inhibition in the presence of other people. Shy persons avoid and flee from social situations because they feel tension and fatigue. As a result, the person becomes isolated and wastes social learning opportunities.

Shy behaviour includes three basic manifestations:

- **Meeting avoidance.** The shy person tries by all means to find excuses (sometimes incredible stories) to dodge an appointment, party or meeting.

- **Anxiety.** Excessively shy persons manifest physiological signs of anxiety such as: agitation, palpitations, sweating, flushing, stuttering, etc. in the presence of other people. Since these are embarrassing symptoms, this fear feeds itself.

- **Embarrassment to speak publicly.** The shy person experiences strong affective trauma when he/she has to address a group or audience. The barrier is such that it may become extremely difficult for a person to address the group. This becomes a serious problem when the person's profession demands public speaking.

The outreach of shyness is vast and it touches a number of important areas, as shown in the following table:

Individual consequences	Interpersonal consequences	Work consequences
Shy people are unhappy with their condition. They observe the talkative and resourceful persons and long to be like them. This frustrated wish may lead to depressive symptoms. They are also inclined to suffer from psychosomatic illnesses (especially digestive types) due to lack of interaction to release their emotions.	*The shy person lacks the regular ability to nourish social relationships and his/her skills become increasingly impoverished.* *As far as courting is concerned, the timid person suffers in the process. As a result, he gives up because of his failures.*	*The shy person is bound to reject many professional opportunities because they require interpersonal skills.* *And even the traditionally solitary professions increasingly require teamwork and more interpersonal interaction.*

TEST YOURSELF ::

Answer True or False as you identify with the following statements:

Am I shy?	T	F
1. In a group, interesting things come to mind, but I do not speak because I feel embarrassed.		
2. It is difficult for me to initiate a conversation with unknown persons.		
3. When I have to speak in public, I begin to sweat; even my pulse races and I feel muscle contraction.		
4. When someone reads my name aloud, I flush and get nervous.		
5. The presence of the opposite sex makes me feel uncomfortable.		
6. If after having made a purchase, I observe that it has a small defect, I keep it to avoid the embarrassment of an exchange.		
7. If my opinions clash, I yield to avoid confrontation.		
8. It bothers me when someone jumps a queue, but I do not say anything to avoid embarrassment.		
9. I do not complain when someone known calls me at undue hours.		
10. I don't like to borrow money, even when it is a small amount.		
11. If when I leave a shop I realise that some money is lacking in the change, I prefer to lose the money rather than demanding what is fair.		
12. If I am served a drink different from what I have ordered, I take it if it is not very different.		
13. In a half-full auditorium I prefer to look for a seat separated from the rest of the people to avoid conversation.		
14. If someone smokes in a non-smoking area and the smoke bothers me, I move away rather than telling the smoker that smoking is not allowed.		
15. If a vendor comes to my door, it is very difficult for me to say 'no,' and sometimes I buy the item even if I do not want it.		

Interpretation:
- If you have answered T to less than 5 statements, you are far from being shy.
- If you have answered T to 5-10 statements, you are in the middle range. If you wish to put aside part of your shy behaviour, follow the advice included.
- If you have answered T to more than 10 statements you have a high level of shyness. This condition may cause you problems and we recommend that you follow the advice of this chapter carefully or seek professional help to overcome the barrier.

How to overcome shyness

Shyness has a strong **hereditary** component, especially if the shyness is very extreme. Nevertheless, the tendency may be modified when circumstances demand it or when there is a strong determination or motivation to change on the part of the shy person.

Apart from the advice of the Self-help box (see next page), there are other pieces of advice that

Gems of Ancient Wisdom

'For God did not give us a spirit of timidity, but a spirit of power, of love and of self-discipline' (2 Timothy 1:7).

VICTORY OVER INHIBITIONS

Henry, a college student, was very dissatisfied with his shy and inhibited style. Quite frequently he would harbour self-destructive thoughts and felt incapable. He knew the root of his problem: a very low self-esteem. The behaviour that made him feel most miserable was his failure to participate in class with his ideas and questions. He felt unable to raise his hand and speak.

The self-help plan had two parts:

1. **Overcome his very low self-concept.** Henry accepted his problem and decided to change his way of thinking. Then he made a list of his good qualities and carried it in his pocket. Often he mentally repeated them and assured himself that he could improve his weak points. He decided not to compare himself with others anymore, as doing so brought much frustration. He frequently remembered Jesus' sentence: 'Which of

you by worrying can add one cubit [18 inches] to his stature?' (Matthew 6:27). He understood that he could not attain certain qualities of others; however, Henry possessed admirable qualities others did not have. He also confided his problem to a friend, and his friend helped him and gave him assurance about his valuable qualities.

2. **Set up acceptable steps of behaviour in class.** Once he gained self-confidence, Henry was much closer to behavioural change. He set the objective to participate at least three times a week. With the help of his friend, he rehearsed at home several ways to ask questions and how to present ideas naturally and not pedantically. He kept record of his achievements each week and noticed that his interventions became increasingly more relaxed. His best reward was when a working team realised that Henry was a good thinker and they asked him to join their group.

are offered below and may be useful to reach victory over shyness.

- **Identify the problem behaviour.** Do not generalise saying: 'I am a disaster and I am no good. I will never overcome my defects.' Instead, identify the undesirable behaviours.

  For example, feeling embarrassed when returning a slightly damaged item may be an isolated and insignificant experience that only happens once a year and should not be considered important.

  However, if you feel upset that you lack the necessary assertiveness to go to your personnel director, whom you see every day, and request something that belongs to you, you must do something to overcome the problem.

- **Establish an action plan.** The plan should have two parts: a) a **deep** one, going to the root of the problem (that is, the cause that produces it) assuming that it is known; and b) a **behavioural** one, in order to change existing responses to more desirable ones. For example, a young man may feel inferior and thus feel embarrassed to ask a young woman out. He first needs to work on **enhancing his self-concept** and then **rehearse behaviours** that may bring about good results. The box on the previous page illustrates this with a particular case.

- **Give yourself challenging tasks.** Although hard at the beginning, results may be amazing. If you are shy, accept the job of door-to-door salesperson or commercial representative. This is 'baptism by fire'. You may suffer at the beginning, but the experience and the achievements you obtain will be the extra step toward success. This process has helped many to acquire a personality free from shyness, not only at work but in all contexts.

Sayings of Jesus

'Jesus told the synagogue ruler: "Don't be afraid; just believe"' (Mark 5:36).

ALCOHOL AS SOCIAL RELAXANT

There are introverts that have a few drinks to break the ice and seemingly become more talkative. We need to warn of the **triple danger** of this method:

- It is **temporary**. It is true that the effects of alcohol cause shy people to lower their inhibition. However, the change is not authentic, and when the effects of alcohol wear off, the individual continues with the same tendency.
- It is **dangerous**, especially for shy people. Many consider social drinking harmless. However, the risk of addiction is real, especially for the shy person who, rewarded by feelings of empowerment, may continue to use alcohol in private. And drinking alone is at the threshold of alcoholism.
- One may **repent of what was said** under the effect of alcohol. The sensation of boldness produced by alcohol is not rational, and may make someone say or do something undesirable.

4.03

Jealousy

Where does jealousy lead?

People experiencing jealousy tend to be subject to emotions such as **anxiety** (fear to lose the loved one), personal **insecurity**, **mistrust** and **suspicion**.

Many jealous people fantasise about attacking and destroying the rival person and some actually succumb to violence.

The aggressive reaction of a jealous husband that believes his wife is cheating on him is, in fact, one of the causes of **domestic violence** (see page 222) in marriage. The jealous individual often criticises, scolds, insults and physically attacks the partner.

Effects upon the couple and the family are devastating and the problem requires attention and treatment.

Jealousy is not always in the context of a man or woman towards his/her partner. It can also appear in relation to other people, such a brilliant **colleague** who does a better job than us (see the box below).

As an irrational attempt to feel better, the jealous person tends to gossip and slander the rival and may even attempt physical harm.

BIBLICAL EXAMPLE

Saul's jealousy

Saul was the first king of Israel. He was strong, intelligent and physically attractive; the most handsome and the tallest in the entire nation, according to the biblical story. However, his kingly term ended in defeat and death, partly because of jealousy toward young David. On one occasion, when returning from the battlefield, a group of women danced and sang: 'Saul has slain his thousands, and David his ten thousands.' This made Saul harbour jealousy towards David; and on several occasions, he attacked David in order to kill him. He tried to deceive him and made plans to assassinate David in one way or another. When he did not manage to kill him, he lost his mind and made a series of great mistakes to himself and the nation. He ended his days committing suicide and was succeeded on the throne by David himself.

The story is found in the first book of Samuel.

Envy	Jealousy
• *Desire to have the possessions and attributes that others possess.*	• *Desire to protect his/her own possessions or attributes before a rival.*
• *It can be personal or impersonal.*	• *It is almost always personal.*
• *It causes feelings of inferiority.*	• *It provokes fear of losing.*
• *It provokes resentment and frustration.*	• *It causes mistrust.*
• *It causes guilt.*	• *It impoverishes self-esteem.*
• *Moderate behavioural risks: strong desire to possess.*	• *Extreme behavioural risks: violence against rival.*

How to overcome unfounded jealousy in marriage

Whether male or female, the person suffering from unfounded jealousy can **control** this adverse feeling. It is not practical to blame 'the way I was brought up' or 'the environment where I live.'

The first step in attaining victory over jealousy consists of **accepting the problem** and showing willingness to do something to solve it. It is good to talk about this matter with the spouse and share the concern. The following tips may also be useful:

• **Stop and redirect thoughts of jealousy.** It is common that jealous people fantasise about situations where the spouse is engaged in sexual intercourse with a stranger. For example, the jealous woman sees in her mind the image of her husband embracing and smiling at a younger and more beautiful woman. The solution is to stop those images as soon as they appear and think of something different in order to distract oneself.

• **Develop a behavioural plan.** Identify the habits, stimuli and elements that feed and perpetuate jealousy. For example, avoid watching movies, reading novels or attending places that feed those feelings. Give yourself over to family activities that will strengthen your relationship with your spouse. This will help to keep you far from jealous thoughts. The spouse may help the jealous partner by affirming commitment and fidelity, but he/she should never adopt a position of servitude, as this can feed jealousy.

• **Strengthen your self-concept.** Many jealousy cases find their root in a low self-esteem. The support of the spouse in this area is recommended. Ask him/her for help and contribute to enhance his/her concept as well. Observe the positive and pleasant aspects in your spouse and state them to him/her. Demonstrate through your words and loving acts your admiration for him/her. Do not tease or ridicule your spouse; this may ruin his/her self-esteem.

• **If things do not improve with self-help, seek professional help.** A clinical plan will be set up and, through the series of therapeutic sessions, will help the couple to build up mutual trust. The counsellor will also help the couple to agree on the treatment steps and to establish measures for when the jealous behaviour may reappear.

BEWARE OF JEALOUSY IN MARITAL RELATIONSHIPS

There are a number of adverse effects of jealousy in marriage:

• Jealousy is often linked to **infidelity** ('If she is unfaithful, I will be even more so').
• Marital relationships **deteriorate** significantly.
• Meaningful **communication** disappears.
• Love **vanishes** and all commitments disappear.
• Children receive a **wrong example** of family relationships and develop an attitude that tends to perpetuate this problem into the next generation.

TEST YOURSELF ::

What would be your most probable reaction to the following situations?

<table>
<tr><td colspan="3" align="center">Am I jealous?</td></tr>
<tr><td colspan="3">1. You and your spouse are walking in the street and someone of the opposite sex that you have never seen before greets your spouse warmly. Your spouse recognises the stranger and introduces him/her to you as a school friend. They proceed with their lively conversation.</td></tr>
<tr>
<td>A. I would participate in the conversation.</td>
<td>B. I would remain quiet observing them.</td>
<td>C. I would remind my spouse that we were late (without it being true).</td>
</tr>
<tr><td colspan="3">2. What would you do after the encounter?</td></tr>
<tr>
<td>A. I would not comment; there does not seem to be any impropriety in their friendship.</td>
<td>B. I would ask my spouse about the details of his/her friendship with the person.</td>
<td>C. I would reproach my spouse for his/her familiarity with the person.</td>
</tr>
<tr><td colspan="3">3. You answer the phone and a man's voice asks for your wife (or a woman's voice asks for your husband).</td></tr>
<tr>
<td>A. I would say: 'Who is calling?' and would pass the phone to him/her.</td>
<td>B. I would say: 'I am his wife (or I am her husband). Can I help you?'</td>
<td>C. I would say: 'He/she is not in' (false) and I would question my spouse.</td>
</tr>
<tr><td colspan="3">4. Your spouse gets home two hours later than usual and tells you that he/she was engaged in a long conversation with a neighbour.</td></tr>
<tr>
<td>A. I would totally accept the explanation.</td>
<td>B. I would ask further details to ensure that my spouse is telling me the truth.</td>
<td>C. I would blame him/her for being late and would mention a possible relationship with someone of the opposite sex.</td>
</tr>
<tr><td colspan="3">5. Your spouse gets dressed up elegantly to attend a party. What would you think?</td></tr>
<tr>
<td>A. I would be pleased that he/she looks good and I would tell him/her so.</td>
<td>B. I would wonder why he/she is getting so dressed up and I would feel afraid that there might be someone else.</td>
<td>C. I would show that I am unhappy with the fact, and I would warn that I do not like this.</td>
</tr>
<tr><td colspan="3">6. At the party…</td></tr>
<tr>
<td>A. I talk naturally and feel relaxed with others and I do not mind him/her doing the same.</td>
<td>B. I try to be close to my spouse, as I feel uncomfortable when he/she talks alone with someone of the opposite sex.</td>
<td>C. I warn my spouse not to move away from me and if he/she does so for a moment, I watch carefully.</td>
</tr>
<tr><td colspan="3">Scoring:
Give yourself 1 point for each option 'A'
Give yourself 2 points for each option 'B'
Give yourself 3 points for each option 'C'</td></tr>
<tr><td colspan="3">Interpretation:</td></tr>
<tr>
<td>6 to 9 points
You have an acceptable level of jealousy and there is no danger of falling into undesirable effects.</td>
<td>10 to 13 points
You have a strong tendency to jealousy and should do something to avoid it. Read and practise the advice in this unit.</td>
<td>14 or more points
Your jealousy is fairly marked and you should do something to correct it or you relationship will be in danger.</td>
</tr>
</table>

RESEARCH RESULTS

Jealousy and early age

In an experiment (Hart and Carrington, 2002) carried out with 32 infants of 6 months of age and their respective mothers, each mother was asked to interact, in the presence of her baby, with a doll that uttered syllables (social interaction) and with a Sesame Street book (non-social interaction). Babies showed negative gestures in both situations: furrowed brow, pout and sob. However, negative reactions were more than double for mother-doll interactions, than for the mother-book interactions.

From these observations, it can be concluded that:

- Jealousy appears spontaneously at a **very early age**. In the past, it was believed that jealousy did not develop until 2 years of age.
- Jealousy appears even in **children without siblings**, as all participants in this study were firstborns.
- Jealousy carries a **combination of sympathy** for and **rejection** towards the rival. Babies showed a mix of positive and negative gestures, although **negative ones were dominant**.
- Since jealousy includes sympathy and rejection, children can be **trained with flexibility** in order to prevent pathological jealousy.

Gems of Ancient Wisdom

'For jealousy arouses a husband's fury, and he will show no mercy when he takes revenge' (Proverbs 6:34).

'Love is as strong as death, its jealousy unyielding as the grave' (Song of Solomon 8:6).

Hatred

HATRED AND PHYSICAL EFFECTS

Hatred is one of the strongest and most dangerous emotions that affect health. When hatred is felt in an intense and prolonged way, the risk of contracting and maintaining psychosomatic ailments increases. These are examples:

- coronary disease
- gastritis and other digestive disorders
- skin reactions
- lowering of defences against infection

Hatred is a strong feeling of repulsion towards others and is experienced by many people.

This **dangerous emotion** may appear due to sociological reasons (hatred toward members of a racial group), family conflicts (hatred towards the spouse due to relational problems), professional (hatred toward a colleague who reaches high achievements), ideological (hatred towards those with different values and beliefs), or class (hatred toward the wealthy).

Whatever its origin, hatred causes a number of adverse consequences:

- Proneness to violence (physical and psychological).
- Deterioration of interpersonal relationships.
- Feelings of guilt and emotional dissatisfaction.
- Difficulty focusing and concentrating on noble tasks.
- Difficulty attaining goals and objectives.
- Psychosomatic complications (see the box above).

How to overcome hatred

In spite of being a strong emotion, by preparing to combat hatred, we can avoid it taking over our lives and behaviour. These are our suggestions:

- **Control your thoughts of hatred.** Try to promote positive thoughts towards others, even those you may hate (see the Self-help box on page 211).
- **Reduce your lonely moments and associate with healthy people.** When there is proneness to revenge and hatred, loneliness leads to criticism and desire for retaliation. To avoid this

RESEARCH RESULTS

Hatred prevention

In order to prevent the growth of adolescent delinquency and hatred, **Dacia Gerst** proposed the following preventive measures (Gerst, 2005):

1. **Conflict resolution programmes.** Help young people to use negotiation and verbal skills to solve the problem among themselves as well as when facing the adult world and authorities.
2. **Empathy-improvement plans.** Empathy does not always come naturally and should be increased through stories, photographs, films, etc. in order to promote good feelings towards others and a sincere disposition to avoid hurt.
3. **Impulse-control techniques.** Help adolescents to make correct decisions in the precise moment before displaying anger and rage.
4. **Listening techniques.** Teach young people to attentively listen to verbal and non-verbal messages coming from others. Learn to read not only the words, but also the feelings of the opponent.
5. **Rational problem resolution.** Motivate adolescents to use rational methods, reducing the emotional component of the display of anger and rage.

chain of events, seek the company of people able to lift your mood and provide adequate counsel.

- **Keep active.** Organise your day so that it is full of activities, preferably through interaction with other people. Even for holidays, plan an active and enjoyable day. Too much free time leads to thoughts of rage and hatred (if you have that tendency).

- **Be prepared to love and forgive.** If you really wish to live in peace with yourself, you must take this important step. Stop focusing on the bad things that the other person has done and choose to forgive.

- **Take a first step towards reconciliation.** Some wait for the opposing party to come and ask for forgiveness and seek reconciliation. The other person does the same and enmity remains for years. Put your pride (or self love) aside and take the first step towards friendship.

- **Offer help to your enemy.** Helping your enemy seems like a contradiction. However, quoting an ancient proverb, the apostle Paul says: 'If your enemy is hungry, feed him; if he is thirsty, give him something to drink.

In doing this, you will heap burning coals on his head' (Romans 12:20). The complicated relationships between adversaries mysteriously benefit from the unusual act of extending a helping hand. It is a noble act that brings about precious dividends in relationships.

- **Appeal to God's power.** Pride and hatred are rooted in human nature in such a way that they seem impossible to eradicate. It is therefore necessary to appeal to the supernatural power coming from a kind and loving God who is able to grant additional strength in order to reject hatred.

alternative option

MEDICINAL PLANTS USED TO TREAT HATRED

There are medicinal plants known for their tranquilising effects. They can be used in the form of tea or extract in order to provide additional support to other strategies. These are a few of them:

- **Common hop** (*Humulus lupulus*). It is a great remedy against anxiety and general tension as well as a calming agent to treat pain and insomnia. Its relaxing effect makes it useful for controlling anger, rage and feelings of hatred.

- **Yellow lady slipper** (*Cypripedium calceolus*). It has restorative properties for the nervous system and it is recommended as a natural remedy for irritability (which happens together with impulses of hatred) and for nervous maladies.

- **Skullcap** (*Scutellaria lateriflora*). It is a highly effective neuroleptic plant used as a relaxant and as a nerve tonic. Taken regularly, skullcap counteracts states of nervous arousal and brings about a sensation of calm and stillness.

- **St. John's Wort** (*Hypericum perforatum*). Being among one of the medicinal plants that has received most scientific attention, it is widely used today as an antidepressant. It also works as a sedative, calming of the nervous system and enhancing good feelings and the rejection of hatred and rage.

Lastly, **avoid coffee, alcohol and tobacco**. These substances exert an exciting effect upon the central nervous system, and this may provoke a state of irritability and intensify hatred and revenge.

HATRED-GENERATING SITUATIONS

An exhaustive analysis (Waller, 2001) of historic cases and studies related to hatred and cruelty revealed that perpetrators of the greatest brutalities of the twentieth century were neither psychopaths nor subjects with personality disorders. They were ordinary persons, loved and respected in their settings, balanced, capable, and hard-working. However, they were subject to circumstances that led them to commit horrific hate crimes against their fellow human beings. These particular circumstances were:

- **Group situations** with a level of pressure able to transform ideologies. This context produces in many the impulse to perpetrate extremely sinister acts.

- **Hierarchical situations** with blind obedience to authority; for example, military or scientific authorities. This makes the perpetrator deny his/her guilt, arguing that he/she is following orders, and that responsibility lies with those from above.

Exert great care to keep yourself firm in your convictions, principles, beliefs and values. Remember that peer pressure can be enormous, together with the strength of those at the top of the hierarchy. In this way, you will be able to avoid acts you would have never imagined you would perpetrate.

CHOICE OF THOUGHTS

Hatred nests and grows with thinking and imagination. It can also be reduced and eliminated using positive mental processes. Examine both options presented below and remember that you are the owner of your thoughts and can manage them at will. If you wish to avoid hatred and its consequences, choose positive attitudes towards your fellow human beings.

Thoughts that promote hatred	Thoughts that prevent hatred
• *Images and memories of evil things that my opponent did to me.*	• *Reflection on the causes leading my opponent to hurt me.*
• *Longing that the other suffers misfortune and illness.*	• *Consideration that he/she may be right in certain aspects.*
• *Mental review on how to take revenge on him/her.*	• *Compassion for the opponent.*
• *Ideas that only I am right and the opponent is to blame.*	• *Mental images where he/she and I reach agreement and reconciliation.*
• *Refusing to see, speak to, or reconcile with him/her.*	• *Generous and altruistic forgiveness even when I am in the right.*

Gems of Ancient Wisdom

'Anyone who hates his brother is a murderer, and you know that no murderer has eternal life in him' (1 John 3:15).

'Hatred stirs up dissension, but love covers over all wrongs' (Proverbs 10:12).

4.05
Psychological violence—Mobbing

Mobbing or **workplace psycho-terror** is a form of harassment in the work environment which is causing growing concern. The perpetrator threatens, hurts, criticises, subdues, humiliates and intimidates the victim. This is done in a subtle manner, generally when they are both by themselves, in order to avoid disapproval from other employees. Rarely does mobbing go together with physical aggression or sexual harassment. The process is strictly psychological.

Depending on which study is consulted, between 3 and 12% of surveyed people have been victims of some type of psychological aggression. Without an apparent reason, **the aggressor terrorises the victim in various ways**. For example, he or she:

- **Ignores** the victim as if he/she was not there or as if he/she were useless.
- **Speaks badly** about the victim, passing well-designed slander on to peers.
- **Isolates** the victim from everyone else.

- **Gives excessive work** (or practically no work) to the victim.
- **Ridicules** the victim in the presence of others.
- **Interrupts** the victim when he/she speaks.
- **Threatens** the victim with dismissal if he/she tells anyone.

The consequences of this activity vary depending on the mobbing intensity and the victim's strength, but the effects can be devastating, causing not only the professional ruin of the victim, but also serious mental disorders like depression, anxiety and even suicide, as listed in the table below.

Somatic reactions	Psychological reactions
• *headaches*	• *lack of concentration*
• *nausea, vomiting*	• *job anxiety*
• *chronic fatigue*	• *feelings of inferiority*
• *insomnia*	• *irritability*
• *panic attack*	• *risk of substance use*
	• *relational problems*
	• *suicidal attempt or consummation*

Psychological harassment at the workplace is difficult to understand, as bullies do not seem to obtain any benefit.

Perhaps it can be explained saying that his/her personality is similar to that of a **psychopath**, who enjoys witnessing ruin, discredit, depression and anguish in someone else.

The beginning of this process normally finds its root in **envy** (see page 236) or **professional jealousy** together with a concrete profile on the part of the perpetrator. Victims also have a particular personality profile that makes them prone to suffer from this type of harassment. The following table shows a few typical traits:

Perpetrator's profile	Victim's profile
• *Perfectionist.* He/she likes to do everything with precision and this skill is used to harass thoroughly. • *Cold and calculating.* The perpetrator prepares each step of the attack in order to do it emotionlessly. • *Insecure.* In spite of his/her image of external adequacy, he/she carefully hides personal deficiencies. • *Selfish.* Basically self-centred, this individual is not able to identify with the suffering of others. • *Double personality.* This person is able to show cruelty and sarcasm to the victim while appearing charming in front of the group. • *Paranoid.* This subject sees hidden intentions in others (for example, interprets that others want his/her job). • *Patronising.* The perpetrator is authoritarian and arrogant with traces of kindness. • *Manipulating.* Good at making up anecdotes and details about the victim, the individual is able to ruin the victim's reputation.	• *Effective.* This person is a good and regular worker with an excellent disposition. These traits may provoke the jealousy of the aggressor. • *Faithful.* He/she recognises authority and is willing to follow instruction and to satisfy the boss. • *Non-assertive.* He/she is longsuffering and does not defend his/her rights. This is perhaps a reason why the perpetrator does the mobbing. • *Altruistic.* A good-hearted person, he/she is given to help others, a reason to be envied by the aggressor. • *Naive.* This person is without malice, always seeing good intention in others. • *Honest and ethical.* The victim is unable to pay back the perpetrator, which may prolong the mobbing. • *Good family/personal situation.* The person enjoys good relationships with family, spouse and friends. • *Well educated.* His/her studies and experience ideally qualify him/her for the job.

Reduce your risk of being a victim

Heinz Leymann, in his book *Mobbing. La persécution au travail* (1996), proposes a number of lifestyle factors that can prevent harassment at the workplace. Consider these useful not only for those who have already suffered from mobbing, but especially for those with some probability of becoming victims of this problem. These are the seven preventive measures as outlined by Leymann:

1. **Keep yourself mentally and physically fit.** Mobbing manifestations have two aspects—psychological and somatic. That is why it is good to be healthy in order to face such problems. Live in a balanced way, compensating for your

---

RESEARCH RESULTS

Workplace mobbing and psychosomatic ailments

Mikkelsen and Einarsenwith, two Danish researchers carried out a study (2002) a group of 224 (55% male and 45% female) employees in factories working at various levels of responsibility. Results showed a **close relationship** between mobbing and illnesses of a psychological and psychosomatic nature.

Participants completed several highly reliable questionnaires and it became obvious that those who had suffered one or more harassment episode/s over the past few weeks experienced the highest levels of dizziness, stomach ache and chest pain.

They also complained of stress, fear of the future, guilt and nervousness.

deficiencies: get exercise if your work is sedentary or engage in mental activities if your job is physically active. Care for your diet so that it is simple and complete, avoiding all kinds of excessively processed or complex food. Sleep the necessary hours and adopt a positive attitude towards life.

2. **Increase self-confidence.** The goal of mobbing is to ruin self-confidence and destroy any self-value and self-respect that a victim may have. It is therefore imperative to convince oneself of personal abilities, capacities, moral strength,

and value. For the believer there is a further step: confidence in God as infinite strength. Above self-confidence, which is always limited, there is the benefit of surrender to the Supreme Being who wishes the best for us. His alliance makes us invincible against harassment.

3. **Care for your reputation.** The poor public opinion of the victim is due to the discrediting activity of the accuser. However, a well-established reputation with an impeccable history is almost impossible to ruin.

    Therefore, if there is anything doubtful in your professional activity, eliminate it at once. Be blameless in everything that depends on you. Then comment with others your ideas of being faithful and thorough at work. Make known your sense of honesty; in case of need, someone who knows the truth will come to your aid.

4. **Strengthen your social support system.** It is always comforting to count on your spouse, family or friends when it is time to talk about doubts and conflicts. In case of possible mobbing, this support is basic to survive the experience.

    However, a common tendency of victims is to remain silent and not share the problem with anyone. Avoid this wrong attitude and practise interpersonal relationships, as they are a very valuable support to fight psychological harassment at work.

5. **Stabilise your finances.** In principle, nobody should live obsessed with the fact that she/he may be a victim of mobbing with the possible financial struggles this may cause. However, one should be prepared in case it happens. Therefore, do not allow yourself to be without any savings or resources (see page 266).

    In the unlikely event of having to face a series of expenses (legal, medical, or job searches) caused by workplace psycho-terror, you will be able to handle it.

6. **Increase your ability to manoeuvre.** Keep all possible options open. Avoid having to remain in your job like a caged animal. This can be achieved by maintaining outside possibilities of employment, location and activity. It can also be achieved by holding parallel activities (professional or recreational) that help you to remain vibrant and excited.

    This will provide necessary leisure and will of-

self-help

MOBBING AND ASSERTIVENESS

To combat workplace harassment, assertiveness is absolutely necessary. Being assertive means being able to communicate one's position and feelings expressively, directly, honestly and with dignity. A number of specialists have suggested that it is desirable to learn this skill **in group** (Lange and Jakubowski, 1976); that is why it is recommended to join a group (see page 316). In any case, the following personal advice may become very useful:

- **Outline the message.** Prepare in advance a series of points containing the things you would wish to say, including relevant details. Doing this in advance helps to take away emotions and add efficacy.

- **Be correct.** With respect, good manners, and without raising your voice, express your viewpoint and observations clearly and firmly.

- **Do not use too many excuses.** Unless necessary, do not go asking for apologies from the beginning. The mobbing victim does not have to apologise.

- **Do not use threats.** It is more effective to state your position than to threaten to file a complaint. And if you need to do it, do it without warnings or threats.

- **Do not corner the opponent.** Avoid doing what the perpetrator does; that way you will gain everybody's respect and you may end up with a balanced solution.

fer support for your mental health. Putting all your energy and hope into the current job may be catastrophic if a psychopath declares war on you.

7. **Improve your assertiveness.** The person lacking assertiveness is one of the easiest targets for the attacker. When this individual observes someone with high professional capacity and ethical principles who is not assertive, he or she assesses him/her as an easy victim, with less risk to the perpetrator. This is why it is very useful to be skillful in assertiveness, as it solves difficulties in interpersonal relationships (see the box on the previous page).

How to face workplace psycho-terror

You can practise these tips:

1. **Channel your rage towards surviving.** One of the most natural reactions towards those who slander us or try to ruin our lives is that of rage. However, this is not advisable; it is better to use the accumulated energy used up in rage in pos-

itive ways. Seek the support of others or find beneficial alternatives.

By doing this, the psycho-terrorist's plan is spoiled, as he/she wishes to cause rage to the victim. This will free the victim from the burden of rage. Use self-instruction to prevent anger. Tell yourself: 'If I remain calm, I have the upper hand; if I lose control, I am giving it to my opponent. Seek peace and calm.

Also, use visualisation: Imagine the perpetrator as if you were an observer and not the victimised person ('This does not have anything to do with me').

2. **Instead of taking revenge, protect yourself.** Personal protection consists of seeking advice and emotional support from a dear person and maintaining inner mental balance.

If, for example, an opportunity of a new job arises, accept it and move on with your life. Be careful not to fall into the dynamics of saying: 'I have been offered a new job but I am not accepting; I am staying to complicate the life of my opponent.' Be practical and save yourself some suffering.

3. **Cultivate assertiveness and self-esteem.** These are the two basic factors to avoid personal destruction. Follow the simple tips of the box on page 214 and increase your self-esteem (see page 28).

4. **Consider the perpetrator as someone with problems.** If you look at the aggressor as a bad and corrupt individual, you will experience anger, rage and desire for revenge. This may work against your mental and physical health.

   See your accuser as someone with serious personal problems causing him/her to behave in anomalous ways. This will help you break the chain of hostility and resentment.

5. **Minimise the situation.** It is difficult to do this, as it is hard to face an absurd and irritating circumstance. However, once the first crisis is over, it is possible to deactivate the emotional burden of mobbing in order to deal with the problem in a more relaxed way.

   Try to inject a little humour into the situation. Ultimately, you will need to free yourself from the role of suffering victim, the object of all offences.

BEHAVIOURS TO AVOID

Mobbing victims tend to display certain reactions, usually unconscious, that cause them further suffering. If you suspect that you may be a victim of psychological harassment, **avoid the following**:

- **Denial.** If you have observed some aggressive evidence beyond one or two isolated events, you should accept that the other person is trying to hurt you. Many take months to admit that mobbing is touching their lives.

- **Aggression.** Do not react aggressively. Use correct manners. Any mistake in this will put you at a disadvantage, as the perpetrator will have something with which to accuse you and you may lose credibility in front of others.

- **Identification.** Avoid identifying yourself with the aggressor (Stockholm's syndrome; see page 226), an important risk to all victims. Even though he/she humiliates you, insults you or tells you that you are good for nothing, do not accept it, as it is not true. Hold fast to your belief in yourself and in your worth. Find refuge in a good friend so as not to lose your own perspective.

- **The false hope that everything is soon going away.** It is very improbable that the perpetrator ceases to hurt the victim. It is better if you accept the situation and actively start to do something to remedy the problem.

The biblical solution

Returning good for evil does not seem to have much logic in human terms, but it is the inspired suggestion from the Holy Scriptures. In Solomon's writings, Proverbs 25:21 states: 'If your enemy is hungry, give him food to eat; if he is thirsty, give him water to drink.' It is difficult (though not impossible) to be kind and helpful with those who, intentionally and persistently, are trying to hurt us. But it is worth trying, as results may be comforting. Consider the following steps:

1. **Ask God for help.** This is an extremely difficult plan from the human viewpoint. There are few willing to swallow their pride when involved in situations where they are right before an unscrupulous opponent of dishonourable acts. It is a paradox to love your enemy (instead of hating him). Therefore, in order for this plan to be genuine and not sarcastic or cynical, it should be understood that divine help is necessary. Pray to God and ask him for strength so that you can do what Jesus did with his own enemies—love them and respect them.

2. **Grant forgiveness.** It is true that you are completely innocent and the opponent totally guilty. However, you need to think that you are the first beneficiary of your forgiveness to others. In addition, if there is any possibility that the person may be redeemed and influenced not to act this way with others, he/she should be forgiven. In this way, he/she will witness a generous and noble behaviour, which may produce reflection and right behaviour.

3. **Show a cordial and kind attitude.** As you forgive your offender, you have the option to speak to him/her kindly, face to face, and naturally. Offer yourself to help in whatever you can or even provide a small demonstration of kindness or appreciation. This may trigger an unprecedented positive reaction. If this does not work, you have done what the apostle Paul recommends (see Gems below): '...as far as it depends on you.'

Gems of Ancient Wisdom

'Do not answer a fool according to his folly, or you will be like him yourself' (Proverbs 26:4).

'If it is possible, as far as it depends on you, live at peace with everyone. Do not take revenge, my friends, but leave room for God's wrath, for it is written: "It is mine to avenge; I will repay," says the Lord' (Romans 12:18, 19).

'Let us not become conceited, provoking and envying each other' (Galatians 5:26).

4.06
Sexual harassment

Sexual harassment happens when someone at work or at school sends insistent and offensive messages of a sexual nature to another person, making him or her feel uncomfortable. These are some of its forms:

- Erotic comments or jokes.

- Sexual gestures or looks that, in the judgement of an impartial person, are inappropriate.

- Pinching, caressing, or rubbing or pushing up against the person in such a way that the action appears natural, while it actually causes shame, humiliation and even anguish to the victim.

- Touching oneself or displaying signs of a sexual nature in the presence of the victim.

- Notes, drawings, or e-mails of a sexual nature targeted at the victim.

- Obscene jokes shared with the harassed person.

- Chasing or placing pressure upon the victim in order to obtain sexual favours.

- Threats ('We are not going to promote you.' 'I will make sure that your salary is frozen.' 'You are going to lose your job…') if the person should turn the harasser in or refuses the requested acts.

It is common for harassment to be performed by a **higher-ranking** person in authority over a subordinate. In the school context, the perpetrator may be a teacher who sexually harasses an adolescent; or perhaps a boy or girl who plagues a younger or weaker one.

This type of harassment from 'strong to weak' reveals the **abusing and insensitive personality** of the harasser. He/she does not recognise the tremendous damage caused, but only seeks to satisfy his/her own sexual appetite.

The most common occurrence is from male to female. Victims are normally **inhibited, weak or introverted women** who are perceived by the harasser as easy targets for sexual gratification.

Harassment may also happen from women to men, although it is less common. In these cases, it is performed by a woman over an inhibited, prudish or shy man, not necessarily for sexual gratification, but to have fun at the expense of a victim who takes these actions as something very embarrassing.

Consequences of sexual harassment

In spite of the fact that sexual intercourse is not necessarily performed, the victim suffers from a number of symptoms:

- Insomnia.
- Headache and stomach ache.
- Appetite variation.
- Feelings of guilt and shame.

- Fear, frustration and tearful episodes.
- Poor social and professional achievement.
- Sensation of impotency to stop the harassment.
- Fear to ruin his/her own reputation.

Preventive measures

The best platform to significantly reduce sexual harassment is the **work environment**. A company or corporation aware of this problem will have preventive measures in place. If not, employees should suggest the implementation of such **measures** to eliminate the problem. These are a few effective preventive measures:

- **To develop a harassment policy.** It is very useful to have a document stating what sexual harassment means and the steps to follow when this problem is observed or someone is the victim of such behaviour. It should also stipulate the consequences for those who are caught or for those who repeat.

- **To organise talks and seminars for employees.** This can be done as part of a systematic plan. Perhaps yearly, as part of general personnel topics, the psychological and legal implications of this problem can be discussed.
  If sexual harassment is more than an isolated occurrence, an exclusive seminar on sexual harassment should be put in place. Instruction can be provided to teach everyone how to develop an assertive way to reject such attempts upon them. Usually firm, serious and courteous rejection of the attempt by the potential victim ends an incident.
  It is also useful to discourage the use of provocative attire or sensual manners that may encourage sexual advances.

- **To organise talks and seminars for personnel management.** Everyone who is in charge of personnel supervision (even those supervising a small number of employees) should receive special instruction. These seminars are to prevent managers from engaging in harassment themselves (if the problem exists) and to teach them how to handle possible incidents between employees.

- **To prepare a safe environment.** The physical and social settings of the workplace may favour or discourage sexual harassment. For example, enclosed offices or workrooms should be fitted with glass doors or windows that allow visual inspection from outside. When the job requires working in pairs (for example police patrolling in two's), it is important to carefully choose partnerships that do not promote sexual harassment, perhaps combining same-sex teams or teams of proven reputation.

- **To intervene at the appearance of any sign of harassment.** Make sure that the work environment does not include anything that may constitute sexual harassment (for example, nude photographs on display, as they may provoke offence or facilitate harassment). It is much simpler to warn against these practices than to face a full-blown case of harassment.

- **To take all sexual harassment complaints seriously.** Sexual harassment must be documented, but even weak evidence should be taken seriously and measures should be taken to gather additional facts in order to ascertain the truth.

At some time, you may be involved as a witness or spectator of someone else's harassment. In these cases, take the initiative and do not condone what is happening. Show disapproval, speak to the victim and offer your help.

In any case, be careful if the victim is of the opposite sex, as circumstances make the victim especially sensitive and suspicious of everyone who offers help.

How to solve sexual harassment

Sexual harassment requires an external and firm action against those perpetrating it. It is very unusual that this problem disappear by itself. Furthermore, the actions of the harasser will become stronger if consequences do not follow.

If you are a victim of sexual harassment, you need to act, as others may never find out what is happening. You need to be courageous and send alarm signals. You may need to talk about harassment details to various people.

Thanks to the integrity of women who have denounced the behaviour, there is today an attitude of understanding, support and protection towards women that have been the object of sexual harassment. The box on the adjoining page suggests the steps to follow in order to combat the problem.

Gems of Ancient Wisdom

'His master's wife took notice of Joseph and said, "Come to bed with me!" But he refused. [...] One day he went into the house to attend to his duties, and none of the household servants was inside. She caught him by his cloak and said, "Come to bed with me!" But he left his cloak in her hand and ran out of the house' (Genesis 39:7-8, 11-12).

SEXUAL HARASSMENT AT SCHOOL

Harassment at primary and secondary schools takes multiple shapes:

1. Harassment from teacher (or authority figure) to student.
2. Harassment from teacher to teacher.
3. Harassment from student to student.
4. Harassment of a student to an authority figure (for example, a teenage boy to a young, shy and attractive female teacher).

Not every modality listed happens in every institution, but sexual harassment is relatively frequent, especially the first three examples.

If you are a father or mother and know that this problem may exist, talk to the management and suggest measures of prevention and action.

If the situation is not clear, request that students be asked in a safe and respectful environment to find out whether or not harassment exists.

Demand preventive measures and action against occurrences.

IF YOU BELIEVE YOU ARE A VICTIM OF SEXUAL HARASSMENT...

If you have been or are being the object of sexual harassment, consider the following steps:

- If you are not sure whether your experience is sexual harassment, **share your suspicion** with someone you trust, like an intimate friend.
- **Talk to the person harassing you** and let him/her know that those words, attitudes, gestures, etc. produce disgust and request him/her never to do it again.
- **Make sure** that your manner of dressing or acting is **not provocative**. If you are in doubt, ask someone trusted to assess the situation sincerely and objectively.
- **Take care of your mental health.** The effects of sexual harassment are multiple and adverse, and you must protect yourself. Share with a close person you can trust the things that have happened (or are happening) and open up to that person. If you do not find anyone with whom you can confide your experience, look for a professional counsellor or psychologist. Your mental health is very important and you should take care of it.
- Even though you may feel guilty (a very frequent emotion in those suffering from sexual ha-

rassment), **do not think that you are to blame**. The harasser is responsible and he/she is trying to take advantage of you to satisfy his/her sexual desires.

- Someone in your company's management team or other people who do not want to complicate their lives may try to persuade you that what you are saying cannot be so or that it is not possible that the accused person could do such things. **Do not get discouraged.** It is a common reaction that should not stop your efforts to eliminate this social illness.

As soon as you decide to **file** a complaint with your company (which should be **immediate** if your harasser has not stopped after your statements), remember the following points:

- **Find out** if there is a policy and who, according to that policy, is **the person with whom you should file your complaint**. In this way, you will avoid having to talk to many people.
- **Accumulate records of the events**, with date and circumstances of all incidents of harassment. If you have received written notes or drawings, keep them as proof.
- **Think of witnesses** that may have been present when the harassing behaviour occurred.
- If your immediate superior does not listen to your complaint, **do not give up and go to higher levels** of administration. Nobody will blame you if you have followed due process. If you do not feel sure about going alone, ask a good friend to go with you.

Marital violence

Mistreatment in the context of the married couple is a **complicated problem** due to the following reasons:

- **It is more common than we imagine.** It is quite widespread, even though victims are usually silent. It is present in all social groups, and in all professions, cultures and religions.

- **The aggressor rarely changes** and, in spite of promises, tends to repeat the behaviour.

- The aggressor **suffers from low self-esteem** and compensates for this need by intimidating and hitting the spouse. This sense of power/authority favours relapse.

- The attacker **blames the victim**, arguing that she provoked him to violence.

- **The victim experiences feelings of anxiety**, despair, guilt, fear and shame. He/she denies the problem, holds onto false hopes of a solution, keeps quiet and perpetuates the suffering.

- The victim **does not realise the high level of risk he/she is taking**. And if she realises, she does not believe there is a way out and does not know what to do or to whom to go.

Prevention measures

Prevention should occur from several fronts: the victim, the perpetrator who wishes to recover, and friends and family of the couple.

If you are the victim

- Do not take signs and warnings lightly. Consult the box on the page 224. Assess your risks and seek help if you are in danger.

- Speak about this with an intimate friend or someone close to you.

Therapeutic limitation

A team of experts from the State University of New York conducted a comparative study (O'Leary *et al.*, 1999) between two types of therapy for the treatment of marital violence:

1. **Group therapy by gender.** Men and women participated separately in group therapy sessions and received instruction to prevent violence in the couple. This procedure presumed the responsibility of aggressors (males) teaching them how to control their impulses and other preventive strategies. The therapist of each group was of the same gender as participants.

2. **Couple-focused therapy.** Each couple privately attended the corresponding therapeutic sessions where neither of the two was presumed to be responsible for the violence. The plan was to teach skills to help in their relationship and to improve mutual communication. Therapy was carried out by two counsellors, a man and a woman.

Participants were made up of 75 volunteer couples where the male had displayed moderate or severe violence against the female partner in the previous 12 months. Each couple was assigned one of the therapeutic options and treatment progressed.

Results showed **no significant differences between one method and the other.** Both were moderately positive. By the end of the treatment, violence ceased in 39% of the couples. However, one year later, only 26% of couples were free from violence. Half of the couples abandoned the therapy, which is a normal rate in marital aggression treatment.

From this, as well as other similar studies, we can learn that...

- therapy only helps in a limited proportion of cases.
- results weaken with time.
- many abandon treatment.
- in the majority of serious cases, the intervention of social workers, police, and judicial measures are needed in order to free victims from danger.

- Observe your partner and the changes in his personality, words, messages, accusations, etc. that may announce violence.

- Prepare an emergency plan to protect yourself and your children in case of need.

- Arrange for a place (for example, the house of someone you trust) as a refuge in case things get complicated.

If you are the aggressor

- Examine the consequences that may result from your behaviour.

- Admit that you have a problem and that you need to seek professional help.

If you are a close friend or family of the victim

- Do not judge nor criticise her attitude or inability to face the problem.

- Spend time listening to her to understand her and to help her.

- Encourage her and let her know that she is not alone and she should not blame herself.

- Offer practical help: her children, her work, looking for a lawyer, for a refuge, etc.

- When advising, consider her personal safety and that of her children.

- Be patient, as changes may be quite slow.

How to solve the problem

In the first stages of marital violence, solution to the problem should be attempted through psychological intervention.

These are examples of psychological treatment for the *perpetrator*:

- **Thought control.** The aggressive husband must learn to identify thought content preceding violence. Impulses tend to follow negative thoughts towards his wife or after having observed some detail that he dislikes in her.

When such thoughts take over his mind, he needs to reject them and adopt non-dangerous thoughts. He can also instruct himself: 'Calm down, Martin, go take a walk to relax yourself…'

- **Behavioural plan.** The behaviour of the aggressor tends to feed itself with details, events, observations or behaviours that serve as stimuli. The goal is to identify these and avoid them. In this way, the chain leading to the violence is broken.

These stimuli may be certain types of readings or movies, the company of someone else, the use of alcoholic beverages, visiting certain places or the submissive attitude of the victim-spouse.

- **Self-concept enhancement.** The perpetrator normally suffers from serious self-esteem deficiencies and needs to develop self-esteem in a healthy manner.

He needs to embark upon constructive tasks that bring self-confidence. He also needs words and gestures of approval when he manages to do things well and when he makes progress towards the freedom from aggressive behaviour.

Likewise, the *victim* needs to introduce changes to support her husband's recovery or to leave the relationship if necessary:

- **Self-esteem development.** It is necessary that the victim, in spite of her situation, be reassured that she has dignity, talent, and possesses value and desirable qualities… She needs to focus on such ideas and reject all adverse thoughts towards herself.

DOES YOUR PARTNER BEHAVE LIKE THIS?

Does he...

1. often use harsh and accusing words against you?
2. play heavy jokes on you in the presence of other people?
3. make fun of you and your family?
4. insult you when he is angry?
5. blame you when he becomes angry?
6. control everything you do, where you go and who are you with?
7. threaten you with hitting you and your children?
8. tell you that jealousy is a sign of love?
9. put pressure on you to make love when you do not wish to do it?
10. hold you with strength and raise his voice?

If you have answered YES to more than one question, you could soon become the victim of physical violence from your spouse or boyfriend.

Practise preventive measures and prepare yourself and your children for protection in case of need.

- **Practise assertiveness.** She should gain practice in communicating with her husband, in a correct and firm manner, the limits—zero aggressive behaviour. She also needs to establish in clear terms what the consequence would be if he goes beyond the limit.

- **Prepare a way out from the crisis.** Women who are victims of abuse need to have a concrete plan to abandon the relationship with guarantee of personal safety in case he does not respect the ultimatum. Someone should be near to guide her through these difficult steps.

When the abusive behaviour does not cease, the alternative is of a legal and social nature. The perpetrator is **accused** and may be arrested and **processed** in a court of law. The victim needs advice to seek the most appropriate steps in her particular situation.

The abused spouse is offered refuge by local authorities, non-governmental organisations, or churches, in order to keep her and her children safe and to provide for their physical and emotional needs.

When the victim is a male...

More than 95% of cases of violence in couples are perpetrated by males upon females. However, there are situations where the male is victim of female violence. Typically, these are the steps followed by the male victim:

- The woman dominates her husband with her words, actions and attitudes. She shouts, insults and blames her husband.
- Verbal violence is transformed into physical violence and she hits, slams or kicks her husband.
- Even if he is stronger, he does not react violently. Using physical force on a woman would be abusive or cowardice.
- He feels uncomfortable in her presence and prefers to be away; he needs time to be alone and at peace.
- Psychological (rather than physical) pain increases because of the treatment received at the hand of his partner.
- He feels deep embarrassment and keeps quiet so that nobody finds out his humiliating situation.
- He thinks that if he were to tell people, they would probably not believe him and/or they would make fun of him.

Gems of Ancient Wisdom

'Husbands, love your wives and do not be harsh with them' (Colossians 3:19).

4.08
Stockholm syndrome

The Stockholm syndrome, or process of identification with the aggressor, is a contradictory phenomenon. It consists of the emotional attachment towards those who keep us captive or who exert violence against us. The name comes from an incident that happened in Stockholm, Sweden, in 1973 (see the box below).

This situation does **not only take place with hostages** but also with abused children, battered wives, prisoners of war, concentration camp captives and sect members.

These persons suffer abuse and humiliation; yet, they show **loyalty to those inflicting physical and psychological pain**. It is difficult to explain this attitude. This strange phenomenon may be due, in part, to the following characteristics shown by the victim, who:

1. Perceives the aggressor as a danger or threat.
2. Does not see a way of escape and adopts the unconscious attitude of befriending the aggressor as a possible way to stop the mistreatment.
3. Fears that any attempt to escape or confront the aggressor will cause the latter to retaliate. As a result, the victim opts for 'good relations.'
4. Observes some act of sympathy, kindness or tenderness in the aggressor, thus reinforcing faithfulness.
5. Hears the aggressor campaigning against those who want to rescue the victim (police or family). This influences the victim.

How to face Stockholm syndrome

In its original sense, Stockholm syndrome is rather rare. However, the concept is utilised **today** to understand those found in similar situations, **especially cases of battered wives** who seem unable to abandon the abusive relationship where they are receiving bad treatment (see page 222).

What to do in these cases?

Advice for her

- **Imagine life without him.** Make a rational analysis, managing life by yourself with the support of your family. If you have children, envision them out of the bad relationship.

The event that coined the term

Stockholm, 23rd August 1973. Two criminals, one of them a jail fugitive, entered a bank shooting at the air with automatic machine guns and shouting at the employees: 'The party has begun!' Assaulters took three women and one man as hostages, attaching dynamite to their bodies and keeping them inside a safe for more than five days.

After the liberation, the hostages, who had been threatened and mistreated, offered clear signs of loyalty to the kidnappers. During their captivity, they had developed a positive emotional attitude towards the aggressors, and they were convinced that the captors had protected them from the police. Furthermore, at the trial, one of the captive women organised a fundraising campaign in favour of the criminals.

This event led to the name *Stockholm syndrome* for the reaction of attraction towards the aggressors shown by mistreated, humiliated and captive people.

- **Nourish your self-esteem.** Think of your strengths, your determination and your love for your children (if you have children). Examine your achievements.

- In spite of the fact that your partner may not like it, **keep in contact with someone close** (for example, a lady friend) with whom you can talk and preserve your mental health.

- **Pray to God** and ask him to give you wisdom to make the best decision. Reflect on Ephesians 3:20: 'God is able to do immeasurably more than all we ask or imagine…'

Support to the victim

Family and close friends need to be available without interfering or precipitating events. Seeing that the woman is unable to break ties with the perpetrator may be frustrating to many, but it is necessary to be patient. In her irrational thinking, the victim sees her partner as a danger and, at the same time, as a refuge. She needs time and influence to see things clearly.

Of utmost importance is to remain in **regular contact** without inquiring too much about the relationship. In this way, she will realise that her family continues to love her and respect her and are available to help in case of need.

TEST YOURSELF ::

Answer YES or NO to the following questions to assess your risk to live in a relationship that could be categorised according to the Stockholm syndrome:

Am I a candidate for Stockholm syndrome?	YES	NO
1. Is your couple relationship the only way to survive physically and psychologically?		
2. If your relationship should suddenly break, would you be left in financial ruin?		
3. Has your partner shown abusive behaviour (extreme shouting, hitting you or objects) followed by repentance?		
4. Has he displayed tenderness and kindness soon after a violent episode?		
5. Has he ordered you not to talk with a certain friend or relative?		
6. Have you felt rejection towards your own family when they have advised you to leave your relationship?		
7. Have you thought of abandoning the relationship and considered yourself unable to do so?		
8. Has your partner threatened you with some extreme reaction if you leave him? (For example, 'If you leave me, I'll kill myself' or 'If you leave, I'll snatch your child').		

If you have responded YES to one or more questions, you may be in a dangerous relationship and it may be difficult for you to leave by yourself. Trust your situation to someone close or go to a psychologist or lawyer to obtain good advice.

4.09
Sexuality disorders

Given mutual attraction, the necessary stimuli (visual, tactile, etc.), a favourable environment and agreement, it is normal for a man and a woman to desire the initiation of sexual play leading to its consummation through intercourse and orgasm.

However, not all people experience this. There are those who, even with adequate stimulation, do not feel sexual desire. Others do feel the desire, but never reach orgasm and are frustrated. Still others feel disgust with anything related to sexuality, and this prevents a healthy sexual life.

Furthermore, there are men who experience a strong impulse to attain sexual satisfaction through ways other than the normal intimate encounter between a man and a woman. These individuals find satisfaction in strange ways, peeping at others who are unaware of the observation, using children as instruments of sexuality, or showing their genitals to an unknown passer-by. These are sexual deviations (or **paraphilias**) through which some attempt to achieve satisfaction, which is only partially attained due to the consequent remorse, psychological restlessness and relapse.

Sexual desire disorders

Heather's case is typical of **inhibited sexual desire**. After two years of being married and only occasionally having sex, Heather never has made love with desire. She always complains and does it to please her husband. Due to her prudish training, she considers sexuality as an animal passion with only procreative purposes. The extent of her problem sometimes gets to the point where she is horrified of sex, especially of intercourse. Although less frequent, there are also men that feel repulsion to touch their partner's genitalia or to attempt penetration.

Orgasmic disorder

This problem, experienced by both men and women, prevents the person from experiencing intense orgasmic pleasure. The affected individual feels sexual arousal and enjoys sexual play. But at the time of orgasm, he or she does not experience the corresponding climax and feels frus-

trated. The man with this disorder achieves erection and feels desire to continue. But once penetration has occurred, he does not feel pleasure and does not ejaculate. Eventually, he gives up out of boredom. Likewise, the woman feels sexual arousal, lubricates abundantly, but does not achieve orgasm through the action of the penis or by direct clitoral stimulation.

Exhibitionism

Exhibitionists (always males) attain sexual arousal by **showing their genitals** to an unknown woman without intent to touch her in any way. Her typically frightened reaction brings pleasure to the exhibitionist, who masturbates later on.

This type of man feels insecurity towards his sexual ability and himself. He feels ashamed after each act and vows to quit this practice. Often, he has had a troubled childhood with domineering, frightening parents who were closed-minded in sexual matters. The behaviour appears in moments of psychological tension or stress.

Voyeurism

The voyeuristic person attains sexual arousal **observing another person or persons in erotic situations**. Individuals are not aware of the presence of the 'peeping Tom.' This brings the observer even greater satisfaction. The majority of people with this disorder are heterosexual men of all civil statuses, who peep through windows, public toilets, on beaches or in parks where they end up masturbating. There is practically no risk of aggression. When an observed person finds out someone is looking, the voyeur runs away and loses his arousal. Like exhibitionism, voyeurism intensifies during times of anxiety and stress.

Paedophilia or abuse of minors

Paedophilia (also called paederasty) consists of reaching **sexual arousal through contact with a boy or girl** who does not wish or does not understand what is going on. Paedophiles are normally male, older than 35, who take sexual advantage of boys and girls of less than 12 years of

 *self-help*

HOW TO FACE SEXUAL DYSFUNCTIONS

Prevention

- **Provide balanced sexual education to children and adolescents.** Talk naturally and openly with them about sexuality and the responsibility it entails. A puritanical approach, full of taboos and secrets, favours sexual dysfunction in adulthood.

- **Protect children from any form of sexual abuse.** Being a victim of these traumatic experiences increases the risk of sexual dysfunction (see the Case below).

- **Encourage adolescents to postpone their first sexual experience.** On their first time, they normally do it quickly, with fear, with pain during penetration, and without true love and romanticism.

Facing the problem

- **Approach the sexual act in a relaxed manner, free from fear and apprehension.** Lack of sexual desire or lack of orgasm are increased by a nervous attitude or by anticipated failure of the sexual encounter.

- **Nourish your marital relationship.** You need his/her help in order to overcome disorders. A relationship full of love and understanding always helps sexual desire. Practise carefully and respectfully the sexual aspects that your partner enjoys.

- **Talk with your partner about these problems.** In the adequate place and moment, state your needs, fears and doubts. In many cases, the mere fact of talking brings about improvement.

- **Seek professional help.** Sometimes, the complexity of the problem necessitates the intervention of a specialist—a sexologist. He/she will teach the couple in the correct attitude, the preparation for loving foreplay, or the way to control the specific muscles involved. The specialist is an educator and will not ask for any demonstration. The couple is to practise in intimacy the advice given. They should return to the counselling office to report.

Sayings of Jesus

'And if anyone causes one of these little ones who believe in me to sin, it would be better for him to be thrown into the sea with a large millstone tied around his neck' (Mark 9:42).

age. He tricks the victim, promising toys or sweets if the child agrees to touch or be touched in erogenous areas. He sometimes achieves the sexual act. The aggressor ensures silence from the child by threatening to take revenge if the child says anything. Frequently, and because of fear, confusion and ignorance, children do not speak about this and end up suffering posttraumatic problems, sexual dysfunctions and general emotional instability.

Sexual abuse of children tends to happen in **family settings** and it is believed that 85% of the times the act is perpetrated by the father, grandfather, uncle or other adult relative. The frequency of the problem is often higher than believed, because the paedophile goes undetected. He is seen as a loving family member, a sociable neighbour, or the Boy Scout leader. The WHO estimates that the proportion of European women who have been object of this type of sexual abuse may be as high as 40% (and 20% for males).

PRACTICAL CASE

Woman with sexual aversion

The companion book of cases to the DSM-IV (1994) refers to the case of a woman with sexual aversion. She was young, married, and was unable to touch or even look at her husband's penis. Her problem started to improve after a strange event. When her uncle, a renowned musician, died, she attended his funeral, where speeches were made, lauding his creativity and great performances. When she heard the statements, she began to experience intense anger without knowing why.

Later on, she recalled something forgotten. During the lessons she had received as a child from her uncle, he took sexual advantage of her, teaching her to caress his penis to the rhythm of metronome.

In fear and confusion, she never said anything to her parents. Bringing these events to awareness was the beginning of her healing. She went to a sex therapist and talked about these things with her husband. This helped her to reach normality.

4.10
Competitiveness

Many people find themselves in competitive situations, fighting others in order to reach a goal, seeking a reward or gaining authority over others. Competitiveness may be present in business, politics, education, sports... Competitive contexts have some advantages (all questionable) and also disadvantages:

Advantages

- It is a source of motivation.
- It yields high achievement.
- It helps participants to enjoy the event(s).
- It helps in the selection of the most capable individuals (in politics, finances, etc.).

- It builds character and self-confidence.

Dangers

- It inflicts psychological pain to losers, as the winner reaches the goal at the expense of many who do not get there and whose self-esteem is diminished.
- It produces stress, which is good within reason, but which may easily become excessive in competitive situations.
- It favours unethical practices, such as doping in sports, corruption in politics, or lies in business.
- It promotes jealousy, mistrust, and disdain towards the opponent. It also limits one's capacity to love others.

Benefits of cooperation

A team of researchers carried out a study (Karlin, Brondolo and Schwartz, 2003) among 70 participants, all traffic police (male and female) in New York City. The objective was to study the **relationship between their cooperative efforts and blood pressure**. Police officers gave information on the quality and quantity of support and encouragement they received from their colleagues. Their blood pressure was taken every 15 minutes across the days when the study took place. Results showed a clear relationship between the support provided by colleagues and moderate blood pressure. In other words, those enjoying the understanding and help of peers had **less stress and better vascular health**.

Another study (Shui-Fong Lam *et al.*, 2004) is only a sample of many that have shown similar results: Competitiveness causes high achievement, but only under certain circumstances and always with several drawbacks. This team of researchers from the University of Hong Kong studied a group of 52 seventh-year students in their natural environment—the classroom. Pupils were assigned to one of two typing classes: a) competitive environment or b) non-competitive environment. Students in the competitive class achieved better results than their counterparts.

However, those in the competitive environment were focused only on the results, and were not interested in learning more and better. Furthermore, 'being defeated' caused these students to evaluate their ability negatively, something that did not happen among the non-competitive group. Levels of activity enjoyment were also lower among competitive students.

How to attain achievements in non-competitive contexts

The best alternatives are **cooperation** and **'competition' with oneself**. The results may always be compared with those obtained in competitive contexts, but without the side effects of competitiveness. Consider the following strategies:

- **Become accustomed to teamwork**, as the variety of skills and perspectives will enrich both the process and the outcome.

- **Organise cooperative activities** in order to distribute tasks according to the various capacities represented in the team.

- **Work in cooperation**, as this environment permits the exploration of new ideas, risk-taking behaviours and the application of creativity, all without the fear of failure, as the team approach supports each member and there is no single winner or loser.

- **Negotiate, support and cooperate.** These behaviours enhance the probability of success and ensure growth of relationships, so important for mental health.

- **Apply your efforts towards the established goals for your team** and avoid being influenced by the goals and actions of your opponents.

- **Practise fellowship**, friendship and care.

- **Encourage others (even your opponents) to obtain higher achievement**, as the better the result, the greater the benefit for all.

- **Avoid obsession with the final result** and try to do everything thoroughly. Quality will result without anguish or anxiety.

Gems of Ancient Wisdom

'Carry each other's burdens, and in this way you will fulfil the law of Christ' (Galatians 6:2).

'Do nothing out of selfish ambition or vain conceit, but in humility consider others better than yourselves' (Philippians 2:3).

4.11
Kleptomania

A strange impulse

Kleptomania is the **inability to resist the impulse to steal**. This motivation does not come out of necessity, nor as a rejection to or revenge against the shopping business. The affected person experiences a very strong desire to go to a shop, pick up something and take it without paying for it. At the beginning, shoplifting is for items of small value. Then the cost progressively increases because the greater the value, the more intense the thrill.

Once out of danger, stolen objects are given to others or stored in a hidden place. The kleptomaniac finds reward, not in the stolen item, but through strong emotional arousal before, during and after the act. Kleptomania is also an anomalous way to discharge tension. It is believed that the root of this behaviour is in internal conflicts that cause emotional unbalance.

The problem tends to appear early in life, during childhood or adolescence, and continues for years. This happened to Cassandra, member of a wealthy family and with no need of anything. However, one day when she felt very anxious and burdened with tension, she felt the impulse to steal and she successfully accomplished the deed. Since then, she utilised the same technique hundreds of times to find excitement and relaxation. Finally, she went to the psychiatrist, but only after she was caught.

RESEARCH RESULTS

Kleptomania is not usually the only anomaly

A comparative study (Bayle *et al.*, 2003) between patients with kleptomania and patients with a variety of psychiatric disorders revealed that patients with kleptomania had the highest co-morbidity rate between this disorder and…
- chemical addiction.
- depression.
- other types of impulse-control disorders (violent episodes, pathological gambling, self-mutilation and pyromania).

THE MAJORITY OF THIEVES ARE NOT KLEPTOMANIACS

Shoplifting is a growing problem with serious implications to consumers. Many are mistaken into thinking that a great number of people practising shoplifting are kleptomaniacs.

Even delinquents attempt to present this condition as an excuse and to plead innocence. However, clinical data show that **less than 5%** of thieves are kleptomaniacs.

Treatment for kleptomania

The most promising form of treatment includes both psychological and medical approaches. These are the steps followed in **psychological interventions**:

1. **Firm prohibition of stealing**, not granting the patient any option to use this as an escape from adverse feelings.

2. **Use of skills** such as thought control, relaxation, and distraction **to overcome the shoplifting impulse**.

3. **Deep psychotherapy sessions** in order to find out and eliminate the likely root of the pathological behaviour.

4. **Treatment of other co-morbidities** that often accompany kleptomania, such as depression and drug addiction and dependence, which are among the most common.

The other approach is **medical (psychiatric)** and consists of prescribing drugs to alleviate the impulse that leads to stealing. The following drugs have helped many to reduce their impulse. However, before using them, consult your doctor or psychiatrist:

1. **Tricyclic antidepressants** (for example, imipramine and nortriptyline).

2. **Serotonin reuptake inhibitors** (for example, fluvoxamine, paroxetine and fluoxetine, widely known as Prozac®).

3. **Lithium salt**, a medication utilised for manic depression.

ANTI-DEPRESSANT INGREDIENTS FOR KLEPTOMANIA

Results of several studies (Christensen, 1993 and 1997; Christensen and Redig, 1993; Markus *et al.*, 1998; Young, 1993) have revealed that the intake of foods high in tryptophan and folate have a benign effect upon depression.

Since many chemicals used to treat kleptomania are also antidepressants, the following, in their natural state, may be beneficial to reduce kleptomania:

- **Tryptophan.** This substance is contained in all types of grains, legumes and roots.
- **Folate** (folacin or folic acid). It is a form of vitamin B, present in high proportion in chickpeas (garbanzos), lentils and kiwi.

TO OVERCOME THE HABIT

- **Make the decision to completely give up** the behaviour.
- Use **self-control techniques**: reject the thoughts that lead to stealing, reduce the amount of free time, keep busy, enjoy simple activities.
- **Avoid the use of alcohol and nicotine.** They can make you lose control.
- **Seek help from a friend or family member** to support you and observe you during the difficult process of overcoming the habit.
- **Join an organised group** of Kleptomaniacs Anonymous (see page 316).
- **Solve old problems** and relational conflicts that may be in your past.

4.12

Affective loneliness

Even though it may sound like a paradox in our overpopulated world, many suffer from loneliness.

Grace is single and 40 years of age. She lives alone. Her mother passed away a few months ago; eventually, the sorrow caused by this loss came to an end. However, Grace feels lonely and longs for company. A great deal of her time is occupied by professional activities. She maintains good relationships with her companions. She gets along with her siblings, nephews and nieces. Nevertheless, when she gets home, she feels sad and overcome by a sensation of loneliness and isolation that she fears is going to end up in depression.

There are persons who do not mind being alone. They engage in occasional social contacts and enjoy the independence and freedom of being alone. However, loneliness is a source of pain and imbalance to many.

Who runs the highest risk?

It is normal and natural for human beings to live in company and receive benefit from their social environment. But lack of social interaction affects different people differently. Who tends to especially suffer from loneliness?

- **Those with a dependent personality.** Those with a natural need for affirmation and encouragement from friends and family suffer from loneliness and experience feelings of inadequacy, sadness, insomnia, lack of appetite (or excessive appetite), and despair.

- **Those in an isolated profession.** There are occupations that require prolonged absence from home and place the person in a situation of risk. There are also professions of a solitary nature—long-distance lorry driver, ranger, cattle herder, lighthouse operator, etc.—that require long hours of aloneness.

- **Those living alone.** Being single, widowed or divorced force many into the circumstance of living alone, and such people may end up suffering from loneliness. A growing tendency, due to the high price of accommodation, is to share a house in order to reduce expenses. This arrangement may become an added benefit to prevent loneliness.

- **Those living in urban settings.** Big cities, with the highest density of population, have increased levels of affective loneliness. Living in the city

leads to isolation and contributes to the loneliness of many.

- **Information technology users.** Many spend long hours before the computer and exhaust the opportunity to spend time relating face to face with other people. This may also cause affective loneliness.

- **Elderly people.** With retirement there is a tendency to isolation. The gap of separation from younger generations widens and the quantity and quality of company diminishes. This may affect health (see the box on the bottom of this page).

How to face loneliness

Loneliness can be alleviated and eliminated. Try the following tips:

- **Be the first to search for friendship.** Instead of waiting for others to come to you, take the first step. Suggest some specific activity (sport, game, walk, or invite someone to your home). Do not make encounters too long in order not to tire others. Observe whether the relationship develops.

- **Study your attitude and behaviour.** Have you ever thought whether you are a barrier to your friendships? Reflect intimately on your behaviour with friends and family. Ask yourself:

✓ Are my opinions negative or hopeful?
✓ Do I show interest in the other person or do I just speak of myself?
✓ Do I often smile or keep a sombre face?
✓ Am I willing to offer my help or am I constantly asking for help?
✓ Do I do things as I want or am I open to the suggestions of others?

- **Do not think of rejection.** Children establish friendships instantly because they do not worry whether or not they will be accepted. Show a forthright, sincere and frank attitude.

- **Try to join a volunteer work group.** Persons who offer their time and abilities to help others are easily accepted. If you join one of these groups, you may be able to solve your problem of loneliness, apart from rendering a service.

- **Seek spiritual support.** If you are a believer, talk to God as to a friend. Prayer is better than chanting (or reciting). In your prayers, express openly and sincerely your fears and most intimate dissatisfactions. The Bible assures us that for those with faith in God everything is possible, even finding a solution to the problem of loneliness.

Gems of Ancient Wisdom

'Though my father and mother forsake me, the LORD *will receive me' (Psalms 27:10).*

RESEARCH RESULTS
Loneliness and cardiovascular disease

A study (Sorkin, Rook and Lu, 2002) carried out by researchers at the University of California at Irving showed the existing relationship between loneliness and cardiovascular disease. A group of 180 senior citizens, who had an average age of 70 and who resided in assisted living centres, participated in this longitudinal study on health. By means of one-and-a-half-hour interviews, medical examinations, self-control records, the UCLA lonely scale, together with other psychological tests, data were collected on loneliness rates and the probability to suffer from any coronary disease.

The results revealed that **the greater the loneliness level, the higher the risk of coronary ailment**. Therefore, it is extremely important that people (especially those who are elderly) have an optimal level of social support in order to enjoy a healthy heart.

4.13
Envy

- Slanders the envied person.
- Tends to perceive his/her own achievements as insignificant.
- Tends to perceive others' achievements in an exaggerated way.

There are persons who look in admiration at the attainments of others, wishing to reach similar levels. This should not necessarily be considered as envy. In fact, it may help someone to achieve great goals. Or it may become a healthy way to channel envy. It can be dangerous, however, if taken to an extreme.

How to overcome envy

Eradicating envy cultivated through years of habit takes time and requires perseverance. It can be achieved, however, through a **thinking and action plan**, including the following components:

1. **Enjoy what is yours.** Whatever one is or has is always relative when compared to that of others. Do not covet what others have, as it is dangerous. Examine your qualities and belongings; recognise their value and the happiness that they bring to you. This is positive, edifying and helps to prevent feelings of envy.

2. **Perform altruistic acts.** Envy may be effectively fought by performing unselfish acts for the envied person. This seems like a difficult step but its effect against envy is very clear.

Charles envied his work colleague with all his soul. He envied his personal assuredness, intelligence and material wealth. When the wife of this colleague suffered an accident, other mates (in-

Envy is a very common tendency and it causes negative effects upon physical and mental health. It appears at a very early age (it is already present in infants who are 8-10 months of age) and tends to remain for years. People tend to hide it, as it is considered socially unacceptable. These are some typical behaviours of the envious. He or she:

- Wishes vehemently to possess the attributes or belongings of others.
- Tends to have a secret plan to obtain what he/she envies.
- Experiences a negative attitude towards the envied person.
- Becomes happy with the opponent's failure and sad with his/her achievements.
- Uses sarcasm (at times silence) towards the envied person.

cluding Charles) set up a rota to help the family. In the middle of the busy activity, Charles felt great relief from his envy and understood that it was helping to free him from this problem.

3. **Practise healthy praise.** The achievements of others may serve as a source of motivation to attain our own aims. If you experience envy, make an effort to transform it into an incentive for you to reach high aims, moving away from the negative emotions that accompany it.

4. **Set up personal goals and aims.** If your ends and means are clear, other people's actions will influence very little. But if you lack a plan for your life, the impression of success that you observe in others will adversely affect you.

5. **Understand that the other person also has problems.** In rural contexts, it is said that the grass is greener on the other side of the fence. Even when the qualities and possessions of others may impress you, remember that what looks enviable may be disagreeable.

ENVY DOES NOT STAND ALONE

Envious persons tend to possess other adverse characteristics. It is therefore good to avoid envy as it may come accompanied with the following feelings:

- **Selfishness.** The envious is constantly self-centred and lives with the desire to obtain what legitimately belongs to others.
- **Anxiety.** The envious suffers from fear and uncertainty about the future, as he/she does not know whether he/she will be or have more than his opponent.
- **Inferiority.** The envious person is not happy with him/herself. His/Her self-concept is frail, feels inferior to his/her counterpart, and wishes harm to this person while imagining his/her own self-exaltation.
- **Immaturity.** Those who suffer from envy are unable to reason as intelligent persons, unable to put themselves in the others' shoes, and to think of the person apart from his/her possessions.

Gems of Ancient Wisdom

'A heart at peace gives life to the body, but envy rots the bones' (Proverbs 14:30).

BIBLICAL EXAMPLE

Joseph's brothers

The patriarch Jacob had 12 sons and he loved Joseph the most of all. This fact deeply bothered the older brothers, to the point that they hated him.

As if it were not enough, one day Joseph told his brothers about a dream he had. The dream seemed to announce that in the future he would rule over his brothers (later fulfilled). Then he had another similar dream and he again conveyed it to his brothers. The Bible says that Joseph's brothers envied him. As a result, they decided to kill him when they were away in the country. But they changed their minds and resolved to take away his robe, and to sell him to traders. They stained his robe with goat's blood and showed it to their father to make him believe that a ferocious animal had devoured him. This filled Jacob with sorrow.

Although the story of Joseph and his brothers contains elements of jealousy, this is a very clear case of envy. The full account is in the book of Genesis, chapter 37. (See also the Biblical Example box on page 116).

4.14

Living in multicultural settings

The history of mankind has always witnessed cultural and racial pluralism as peoples move from place to place due to various reasons. At their arrival at a new destination, they encounter other groups who have settled prior to them. The resulting mix always produces **tension**. The original settlers claim their right to the available resources for themselves and for their families. This tends to create conflict that affects latecomers in a special way.

Multicultural life is widespread today. The many wars and tribal conflicts throughout the 20th century, religious and political intolerance, labour diversification, seasonal migration and the availability of transportation and communication have caused this problem to grow immensely. And this reality has created the need to solve the subsequent problems.

Whenever there is an **open, flexible and understanding attitude**, results may be optimal. However, when the outlook is purely selfish, the

CONSEQUENCES OF A XENOPHOBIC ATTITUDE

Racism and xenophobia never solve the difference between individuals of contrasting cultural backgrounds. Furthermore, they produce feelings and emotions of great danger to physical and mental health. These are a few examples:

- **Dogmatism.** This is the rigid drive to impose one's own ideas. When this is not achieved, dogmatic persons experience frustration and anger.
- **Intolerance.** This is the disapproval of what others think. It causes discomfort and impedes any opportunity to learn from others.
- **Rivalry.** This is the unhealthy desire to be better than the neighbour. It produces low achievement, resentment and stress.

- **Hostility.** This is the classification of the opponent as enemy. This personality style is known in psychology as 'type A,' and is associated with coronary disease.
- **Hatred.** This is a very adverse xenophobic reaction—the antithesis of love. It produces unhappiness and favours the development of psychosomatic diseases.
- **Violence.** This is physical or verbal aggression, which can be classified as a crime, and one in which a xenophobe may find him/herself involved.

outcome is **racism** and **xenophobia**. The consequences are outlined in the box on the previous page.

How to promote intercultural and interracial life

Good legislation that protects minorities from discrimination is very important. Also, the provision of certain privileges or subsidies to those who are more susceptible of becoming marginalised ('positive discrimination') is fundamental. But these are only the first steps. Authentic multicultural promotion happens when traditional institutions provide a **thorough education of respect and acceptance** of all races and cultures. These institutions are:

- school
- family
- mass media
- state

Lastly, the application of **Christian ideals** at all levels is a sure solution to promote multiculturalism. Although very often Christians do not live up to the standard of their beliefs, Christianity can offer the most reliable guide to live in community, provided that it is not applied by force.

To follow Jesus' teachings is a guarantee of success not only among races and cultures, but for all types of human relationships, as well. These are some basic Christian ideals: **love** (to friends and enemies), **peace** (not only as absence of war, but as a way of life and interaction) and **understanding** of all tiers of class, race, culture, religion, age, gender and lifestyle.

BEWARE OF CULTURAL ASSIMILATION

Cultural assimilation is one of the goals of societies that receive immigrants. For example, it is expected that an Ecuadorian family, who go to Spain in search of work and a future, become 'assimilated' into the Spanish culture and customs. In other words, they should begin to think and behave like Spaniards.

However this is a limited concept that prevents full cultural enrichment. It is true that those arriving should **accept norms and customs from the host country**. However, ideally, both cultures would accept the good from each other. Local people can benefit from the contribution of immigrants.

Gems of Ancient Wisdom

'When an alien lives with you in your land, do not mistreat him. The alien living with you must be treated as one of your native-born. Love him as yourself, for you were aliens in Egypt. I am the LORD your God' (Leviticus 19:33, 34).

'There is neither Jew nor Greek, slave nor free, male nor female, for you are all one in Christ Jesus' (Galatians 3:28).

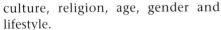

Chapter Summary

How to face challenges (resilience)

5

Steve lost his job three months ago. For weeks, there had been the threat of retrenching at the information technology company where he worked. All that time Steve feared the worst. Finally, he and a dozen others were laid off. The first few weeks were very busy: sending his curriculum vitae everywhere, visiting firms, talking to friends to find possibilities of employment... But when he did not obtain immediate results, he became discouraged. In a state of constant dejection, he could not sleep, had no appetite, and did not have aspirations for anything... He was always plagued with the thought that he would never find a job again. His self-esteem was at its lowest and he started to use alcohol as a refuge.

His wife was instrumental in helping him to rise above his discouragement. With patience and much care, she brought him hope for the future. She reminded him of his many past achievements, she helped him in the task of looking for employment and she was closely involved in his preparation for the job interviews. She also helped him to stay active, thus avoiding too much rumination. With this assistance, Steve regained his self-confidence, put drinking aside and he soon found a temporary job. This is not the goal of his life, but now Steve knows that he will find a regular and well-paying job.

Chapter Highlights

- In the midst of adversity we should understand it is a **universal** phenomenon, not being too demanding on ourselves, and considering the **finiteness** of problems.

- The resilient patient **fights** the disease, follows medical advice, gains courage and finds support in others. In this way, he/she can overcome or at least neutralise the illness' effects.

- There are people who prefer not to think or talk about death, as they view it as unpleasant. However, a **balanced dialogue** about it can help one to face it.

- Lack of activity is a strong obstacle to combating pain and suffering. In most cases, it is better to break the pain barrier and the accompanying vicious circle.

- The feelings related to divorce are typical when experiencing a **loss**. If you are in the midst of divorce, you should understand that all these events are normal and will not last forever.

- Parents of small children are in the best position to guide their children in the path of **peaceful relationships**. Teachers of preschool children can also take this important role.

- The **impact of war** is such that the person needs to adopt measures concerning his/her mental attitude facing the conflict, behaviour during the conflict, and also after it.

Resistance and overcoming

It is hard to explain how an outcast or marginalised individual resists the effect of misfortune, obtaining strength to reach goals against all odds. This is not a natural pattern in human expectations.

The same can be said of people directly affected by violence or natural disaster who resist the impact of trauma and recover, showing strength superior to individuals who have not been submitted to devastating circumstances.

This power to overcome stress caused by extremely difficult situations and to bounce back victoriously in spite of adversity is called **resilience**. This chapter deals with a variety of difficult situations that can happen to anyone. It offers suggestions on how the affected person can use resilience to bounce back and rebuild his/her life.

Terminal or chronic disease (unit 5.01), or the panic associated with epidemics, may be even worse than death itself. Those touched by such situations need to follow practical steps of resilience. And not only those affected by illness, but the people near them… Family, nurses, neighbours, friends… can all be instruments of great relief. To face such situations, one needs to be equipped with thorough preparation.

The **death of a dear one** (unit 5.02) is one of the strongest stressors experienced by most people. In addition, everyone will one day be called upon to face their **own death** and can learn to approach it with dignity.

Negative situations (unit 5.03), such as **divorce** (unit 5.08), bankruptcy, **unemployment** (5.07), **single-parent families** (5.09) and many other experiences, can bring much **suffering** (5.04). Preparation is required to face these problems so as not to allow one to be ruined by circumstances. Instead, when adversities are taken as a challenge and with a good amount of resilience, the person can end up in a better position than before the negative experience.

Work and traffic **accidents** (unit 5.05) are the cause of many handicaps and death. Victims of accidents, together with the persons caring for them, need to have an attitude that allows them to take these unanticipated misfortunes, survive, and redo their lives successfully.

These days, more of the population seem to be facing catastrophe of one form or another. A great deal of resilience is needed to face such circumstances. Only a few generations ago, **terrorism** (unit 5.06) was relegated to isolated and specific situations. Today, it crosses all geographic boundaries, and has become a universal reality that affects everyone. Knowledge about how to respond is needed if one is to survive a terrorist attack or help others to do so. All of us need to be prepared for such an eventuality.

Street and school **violence** (unit 5.10) is a growing phenomenon and it must be prevented. Children and adolescents should know what to do in order to avoid being victims of aggression. Likewise, it is necessary to have therapeutic means and self-help strategies in place for victims of this serious problem.

Human beings have little control over the occurrence of **natural catastrophes** (unit 5.11) which have increased in recent decades. These unexpected events take the lives of many and leave others unprotected— orphans, widows and people subject to risk of illness and death. Such traumatic situations demand much resilience on the part of the affected person, as well as a helping hand from those who have not been touched by calamity.

War is even more disturbing (unit 5.12), as it is obvious that, unlike natural disasters or accidents, it is man who determines whether or not to go to war. Victims, who are almost always detached from the ideological or political reasons behind the war, must try to survive in the midst of confusion and suffering. Here also, resilience plays a fundamental role in surviving the devastating effects of hostile encounters.

Illness

The mood of the ill person affects, to a great extent, the course of the illness. It is well known in the medical community that people who show a positive outlook and a desire to live strengthen their immune system and resist illness better.

It is also known that patients have a greater probability of overcoming illness if they possess a good social support system and a hopeful attitude.

When a patient receives the diagnosis of a serious disease, the course may follow very different paths depending on his/her personal reaction. Where there is lack of resilience, the patient is filled with **fear**, **anxiety**, and **negative worry**. Thoughts become sombre and defences weaken. The illness takes over and causes fatal consequences.

On the other hand, the resilient patient fights the disease, follows medical advice, gains courage and finds support in others. In this way, he/she can overcome or at least neutralise the illness' effects.

How to face illness

If you have been diagnosed with a serious disease, you should understand that your attitude will affect its course.

The following tips are helpful for those fighting disease:

- **Practise cheerfulness.** Try by all means to entertain a good disposition. Visit healthy and lively places, relate to people who are cheerful and manage your thoughts so that they do not end up in negativity or despair.

- **Cultivate hope but do not forget reality.** An attitude of hope and the certainty that you will overcome the disease are decisive factors to achieve wellness.

Think of recovery and you will see your condition improve. But be careful not to set your expectations too high (see the box on the adjoining page).

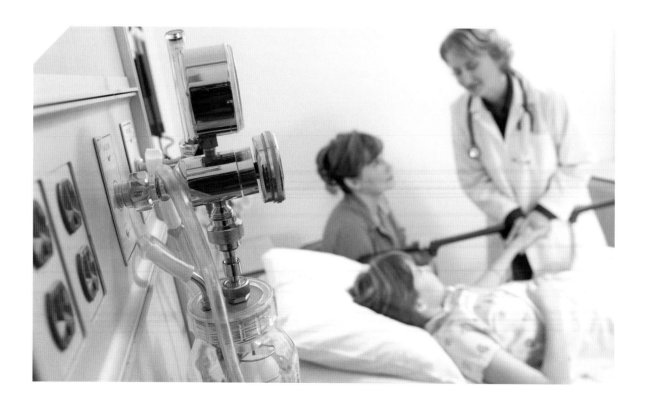

- **Seek support in others.** The role that loved ones play in the course of treatment of the ill is clearly and decisively shown in many studies. Many experts consider this as the number one factor. Therefore, seek the company of persons who love you and understand you. Speak with them about your illness, your feelings and your expectations. If you are friends with an individual who is ill, make efforts to be with and encourage him/her.

- **Maintain a reasonable level of activity.** Except in extreme cases, the sick person can continue to contribute and do useful things. It may be reading, writing, a house chore, a pastime, telling a children's story, or whatever. A useful activity is extremely important towards healing and to favour general well-being.

- **Seek spiritual support.** Faith in a caring and loving God is a crucial factor in support and healing. Try praying to God in submission, asking for your hopes and desires. If you are not used to doing this, ask a religious person to pray with you.

How to help others

Many times the illness does not affect us directly, but a **family member or friend** suffers from a chronic or severe disease. In these cases, the sick requires emotional support and strength from loved ones.

If you are in this situation or know someone who is, try the following suggestions:

- **Listen to the ill person.** Not all sick are willing to talk, but if they are, listen attentively to them, showing interest and an open attitude. When they cannot talk, you can speak in calmness and serenity. Hold their hand and show your care and closeness.

- **Talk about the illness.** When the right moment comes, talk openly about the illness, its prognosis, symptoms and treatment alternatives. The patient needs information in order to choose alternatives and prepare mentally at each step. He/she may ask for your opinion; if so, you should use your judgement to present your viewpoint.

- **Do not scold.** It is normal that patients complain, and some may even curse the doctors or God. Do not reply with sermons. Rather, listen carefully and try to understand how the patient feels and why he/she speaks that way. If you notice that the conversation is affecting them too negatively, carefully try to change the topic.

- **Carry out an activity with the patient.** If the person likes to read, play a game or pastime, or watch TV, accompany him/her whenever possible and be patient even though you may have more 'important' things to do.

- **Connect with the patient's social circle.** Become friends with the patient's friends and relatives. This attitude will expand your social network and will strengthen relationships.

RESEARCH RESULTS

Beware of expectations that are too high

Karin Nordin and her associates at the University of Uppsala in Sweden worked with a group of 85 patients who had been diagnosed with gastrointestinal cancer. Together with the patients, a number of spouses also responded to questionnaires.

The goal of the study (Nordin *et al.*, 2001) was to ascertain the level of satisfaction produced by values such as harmony, relationships, mobility and future expectations.

Data were collected at the time patients became aware of the diagnosis, one month later, and two months later. One of the most revealing findings was that **patients who were able to reduce their expectations** and adjust to their new condition as cancer patients experienced **more satisfaction, less anxiety and less depression** than those who aspired to a total and absolute recovery.

In order to avoid deep disappointment if you suffer from a serious disease, you should understand that pathologies tend to leave sequels and that an absolute and complete recovery is improbable. Adjust your expectations to reach a notable improvement that allows a reasonable quality of life, albeit not perfect.

self-help

THE PATIENT'S FEELINGS

What should you do with those feelings and emotions that overtake a severely ill patient? Whether you are the patient or a friend/relative, the following emotions are very common and you should be ready to face them:

- **Denial.** Any traumatic situation, including the news of a serious disease, may cause the patient to deny reality. It is important to make a special effort to accept and face the situation without thinking that it is something impossible. We should explain to the patient that the diagnosis is firm and there is no use in denying it.
- **Fear.** Fears of disability, pain or death are common in the ill. The best way to combat this feeling is through the support of a close friend or loved one giving the assurance that he/she will be there no matter what happens.
- **Anger, rage.** The patient tends to get angry and curse life and God. We should not scold the patient for such an attitude, as it is a natural reaction to pain,

frustration and a sense of injustice that can overcome the patient.

- **Guilt.** Feeling guilty for having done something wrong and believing that the illness is a punishment is also common. We must assure the patient that the ailment does not have to be linked to something one has done. Evil is ever present and often touches people indiscriminately. And even when the patient bears responsibility for the illness (for instance, a drinker suffering from cirrhosis of the liver), he/she needs to understand that God is willing to forgive him/her and grant faith and hope in the resurrection as well as eternal life.

The best attitude is **acceptance of reality**. This does not mean giving up and abandoning oneself to fate, but to face challenges, remembering that there are certain limitations that may not be avoidable.

How to prevent alarm

A tale from the 14th century (the time when the black plague razed the entire European continent and eliminated a fourth of the population) tells that a traveller walked by night to London. In the midst of the darkness he met two strangers with whom he started to converse and he soon learned that they were Plague and Fear. 'We are ready to kill about 10,000 souls in London over the next few days,' stated Plague. The traveller replied: 'You yourself will carry out the slaughter, will you?' 'No,' replied Plague straight away, 'I will snatch the lives of one or two thousand. Fear will take care of the rest.'

Television, newspapers, radio and the Internet effectively contribute to diffuse news that affect

public health. This may become highly beneficial, especially when news is accompanied by preventive measures to avoid illness. But massive dissemination produces **undue alarm**. Mad cow disease and bird flu epidemics were lived by many with great apprehension. Consider the following points in order to avoid becoming a victim of the lack of control associated with epidemics:

- **Avoid exaggerations and undue alarms.** Collective panic is never good and you should understand that the public easily loses objectivity and good judgement with alarming news, especially when it touches health and life. At such moments, keep calm and remember that the outreach of any epidemics is limited.

- **Practise preventive measures.** You will not attain anything if you worry or become frightened. Furthermore, this attitude will lower your defences. Adopting preventive and hygienic measures to avoid contagion are actions that will help you. Therefore, apply the steps recommended by qualified personnel.

- **Lead a normal life.** You do not need to change your routine substantially; just include the necessary preventive measures and get on with your normal daily activities.

- **Practise positive thinking.** Avoid thoughts of dread and doom. Do not ruminate too much on the idea of contracting the disease or being touched by the epidemic. Distract yourself with other topics and keep on living with confidence.

Gems of Ancient Wisdom

'A man's spirit sustains him in sickness, but a crushed spirit who can bear?' (Proverbs 18:14).

Facing disease

David Spiegel, of Stanford University, has investigated in detail the effect of social factors upon patients with a diagnosis of cancer.

The conclusion is clear: People who enjoy a **positive social environment** extend their lifespan remarkably, as compared with those who lack such support. Specifically, this favourable social support comes in various ways:

- The opportunity to express fears and uncertainties to a close friend.
- The chance to relate to another patient with a similar disease who has learned to bear his/her disease with patience, hope and dignity.
- The availability of family to listen and encourage the patient.

According to **Spiegel**, this support system works for four reasons:

1. The closeness of a friend or relative adds a **practical supplement to medical treatment**. He/she accompanies the patient in the therapy, reminds the patient of the medication and other medical treatments. The general attitude towards the treatment plan becomes more positive and this benefits the patient.

2. Family or friends **help** the patient to lead a **healthy lifestyle** beyond the medical treatment. This encompasses dietary habits, physical exercise, pastimes, etc. In this way, the habits are better adopted and maintained than when they are strictly institutional.

3. The **effect** of social interaction upon the **endocrine system**. Research shows that the internal secretion system in terminal patients who enjoy a good social support context works more regularly and more efficiently than in the other patients.

4. The **effect** of social support upon the **immune system**. It is now known that the secretion of certain hormones (especially the stress hormones) weakens the defence system. Therefore, the mere presence of a loved one may drastically reduce the secretion of those substances, thus providing protection against health deterioration.

Let's add the **spiritual component** to the above list. Patients who believe in God, pray and trust in him view the future with hope, and face their health problems with completeness. Specifically, spiritual life through religious experience has been identified as an outstanding factor that favours good health, as well as helping to develop a better disposition that can accept the future.

5.02
Death

Death is a universal reality. From early in life everyone witnesses the death of others and learns that some day they will face their own death.

In spite of this, people possess a strong instinct for survival, which inspires the desire to live and a certain amount of fear towards dying.

There are those who view death with relative calm and seem hardly affected by it. However, others are tormented by the idea. Sometimes this is due to an existential fear—to cease to be.

Other times, it is caused by an anticipation of the physical pain that often accompanies the passage from life to death. Still other times, it is due to the sadness of separation from dear ones or for the possessions left behind.

How to prepare for death

There are people who prefer not to think or talk about the topic, as they view it as unpleasant. However, a balanced dialogue about death can help one to face it. If you want to be prepared for this inevitable reality, consider the following advice, especially if you suffer from a terminal disease or if you are advanced in age:

- **Seek an adequate social environment.** The presence of some loving family member or close friend is basic. Seek the company of persons willing to be near you and to carry out tasks with you. These people should transmit a cheerful attitude, ease and the desire to live.

- **Follow a regular routine and habits.** Your days should be marked by regular activity with only

continued on page 250

Death and life cycle

In the developmental life cycle, the idea of death evolves and is perceived differently at different stages:

- **Preschool stage.** Children observe that their pet dies or a relative passes away. However, death for them is transitory. They perceive it as something temporary and incomplete, like a dream. In any event, they may become victims of fear. How can we help them avoid fear? Preschoolers dread separation rather than death. We therefore must assure them that they will always be protected and that their parents will never abandon them.

- **School stage.** The school-age child understands death as something sad and permanent, without yet possessing a thorough understanding of its extent. How can we help them to understand death and overcome fear? Speak naturally when the topic arises, clarifying any mistake that the child may have. Explain death as something sad. Do not avoid the topic or treat it as something that is taboo. Believers should explain God's revealed promise of a final resurrection and eternal life.

- **Adolescence.** The adolescent understands death as a definitive, universal, and unavoidable event. Most adolescents do not fear death. Others, even though full of life and youth, may experience a dreadful fear to die. They think of an illness in terms of fatal consequences. What can we do to support adolescents? Allow them to express themselves freely and encourage dialogue on the topic without rejecting their feelings towards death. It is healthy for the adolescent to attend the funeral of a friend or relative in order to feel the extent of the situation. This type of event causes dialogue, which helps to diminish fear.

- **Adulthood.** Adults have a full understanding of death. This is not only general, but specific to death as it will affect them. Under normal circumstances, adults see death as something distant. But they are also aware that illness or accidents may cause it to happen prematurely. What can one do in the face of terminal disease? When an illness that may limit the years of life is diagnosed, it is necessary to look at the past with satisfaction, gratitude and a forgiving attitude to those who may have hurt us. As for the future, it is best to maintain a desire to live as fully as possible, while at the same time maintaining faith in the face of premature death.

- **Old age.** Seniors understand that death is an inescapable reality that may arrive at any moment. Some elderly experience despair, depression, and even contemplate suicide. How can one face death with dignity? Adopt an attitude of gratefulness for having reached old age in a world filled by accidents and illnesses. Reflect on one's own life in calm, never regretting the past. Avoid disappointment over things that did not turn out as one would have wished (which is a futile exercise). Lastly, it is necessary to gaze at the remainder of life with hope.

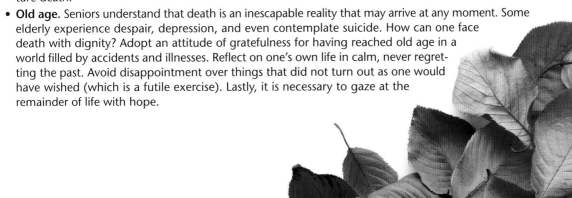

Gems of Ancient Wisdom

'There is a time for everything, and a season for every activity under heaven: a time to be born and a time to die' (Ecclesiastes 3:1-2).

continued from page 248

occasional variations. Depending on your personal capability, there should be more or less vigour in your activities. Avoid inactivity, which leads to weariness and despair.

- **Review your past life.** Thinking of the events of your past life is generally a beneficial activity, especially when reviewing pleasant events. Avoid focusing on unpleasant times. Do not give in to disappointing thoughts and do not wish that you had done things differently. If there were mistakes, you need to accept them in order to face the present and the future with serenity. If you offended or hurt others make sure you ask for forgiveness and obtain reconciliation. Repent from your behaviour and ask God for forgiveness—He is always willing to forgive.

- **Practise hope in a life beyond.** Belief in life after death is shown in many studies to be a beneficial factor in facing death with confidence (see the box below). To believe in eternal salvation and to know that by divine grace it is accessible to everyone is an antidote for despair when facing death. On the other hand, be careful, as believing in hell can lead to terror and discouragement (see the box 'Fear of hell' on the adjoining page).

RESEARCH RESULTS

Death and spirituality in cancer patients

In a study (Lin and Bauer-Wu, 2003) conducted at Harvard University School of Medicine, 43 primary investigations from 14 different countries were analysed. All studies focused on the spirituality of cancer patients at an advanced stage of their illness. The following components of psycho-spirituality were observed:

- Awareness of the spiritual component in their own lives.
- Capacity to face stress successfully.
- Ability to establish satisfactory social relations.
- Sensation of faith.
- Sensation of fortitude and trust.
- Vision of meaning and hope in life.

The study concludes that patients with **psycho-spiritual well-being** enjoy a **greater capacity to face terminal disease and death** than those who do not cultivate that facet. In order to promote psycho-spiritual well-being, the study proposes a good knowledge of the illness, the support from family and friends, a sense of autonomy, feelings of hope, and a sense of life's meaning.

How to help someone else to face death

Accompanying a loved one in the last steps towards death may become as difficult as facing one's own death. This task requires awareness and preparation. Consider the following advice if you are close to someone approaching death:

- **Be physically available.** Without doing any specific thing, just your sole presence will bring support and comfort to the dying person. The proximity of the loved one is the most precious gift that can be offered to him or her.

- **Speak about death if he/she so wishes.** Comments made by the dying person about his/her feelings towards their final departure must be accepted. Speak as naturally as you can and do not dodge the topic or change conversation. Transmit courage, warmth and hope. If possible, pray with the dying, as this will help to bring about peace and calm.

- **Recognise that anger or rage is normal.** The person may complain and even feel frustrated due to the illness. Do not criticise or sermonise. Be quiet and patient. Simply listen and try and draw his/her attention towards another topic or activity.

- **Be willing to listen.** Do not ignore the words of the person approaching death. The suffering individual that feels ignored will interpret this as a rejection.

- **Respect his/her dignity and will.** Unless affected by loss of mind, his/her desires and requests must be respected. Certain invasive medical treatments may be rejected by the person. Respect his/her will and do not try to impose your criterion, even when you think it is best for him/her. Make every effort to preserve his/her authority and dignity.

The last steps

Swiss psychiatrist **Elizabeth Kübler Ross** (1926-2004) dedicated her life to the study of the last phases of human existence. These are the steps observed by Dr. Kübler-Ross:

1. **Denial:** The person does not accept that death approaches.

2. **Anger:** The ill or elderly person feels anger towards the possible separation.

FEAR OF HELL

It is now known that religion and spirituality play a primordial role at the time of understanding and facing death—one's own and that of dear ones.

However, it has been observed that, at times, it is religion that favours fear and horror of death. For example, doctrines that teach everlasting hell with an eternal fire, or those portraying salvation as something difficult to achieve, along with teachings about the suffering that awaits those who are evil, all tend to create **anxiety and despair**.

The true biblical concept of redemption is far better: God accepts everyone, righteous and sinners. He forgives us and saves us from eternal death when, by faith, we accept his invitation to be saved.

Gems of Ancient Wisdom

'For the living know that they will die, but the dead know nothing; they have no further reward, and even the memory of them is forgotten' (Ecclesiastes 9:5).

'I will ransom them from the power of the grave; I will redeem them from death' (Hosea 13:14).

---

3. **Bargaining:** The person makes secret covenants with him/herself or with God to prolong life.

4. **Depression:** He/she experiences sorrow as death approaches. The person now wishes for death to come soon and even sometimes contemplates suicide.

5. **Acceptance:** This is a desirable step as the end nears. A sensation of peace and calm is attained and this can help the person to face the last moments and to die with fortitude and dignity.

It is important to say that, in these last steps, there is a tacit **farewell** between the dying person and the caregiver/s.

5.03

Adversity

Nobody is free from adversity. It touches everyone without exception and all need to face it at some time. These are frequent sources of adversity:

- **Relationships:** Serious problems with the spouse (see page 270), family or friends.
- **Work:** Losing one's employment (see page 266), decreased income and obstacles to professional development.
- **Health:** Temporary illness that interrupts normal life; diagnosis of a serious disease (page 244).
- **Finances:** Loss of income, a wrong investment, bankruptcy in family finance (page 266).
- **Accidents:** Work, traffic, home accidents... (page 260).

The magnitude of adversity varies a great deal. However, there is even more variations in the way people take misfortune. Some face problems and difficulties with determination, while others experience frustration and depression. What enables us to address obstacles with completeness and balance? The answer is **resilience**, or the ability to face barriers successfully.

What to do with adversity?

One should:

- **Understand that adversity is universal.** Everyone has to face troubles and difficulties. In fact, when we look around, there is always somebody in worse condition than ourselves. Understanding this reality may help us bear our burden better.
- **Do not be excessively demanding on self.** When adversity strikes, one should do as much as possible to repair the damage and to solve the problem. But one should not crumble be-

cause the result is not perfect or quick. Due to the adversity, circumstances may be against us and it is not realistic to expect perfect solutions.

- **Avoid regretting the past.** Gazing at a misfortune and saying: 'I could have prevented it... Why didn't I do it differently?' is an automatic and negative reaction. Regretting past events is a source of irritation that can be avoided by controlling one's thoughts. Past errors may be observed as a way of learning in order to avoid future problems. But they should not be taken as a source of frustration for not having done something differently.

- **Consider the finiteness of problems.** As the saying goes, 'Nothing lasts forever'. Experience teaches us that adversities are quite alarming at first but they lose strength little by little. The affected person recovers and, in the end, satisfactory solutions are reached.

- **Do not generalise.** An accident or loss is tied to a specific area of our life and we need to avoid its application to everything else. For example, losing one's job is a serious problem; even so, we can preserve family, friends, values, health and other areas intact and receive enjoyment and support from them.

- **Consider the positive side of adversity.** All adversities are bitter, but from them we can learn lessons of experience and strength. When we remember the difficult experiences of the past, from their beginning to their end, we almost always find that we have learned something. Once difficulties are past, the person realises that he/she has emerged with a special strength. His/her character has become more resistant to difficulties.

Gems of Ancient Wisdom

'God comforts us in all our troubles, so that we can comfort those in any trouble with the comfort we ourselves have received from God' (2 Corinthians 1:4).

'Consider it pure joy, my brothers, whenever you face trials of many kinds, because you know that the testing of your faith develops perseverance' (James 1:2-3).

RESEARCH RESULTS

The ingredients of resilience against adversity

The study conducted by **John Buckner** and his colleagues (2003) clearly showed that development of resilience has nothing to do with the absence of problems. In fact, difficulties provide the platform to develop resilience and to fight adversity. Experts focused their study on a group of 155 subjects of school and adolescent age. All came from an extremely poor background, but only 29% of participants could be classified as 'resilient.' What did those children and youth who were endowed with such special strength possess? The resilient youth demonstrated a consistent ability to:

- Anticipate the consequences of their own behaviours.
- Plan their behaviours and activities.
- Establish goals and priorities.
- Maintain attention and concentration.
- Control their emotions, especially anger and frustration.

The authors of this study labelled this trait **self-regulation skill**. This can be compared to what has always been understood as patience, self-control, ability to endure and self-discipline. All these traits can be taught and learned in order to face small and great life adversities.

TEST YOURSELF ::

Answer True or False to the following statements:

How much resilience do I have?	T	F
1. When I face difficulties, I easily adapt.		
2. When I experience a loss, I recover relatively easily.		
3. I can easily talk to others in the midst of my difficulty.		
4. I know how to calm myself down in a crisis.		
5. I enjoy a healthy self-esteem and I have self-confidence.		
6. I understand that any difficulty is temporary.		
7. In the midst of adversity I try and use logic and not burden myself with emotions.		
8. I see the humorous side of things and I know how to laugh at myself.		
9. I learn from everything around me and I even take advantage of difficulties.		
10. I make provision to avoid problems.		
11. I have become stronger and more resilient due to past adversities.		
12. In spite of difficulties, I tend to face them and wait until the storm is over.		

Interpretation:
- If you have answered T to 9 or more statements, you possess the necessary resilience to face all sorts of adversities.
- If you have answered T to 5-8 statements, you can successfully confront certain adversities but others can cause problems to you. You need to apply the advice offered in this unit and gain resilience by practice.
- If you have answered T to less than 5 statements, you have limited resources to face difficulties and adversities. However, this skill may be practised and developed. Follow the tips of this book and other specialised publications and seek the counsel of a mental health professional, especially if you are in the middle of an adversity.

Pain and suffering

These days, people increasingly complain of muscular pain, headaches, backaches or pain in the legs without apparent reason. They visit the doctor and undergo clinical tests, but everything seems normal. Sometimes, medical science finds the cause and makes a diagnosis, but the patient does not respond to the treatment. In the end, the person resigns him/herself to live with the pain as best he/she can.

Other people suffer more than necessary, not from illness, but from the loss of a loved one, a disappointment in love, academic failure or a failed business. This suffering, psychological in nature, may equal or surpass the intensity of physical pain.

In any case, people affected by pain and suffering need not succumb to such events. They can do something to **ease** their pain and **lighten** the way. It is important to become familiar with various ways of alleviating pain, whether physical or psychological. In this way, the affected person learns to partially regulate pain or discomfort. This helps him/her to avoid the feeling of impotence experienced by those who give in to pain, believing that their only option is to endure it.

THE VICIOUS CIRCLE OF PAIN

Chronic pain, left to the mercy of circumstance, does not go away. Furthermore, its intensity may increase and be further complicated because it is part of a dangerous vicious circle that follows these steps:

1. Pain appears and produces discomfort and irritation.
2. When the affected person does not know what to do, he/she not only suffers but also limits his/her activity as he/she feels intimidated by pain.
3. Inactivity brings about muscular weakness and lack of habit and practice.
4. Further attempts are likely to fail because of lack of exercise.
5. This partial inability brings about despair, rage, frustration, discouragement and anxiety.
6. Pain increases because of the presence of adverse emotions.
7. As pain increases, activity is further limited.

Lack of activity is a *strong obstacle to combating pain and suffering*. In most cases, it is better to break the pain barrier and the accompanying vicious circle.

How to manage physical pain

Chronic pain of any kind is not present 24 hours a day. Even in cases of pain and ailments of a permanent or semi-permanent nature, the level of pain is perceived in variable form at various times of the day.

This becomes obvious when one records pain in a systematic way over one or two weeks (see the Self-help box below). The record will show that pain sometimes intensifies; other times, it subsides; and yet other times, it will completely disappear. It is useful to observe personal attitudes associated with these variations, as well as those events that contribute to increase or diminish pain intensity.

Often, **fixed patterns** may be observed indicating that there are patterns to the intensity of pain according to the time of day. All this information becomes useful in finding ways to manage pain.

PAIN LOG

Keeping a record over a limited period of time can offer much light on the pain process and how it is perceived. Knowing the patterns and circumstances accompanying pain is a great step towards controlling it. The goal of those suffering from pain is to prolong the moments of relief and accept the unavoidable pain. If you suffer from chronic pain, keep a weekly record log to identify the moments of pain and learn more about your ailment:

Day/time	Description of pain	Level (0-10)	What was I doing?	Observations

The following tips do not work with everybody, but they have provided strong support to many. If you suffer from chronic and persistent pain, try them; if you do not need them, try them with someone who may benefit.

1. **Speak about your pain.** Verbalising the patterns of your pain, especially if it affects you emotionally, has a great liberating power. You should look for someone close who is genuinely interested in you and willing to listen to your feelings and frustrations.
   Self-help groups can help. Their members, who share the same problem, are usually highly motivated. In addition, the group provides a place to learn how others face pain. If you are interested in finding a group with similar pain to yours, ask your doctor or search the bulletin boards of hospitals and clinics.

2. **Learn remedies that work for you.** A neck ache can be alleviated with a soft massage, dry heat or adequate muscular exercise. Some treatments work better for some people than for others. A headache may be remedied applying a bag of ice, taking a pain killer, or practising aerobic exercise…

   The key is to find what works for you. If you suffer from pain, try various alternatives and adopt those most effective to you. When the pain comes, use the methods that work. Never disdain the simple or natural remedies (see the Alternative Option box on page 258).

DISTRACT YOURSELF

The human mind cannot concentrate intensely on two things at the same time. For this reason, when someone is totally devoted to an alternative theme, the pain message is not recorded by the brain centres (see the box on page 259). Try the following **imagination and behavioural tasks** in order to distract yourself from pain:

- Think of a past event that makes you laugh. Think of this in detail, including all funny images and dialogues.
- Mentally review a film or a novel you liked. Enjoy thinking of their characters and actions.
- Mentally repeat a tune, poem, a difficult tongue twister or a list of names.
- Visualise yourself as the protagonist in an adventure or performing a heroic act.
- Read something you are very interested in.
- Carry out a rhythmic activity with your fingers or play an instrument.
- Examine your collection (stamps, coins, etc.).
- Listen to someone who tells you a personal experience or events of interest.

3. **Use your mind.** Your perception of pain is greatly influenced by the kind of thoughts you allow your imagination to process. Think of pleasant things and loved persons. Do not fall into negativity and despair. Trust in positive developments and an acceptable solution to your pain or illness.

4. **Remain active.** Keep yourself busy through physical exercise (if possible) or by engaging in some moderate activity. Do something productive and engage in some altruistic task. Avoid being bedridden unless it is absolutely necessary. Activity causes your brain to produce endorphin (or inner morphine), which helps to calm your pain.

5. **Care for your environment.** An attractive and relaxing environment is a great step in pain management. Keep your surroundings clean and neat, with a pleasant aroma and enjoyable music. Seek the presence of congenial people. Likewise, a change in environs (or taking a trip) may exert a positive effect upon pain.

6. **Distraction.** This is an important element and may become highly effective if one possesses techniques of proven efficacy. Use your imagi-

nation to distract yourself and become inspired from the examples of the Self-help Resource box.

7. **Relaxation.** When pain is musculoskeletal, a full relaxation and respiration session may provide better effect than a pain killer. See unit 1.07 on page 40 and follow the progressive relaxation steps presented there. Assess your pain before and after relaxation. If it works for you, put aside half an hour every day for this task, which in many cases will provide physical well-being as well as mental peace.

8. **Faith.** Faith in God and his healing power provides great support to the person who believes. Reading with calm and attention the Book of Psalms or a portion of the Gospels will favour spirituality and will bring relief to your pain and agitation.

A prayer asking for health and relief from pain will not go unanswered. 'And the prayer offered in faith will make the sick person well; the Lord will raise him up. If he has sinned, he will be forgiven' (James 5:15).

BEWARE OF CARING TOO MUCH

Pain and how it is perceived vary from person to person and depend on circumstances. There are people who do not benefit from excessive attention.

For example, Myrtle suffered from rheumatic pain. When she had a strike of pain, her husband and children would comfort her and show her that they cared. Outside of these moments of pain, Myrtle did not receive much attention from her family.

Curiously, she felt the pain more intensely in the presence of her dear ones. It was as if she felt sorry for herself and would suffer more in their presence. It seemed as if she unconsciously wanted to attract their attention through her pain.

In these cases, one should use this method cautiously since giving a patient too much attention may create a barrier to healing.

Pain can also be used as an excuse to avoid an unwanted task: 'I will not visit them today because I have a headache.'

This attitude may cause slight pain to become intensive, as if the patient wants the pain to grow. This manipulation of pain is not only unethical, but it deteriorates interpersonal relationships and intensifies pain sensations.

The person should reflect on the undue use of pain and face it in an open way, sharing the reality and negotiating help and support from others to confront the problem.

When pain is psychological...

Sometimes pain is not from a specific body part or organ, but is of a psychological nature, originating in the 'soul'.

This kind of suffering accompanies a traumatic event, a loss, a disappointment or a time of despair. In such cases, consider the following advice:

• **Escape from inactivity.** Keep yourself busy doing something you enjoy. If the pain is so intense that you cannot maintain a full-time job, reduce your daily hours of work and spend time on something you really like to do. Do not feel guilty because you may be 'producing' less than others.

• **Do something for other people.** In your search for an activity, include helping the needy.

This does not mean a humanitarian donation but a commitment of time and effort to occupy 6, 8 or 10 hours every week.

Contact a neighbours' association, your city hall, or a non-governmental organisation (NGO) about volunteering and join a group.

- **Organise your relationships.** Invest time in pleasant and relaxing conversation. Talk to your best friend about your problems and seek the friendship of healthy, agreeable and altruistic people.

  You will find these people at youth associations, parishes, nature clubs, etc.

- **Organise your attitude.** Your physical and psychological pain depends a great deal on how you consider yourself.

If you pity yourself, you will feel it more intensely. Think of your good luck (there must be good things in your life); think of your personal ability and how to put it to work; nurture an optimistic perspective and gaze at the future in a hopeful manner.

PAIN-SOOTHING PLANTS

alternative options

Rosemary

The herbal and plant remedies listed below have analgesic and calming effects. Try them; one or more may be an effective solution to your pain. Do not become discouraged if they do not work straight away. Persevere for a few days, as nature always takes its time.

- **Rosemary** (*Rosmarinus officinalis*). A general analgesic and relaxant, it helps calm internal pain when taken as an infusion (tea).
- **Willow bark** (*Salix alba*). Willow contains salicine (used in aspirin) and soothes pain in the joints as well as arthritic, rheumatic and sciatic pains.
- **Bay leaf** (*Laurus nobilis*). Bay leaf tea has anti-inflammatory effects, bringing relief to joint pain.
- **Devil's Claw root** (*Harpagophytum procumbens*). This contains strong anti-inflammatory substances to help in the cure of sprains and dislocations.
- **Meadowsweet** (Queen of the meadow) (*Filipendula ulmaria*). An analgesic

and anti-rheumatic plant, it eliminates uric acid and renal stones via the urinary system.

- **Malva** (*Malva silvestris*). Its hand-shaped leaves are effective against pain and swelling. It also favours perspiration, regulates menstruation and is a good anti-spasmodic remedy.
- **Oregano** (*Origanum vulgare*). This soothes digestive pain, especially stomach spasms. It also alleviates menstrual pains.
- **Anise** (*Pimpinella anisum*). It frees the stomach from gases and alleviates the discomfort produced by trapped air. It also works as an analgesic for headaches.

The above-mentioned herbs/plants may be taken as an **infusion by boiling** them for 5-10 minutes. Use an approximate proportion of one tablespoon of dry leaves for a cup of water. Infusions may also be applied directly over the painful area by means of a hot cloth (fomentation). Try the plants from the list to find out which one works best to bring relief to your pain.

Bay leaf

RESEARCH RESULTS

Use of virtual reality against pain

A study carried out by researchers at the University of Washington (Hoffman *et al.*, 2004) revealed the efficacy of a new method of pain management: **computer simulation**. The method consisted of an all-encompassing audiovisual device, which permitted patients to participate in an interactive video (a type of video game adapted to the patients' profile). During moments of intense pain, patients interact with virtual reality, managing to significantly reduce the sensation and intensity of pain.

The logic of this treatment lies in the fact that **pain has a strong psychological component**. When a patient's attention is focused on his/her problems, the pain intensifies. Virtual reality absorbs the person's attention and interest, helping him/her to concentrate on the activity, thus removing pain from the mind. The study centred on burn patients. Pain from serious burns is normally so intense that it cannot be easily endured even with the strongest opiate pain killers. Researchers present the case of a 40-year-old patient with deep burns affecting 19% of the body including neck, back, buttocks and legs. With the audiovisual treatment, the patient managed to reduce perceived pain from 7 to 2 (on a 1-to-10 scale) and the time spent thinking about his burns from 10 to 3.

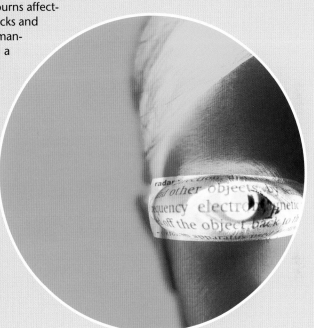

A different study was conducted among adolescents who were hospitalised for burns. A set of video games were used where additional fuel for aeroplanes (a desirable outcome) became available when the patient opened and closed his/her burned hands (an essential, but very painful movement in psychotherapy). The video game encouraged these young patients to carry out the exercise several times. Without the help of the video game, they were unable to perform the exercise.

Gems of Ancient Wisdom

'He will wipe every tear from their eyes. There will be no more death or mourning or crying or pain, for the old order of things has passed away' (Revelation 21:4).

5.05
Accidents

Thousands of accidents take place every day. Many carry loss of life. Others cause serious or mild injuries.

Still others involve great financial loss. In any case, survivors (or those close to them) feel the emotional impact of these events and undergo important emotional disruption.

Sequels cause short-, medium- and long-term disorders. In this unit primary care advice is given that can be helpful when enduring or eliminating psychological pain caused by accidents.

The most common accidents include car collisions, work-related accidents, fires and natural catastrophes.

Aside from the physical damage that may occur, accidents produce **important traumatic effects**. These are some of them:

- **Involuntary mental reconstruction of the event.** The person is overtaken by memories of the accident. These images or words are involuntarily played back mentally. While not necessarily harmful, this can be painful.

- **Anxious response to similar conditions.** Not only actual accident conditions but situations of a similar nature elicit fear and anxiety in the person. For instance, an individual who has almost drowned in the ocean may feel fear in a small swimming pool.

- **Rejection of social relationships.** The victim may avoid relationships with people or experience isolation and may show a lack of emotions.

- **Agitation, edginess.** Accidents are often followed by a general feeling of nervousness and discomfort. The affected person seems unable to experience calm and relaxation. He/she sleeps little and poorly and experiences despair when this problem stretches over days or weeks.

- **Anger and resentment.** Many times the person gets angry and feels animosity for not having done things differently.

How to overcome trauma

(See also page 110).

- **Speak about the accident.** To speak about what happened and how it happened is an important step toward healing and final recovery from trauma. It is therefore important to provide a warm and empathetic environment where the victim can talk about the event and its circumstances (see the box below).

- **Seek positive social interaction.** Recovery from any trauma requires the presence and support of others. People should be empathic, willing to listen and physically near the person.

- **Monitor the cardiac rate.** Cardiac rates often accelerate during the days following the accident. It is, therefore, advisable to practise relaxation and thought control techniques.

- **Avoid the use of toxic substances.** The person affected by accident trauma may turn to high risk behaviours (alcohol or drug use) for comfort. It is imperative to avoid this danger.

- **Avoid feelings of guilt and frustration.** Many victims of accidents feel guilty for having caused the accident, for having survived or for not having been able to avoid it. This feeling obstructs the healing process and should be dispelled using thought control techniques.

- **Understand that symptoms are normal.** Post-traumatic stress symptoms following accidents are normal. We should reassure the person that

---

RESEARCH RESULTS

It is good to talk

Stallard and his team of researchers carried out a study (Stallard, Velleman and Baldwin, 2001) with 40 children who had suffered from traffic accidents in the United Kingdom. The children were submitted to psychological tests on two occasions: at 6 weeks and at 8 months after the accident.

Results showed that the factor that most influenced recovery from the trauma was the **willingness of participants to talk** about the accident and the **understanding attitude** of those who listened. Children who avoided talking about the accident recovered at a slower pace than those who were willing to describe the event and dialogue about it.

This study points to the benefit of open conversation about a traumatic event, discounting the old tradition of burying bad memories.

---

his/her feelings are a normal reaction to an abnormal event.

- **Do not block accident memories.** Remembering what happened in the accident may be unpleasant but it is part of the healing process and should be permitted instead of blocked.

- **Engage in normal activity.** As far as possible, the victim of the accident should return to his/her normal life, take up the daily routines, keep active and rest adequately.

- **Know how to wait for time to pass.** It is necessary to have patience and to recommend this attitude to the affected person. Given time, most cases develop positively without any psychological help. Time tends to heal emotional sores.

5.06

Terrorism

At the dawn of the 21st century the world faces a new type of violence marked by its massive and indiscriminate nature: terrorism!

Examples are the attacks against New York City's World Trade Center (11 September 2001), the Atocha trains in Madrid (11 March 2004), or those of Bali, London, Egypt or India. Events like these may transform the worldview of an entire regional or national community.

A terrorist attack perpetrated in a town or city causes a **sense of loss** in the community: loss of human lives, of safety, of personal freedom, of property, etc.

This causes depressive symptoms (see unit 2.05, page 102). It also brings generalised apprehension and helplessness towards the future ('it could have happened to me; when will it happen again?'), together with anxiety symptoms: 'nerves,' fatigue, lack of concentration, insomnia, muscular tension and irritability.

For weeks or months, affected people suffer the terrible symptoms of **post-traumatic stress**: flashback images of the event, nightmares, startling reactions and an attitude of paranoia.

Although there is nothing positive about snatching life from innocent victims, when the evil is over, **we need to react resiliently** to obtain something positive from the disaster. The boxes on the adjoining page include a number of negative reactions as well as those that may be beneficial once the frenzy is over.

→ Reactions to a terrorist attack

Negative reactions	Positive reactions
• **Sadness.** *Death or physical and psychological injury inflicted by terrorists cause deep pain in other people, especially those living close to the victims.* • **Trauma.** *Survivors, witnesses and even those who simply receive the news of a terrorist attack often display post-traumatic stress symptoms.* • **Rage.** *Anger, rage and the desire to take revenge are natural reactions towards the attackers' cowardice.* • **Anxiety.** *Those living in an environment of ongoing terrorism or among threatened groups experience typical anxiety symptoms.* • **Guilt.** *Terrorist attack survivors tend to feel guilty for having survived. Those living far away may also feel guilty for not being able to do anything about the misfortune.*	• **Immediate altruism.** *After a terrorist attack, many offer their benevolent and unlimited support in terms of money, professional skills, and blood, to provide relief to the victims.* • **Reorganisation of values.** *To live near the scene of a terrorist attack makes people question their values and life habits. Generally, in moments of crisis, people adopt safe and traditional values: family and faith.* • **Adoption of new ways of being.** *After a terrorist attack people adopt unselfish lifestyles filled with more charity and more empathy.* • **Community revival.** *Terrorism and other catastrophes bring life to community approaches and protect people from individualism.*

BE CAREFUL NOT TO LOSE CONTROL

A terrorist act is radically unfair and awakens the rage of even the most peaceful person. This is why it is extremely important to prepare oneself to react in the most civilised form possible in order to avoid acting like those who perpetrated the attack. The following points are to be cautiously considered:

• **Violence.** It is well known that violence begets violence and that in a state of war the most unthinkable brutalities are committed, on or off the battlefield. Terrorism can prepare the stage for revenge and violence. This must be avoided.

• **Racism.** Terrorists that belong to a cultural or ethnic group claim to represent their group, even though this is not the case. Thus, thousands or millions of people belonging to these groups are associated in the minds of others with the terrorists. These people do not share nor do they support the barbaric acts. Nevertheless, they may become targets of discrimination, rejection and even violent attacks because they belong to that race or group.

• **Religion.** Many terrorists embrace the banner of religion and kill in the name of God. This is a mistaken concept of God and of religion that has happened throughout history. However, this wrong interpretation should not be used to blame God, religion or believers. The large majority of religious people (of any religion) carefully follow a lifestyle of goodwill, good citizenship and pacifism.

• **Hatred and dissension.** Terrorism is capable of introducing into society subtle ideological disagreements that lead to hatred among various groups and ideologies. In the midst of acts which produce strong emotions, differences in thought are accentuated and dangerous tensions develop.

How to face the strike

Tackling the pain produced by a terrorist attack is very difficult. Enduring pain caused by natural death, illness, accident or natural disaster is hard, but it is more difficult to face terrorism. Terrorism is **intentional**; it is a carefully planned act against unknown people, moved by ideals foreign to the victims. This is totally incomprehensible to the victims, their families and those who are near.

The advice that follows may be very helpful to those who assist victims, as the victims themselves will most likely be unwilling to read self-help handbooks:

- **Psychological first aid.** The first 24 hours are decisive to survivors, their families and other people that may have received the impact. They should be assisted by mental health professionals or volunteers who possess the skills and wisdom to listen and bear their sobbing, their insults, their shouts or their rage attacks. It is necessary for the victims to let out their conflict and proceed with the normal pain that follows bereavement.
- **Return to routine.** This should come progressively. Affected persons must retake their daily activities without a rush but in a systematic manner. Perhaps they can start with a half-day of work at the beginning and gradually expand to a normal day of work.
- **Learn anti-anxiety techniques** (see the box on this page).
- **Remain close and be prepared to listen.** Over the weeks following the terrorist attack, those who have lost dear ones (or lived through the tragedy) need to have someone near. They should not be forced to talk; but when they are willing to express themselves, someone must be available.
- **Practise social support.** Family, friends and neighbours, with discretion and perseverance, must remain close and willing to give a hand in practical matters and encouraging those affected by terrorism. They should do it on a continuous basis as there is a tendency to help a lot at the beginning and then abandon the victim.
- **Be optimistic.** Communicate a positive vision of life. Talk about positive or neutral topics, not gloomy ones. But when the victim talks about his/her sorrow, listen attentively and without rush, and encourage him/her to continue to talk.
- **Guard hope.** Hope is necessary to continue on with life and to enjoy mental and physical health (see page 64). Many become ill and die because they are always thinking about tragedy. View the future with hope and encourage victims to think of a better future. Invite them to exert faith in God and in eternal salvation. Believing that this life is just the threshold of an eternal and immensely happy future life is an antidote for suffering and anxiety.

  It is worth trusting in the Scriptures' promises of divine protection (reading or listening to the the Gems of Ancient Wisdom on the adjoining page several times until those words echo in the mind, becoming very useful to the affected person).

self-help

ANTI-ANXIETY TECHNIQUES

To fight apprehension, edginess, mental and muscular tension, try these anti-anxiety techniques:
- Breathe in and out deeply and slowly (taking about 8 seconds).
- Practise relaxation (see page 40).
- Get regular physical exercise and enjoy its calming effect.
- Identify your usual catastrophic thoughts.
- Learn to reject those thoughts as soon as they appear and substitute them with positive and edifying thoughts.

How to explain evil

Why do terrorists attack innocent persons? Why do these injustices happen? These are questions that everybody asks when terrorism takes place.

This and many other forms of evil, violence, and covert cruelty continue to exist in the world today. Why does evil exist and how can we explain it?

The only explanation we know is found in the Bible. Evil does not exist because God invented it, but because of the **free action** of his creatures. God created humans and angels and endowed them with freedom to choose. Both angels and humans opted for evil (the Bible calls it 'sin'). As a result of this choice, there is suffering, pain, meanness, terrorism and death.

Will suffering, pain, meanness, terrorism and death always exist? The precious answer from the Bible is *no*. We are promised that the current world order will be replaced by another where those who believe in that salvation will experience total perfection and eternal happiness.

Gems of Ancient Wisdom

'You will not fear the terror of night, nor the arrow that flies by day, nor the pestilence that stalks in the darkness, nor the plague that destroys at midday. A thousand may fall at your side, ten thousand at your right hand, but it will not come near you' (Psalm 91:5-7).

SATURATION BY FREQUENCY

Living in areas where terrorism is in the daily news may make the population insensitive. And the time may come when a new act of terrorism is accepted as an ordinary and irrelevant daily event.

In order to fight terrorism and understand and support those who suffer from it, it is necessary to preserve sensitivity and respect for human life. It is also necessary to condemn those who target the lives of innocent souls.

5.07

Financial crisis · Unemployment

Everyone faces circumstances when money becomes scarce for days or weeks. The necessary adjustments and sacrifices are made and, in the end, the situation balances itself. However, things may reach a critical stage where one owes much more than he/she owns. Under such circumstances, mental and health problems may result. In order to prevent this, a few firm measures must be put into place.

Other times, the fundamental problem is to lose one's job and be unemployed for a long period of time. Becoming unemployed is a very hard emotional blow. This is not only because of the loss of income that accompanies unemployment. It also means a **reduction in the psychological and emotional** flow due to lack of activity, behavioural structure, security, self-esteem, sense of contribution, social interaction and personal development.

Work meets a multitude of psychological and emotional needs. This is why losing it almost always translates into a traumatic loss.

Psychological consequences

A financial crisis may trigger the following reaction in the affected person:

- fatigue and weakness
- weight alteration
- mood fluctuation
- insomnia
- loss of memory
- lack of attention and concentration

The effects of financial crises are comparable to those caused by adverse events such as divorce or the death of a loved one. The affected person may also live through times of anger, frustration and hopeless-ness, followed by periods of hope and anticipation for an opening door.

The consequences of this problem are not limited to parents, but they also affect **children**. The Research Results box on the adjoining page shows how children also suffer with the parent's loss of employment.

It has also been observed that, in families experiencing unemployment, there is increased violence towards the spouse and sexual abuse towards children. Unemployment pressures lead to behaviours that could be avoided if there was an adequate work activity.

RESEARCH RESULTS

The effects of unemployment on children

A relevant study carried out in Finland (Solantaus, Leinonen and Punamäki, 2004) shows the effects that unemployment may cause to families. Participants of this study were 527 families, all of them with at least one 12-year-old child. Parents completed 15 questionnaires on their family situation, the history of work and unemployment, and their family relationships. All subjects had participated in a previous longitudinal study and data were integrated in this study. Children also completed a questionnaire of 112 items designed to identify their mental and behavioural state.

Results show the direct and indirect effects of parent's financial alterations upon their children. Specifically, moments of economic crises, when compared with stable times, showed that children experienced high rates of:

- aggression
- depression
- disobedience

Furthermore, these alterations were observed **regardless of the families' economic level**. In other words, the problems affected those families with savings and emergency resources as well as families lacking reserves.

Unemployment and how to survive it

Anyone can go through the misfortune of losing their job. Facing this situation requires a great deal of resilience if one is not to collapse psychologically and end up in material and emotional bankruptcy. The following pieces of advice are recommended for those facing the adversity of unemployment:

- **Be realistic in assessing your situation.** Avoid blaming yourself for having lost your job. Instead, identify the real cause. In most instances, employees are made redundant due to financial pressures, not incompetence. Do not place the blame on yourself because your self-esteem will suffer and you will have less chance of finding another job. If you are truly responsible, invest time and effort in retraining to compensate for your deficiency.

- **Learn about your rights.** In many countries, unemployed people have rights to income for a period of time. There is nothing wrong in demanding your rights and receiving the benefits

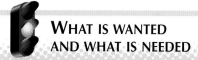

WHAT IS WANTED AND WHAT IS NEEDED

In these times of wild consumerism (see page 186) it is necessary to distinguish between need and want. Before making a purchase or incurring an expense, especially when the financial situation is tight, we need to ask ourselves the question: 'Do I really need it?'

Need: Things we must have in order to survive. They have absolute priority at the time of spending money. These include not only physical needs, but also social and psychological ones.

Want: All things that seem attractive but which we can live without.

This distinction (albeit partly subjective) becomes very useful for controlling expenses. A clear understanding of what is 'need' and what is 'want' will help establish priorities for the best use of financial resources.

offered by the system. Use this income to search for another job and not to take a long vacation.

- **Reduce your expenses immediately.** Control your expenses to adjust to your reduced income. Find economical ways to take care of your food, dress, leisure, etc. You will soon realise that you can live with less if you are careful.

- **Organise your life.** Avoid disorganisation at all cost. Interestingly, there are many people who, having lots of time on their hands, end up without any structure or order. Adopt order in your life; get up and go to bed at regular times and put aside a specific number of hours to search for employment.

- **Seek support.** Before you experience any depressive symptom, seek emotional help from someone close who is willing to listen and to offer counsel. Spend a few moments every day to talk to your best friend or close relative, sharing your activities and your progress. Be open to their advice. You may also find a good source of support in community organisations, churches, clubs or self-help groups.

- **Search for a job in various ways.** In looking for a job, do not limit yourself to only writing letters and applications. Take a multiple-strategy approach. Check the newspapers, internet ads, government employment lists, temporary placements, and even those that do not have a direct connection with your profession. Go out and offer yourself here and there. Speak and listen to others and remember that many jobs are granted through personal referral, more than through organised competition.

- **Offer your service as a volunteer.** If you do not find a job immediately, offer yourself to work as a volunteer in something related to your profession or trade. Aside from providing structure to your routine, activities like these may open doors for permanent jobs in the same place or they may provide good recommendations.

- **Do not forget leisure.** Do not fail to engage in some pastime you enjoy, especially together with other people. Avoid isolation, as it leads to depressive symptoms.

- **Flee from noxious substances.** Unemployed people run the risk of alcohol, tobacco, caffeine… abuse. These are poisonous substances, and they may also weaken your will power and even lead to gambling.

PREPARE YOURSELF FOR AN EMERGENCY

Sometimes a financial crisis may appear, not due to losing one's job but because of a significant, unexpected expense.

For example, a costly car repair, an unexpected medical expense or an expensive home appliance replacement.

A safe way to face this type of crisis, which may not have insurance coverage, is to open a bank account for emergencies, following these steps:

1. Deposit ten percent of your income every month for 10 months. This will provide a solid fund, equivalent to one full month's income to face emergencies.
2. When the emergency comes, use the fund.
3. Replace the amount used in that way over the following months to top up the fund.
4. Use the fund only for emergencies.

This system will help you to avoid financial pressure from emergencies.

Gems of Ancient Wisdom

'Give everyone what you owe him: If you owe taxes, pay taxes; if revenue, then revenue; if respect, then respect; if honour, then honour. Let no debt remain outstanding, except the continuing debt to love one another, for he who loves his fellow-man has fulfilled the law' (Romans 13:7-8).

'I know what it is to be in need, and I know what it is to have plenty. I have learned the secret of being content in any and every situation, whether well fed or hungry, whether living in plenty or in want' (Philippians 4:12).

5.08
Divorce

The decision to get a divorce and to follow the necessary steps is a slow and painful process.

Aside from the implications that divorce has upon work, family and social connections, those going through divorce tend to experience, in more or less extent, the following emotions:

- sadness
- anger
- remorse
- sense of failure
- rage
- guilt
- insecurity
- sense of isolation
- low self-esteem
- loss of identity

Habits and behaviours also undergo changes. For example, those under the effect of divorce may act impulsively (or end up in total inactivity), lose their appetite (or become uncontrolled eaters), use alcoholic beverages or other psychoactive substances, experience sleep difficulties and run the risk of accidents because of lack of attention and concentration.

These experiences are typical when experiencing a *loss*. And this is because, even though it may become liberation, divorce is also a loss: of a companion, belongings, familiar lifestyle, money, social network, self-esteem and plans for a common future.

Both men and women experience negative feelings with divorce. These effects may last several months or even years.

If you are in the midst of divorce, you should understand that all these events are normal and will not last forever.

Symptoms will go away with a little time, patience, and the support supplied by friends and family.

Divorce affects children

While varying from case to case, children always receive the bitter part of their parents' divorce. In the large majority of cases, the effect is **temporary** (about two years from separation), although in some cases, a divorce may leave scars for life.

The table on the adjoining page offers a variety of ways to support children of various ages if they must face parental divorce.

How to explain divorce to children

With the exception of those younger than 3, children have the right to receive an explanation adequate to their age. An appropriate amount of knowledge will benefit them. It is not a pleasant activity, but it must be done. The following tips will help to carry out the task:

- **Choose a quiet moment.** Circumstances around divorce tend to be full of emotional ups and downs. Set a special day apart to explain to your child that you are going to divorce. Do not offer details, but be clear on what is going to happen to the couple, and especially to the children.

Do not focus too much on the past (the pain of the relationship) but rather on the future (the arrangements to be made or the freedom that was impossible before).

- **Think of what you are going to say.** Reflect on the content of your explanation. Ideally, both parents should face the task together, sharing with their children what they have mutually agreed.

- **Do not say it all at once.** In some families, children do not anticipate such news and it may become too traumatic. In these cases, you need to speak little by little until they are told that divorce is inevitable.

- **Be prepared for their questions.** It is common that children ask many questions; and that is good. But you should know how you will answer questions such as:

'What is going to happen with me?' 'Will I never be able to play with Dad?' 'Who is going to take me to school?' 'Am I going to have a stepfather/stepmother?' 'When there are events at school, will you both attend?' 'What is going to happen during holidays?' and so on.

Before approaching the discussion, try to imagine all possible questions that your son or daughter may ask.

In any case, it is of utmost importance to make them understand that they are not responsible for the separation, and that both parents will continue to love them and care for them.

After this conversation or conversations, it is normal that children will feel affected, but this is a regular step in the process of acceptance and healing.

→ How to support children according to their age

A child younger than 5...	A 5- to 8-year-old child...
... will show confusion and fear that his/her parents may reject him/her or that one day he/she may wake up and not find them. Symptoms: sobbing, spoilt behaviour, no bladder control, a greater need for stuffed animals.	*... will feel sad and believe that he/she has to opt for only one parent; he/she will be afraid of being abandoned and will wish for his/her parents to get together again. He/She may experience nightmares and even aggression and rage.*
How to provide support • Show love and care. • Assure him/her that he/she will not be rejected. • Explain where and with whom he/she will be living. • Do not speak badly of the other parent. • Do not become harsh because he/she wets the bed or is attached to stuffed animals.	**How to provide support** • Assure him/her that he/she is loved and accepted. • Convince him/her that he/she is not causing the separation. • Listen to him/her. • Provide love and warmth. • Reject the idea of reconciliation.
An 8- to 12-year-old child...	**The adolescent (12-18)...**
... reacts badly to separation. He/She gets angry, worries about his/her future, and feels fear and shame for what is happening. He/She shows hostility towards one of his/her parents. He/She may also lie, steal, get bad marks and try to escape from home.	*... understands divorce and knows that it is a way out of an extreme situation, but he/she may display certain symptoms: lack of concentration, low school grades, blaming his/her parents for the separation, disobedience and lack of cooperation.*
How to provide support • Give him/her opportunities to speak and dialogue about what he/she feels. • Be patient and not angry at him/her. • Care for his/her social environment. • Answer his/her questions in an honest manner. • Do not speak badly of the other parent.	**How to provide support** • Listen with care and attention whenever he/she is willing to talk. • Do not use him/her as a confidant/e. • Respect and accept his/her friends. • Apply discipline firmly but with care.

How to prevent divorce

Whenever possible, it is best to prevent divorce, applying solutions based on good will before the relationship reaches an unbearable point. A couple may think about divorce in the middle of arguments and temporary crises, but, before taking such steps, it is advisable to attempt solutions to the problems. Remember the following preventive measures:

- **Do not give up because of conflicts.** In the presence of a clash, seek dialogue and avoid discussing matters when angry. Explain your position from your viewpoint without making accusations. Use I-messages ('I believe...' 'I feel hurt when...') instead of you-messages ('You have decided...' 'You don't realise...'). Avoid presenting problems, and offer solutions.

- **Nourish the relationships with loving details.** You have invested a lot in your marriage and should not let the flame of love die. The best way to nourish the relationship is to demonstrate romantic acts and words of love.

AVOID DOING THIS

Certain **mistakes** may produce permanent psychological scars. Because of the high risk involved, try by all means to avoid:

- Using children as messengers to carry hostile, covert messages to the ex-spouse.
- Asking children not to talk about this, or that they should cover that, or that they should not mention that other thing to the ex-spouse.
- Telling lies to children with the pretended excuse that it is better for them. If something cannot be said, it is better to be quiet about it.
- Question children when they come from visiting the other parent in order to find out the ex-spouse's intimate or personal details.

- **Share the family burdens.** Whether it be professional tasks, domestic chores or children's care, help in each one of the burdens. If there are disagreements, express your position with respect and consideration towards your spouse and attempt to reach satisfactory agreements.

- **Do not think your relationship should be a 'Cinderella' story.** Interpersonal relationships and especially marriage relationships are subject to imperfection. The permanently joyous marriage is a myth and married people who wish to be reasonably happy must build their own realistic happiness.

- **Do not abandon the intimate relationship.** Sexual dissatisfaction is at times the reason for a break-up. Do not despise this dimension and try to please your partner. Openly discuss his or her needs and preferences.

- **Seek external help.** When there is no apparent solution to problems, the couple should seek outside help from some impartial person (counsellor, psychologist, spiritual leader or an experienced and trusted person) who may arbitrate and guide to save the couple and to strengthen their ties.

How to survive divorce

When it is not possible to save the marriage, divorce is an imperfect option that requires a great deal of resilience. Apply the following suggestions to face the hard path of divorce:

- **Seek help.** It is very difficult to proceed alone. You need to find someone, a very close person, with whom you can talk and share in your daily afflictions. Your children are not an option to let out your sorrow.

- **Hold onto the reins of your life.** Become determined that you will rule over your own life, and will not live at the mercy of circumstances or feelings that may overtake you. Slowly move on, especially in those tasks performed by your ex-spouse that you must now do. You have to try and believe that you can do them.

- **Focus your feelings.** Feelings and emotions will often surface. You need to be prepared to adequately manage them. Your thoughts determine your emotions and you must control your thinking process. If ideas of hatred (against your spouse or others) take over your mind, you must reject them, distracting yourself or changing activity. You may also use certain emotions in a constructive manner. For example, when rage takes over, apply that additional energy to work hard and demonstrate to yourself the ability and strength you have to do it well.

- **Protect your rest.** Regular and restorative sleep is essential to keep your mind healthy. Therefore, you must rest well in these difficult moments. If you have sleeping problems, read and practise the advice offered in the unit on insomnia (page 86). If this is not enough, consult your doctor or psychiatrist, but do not let much time pass without addressing this problem.

- **Eat adequately.** Lack of appetite is one of the dangerous stress symptoms in connection with divorce. For some people, the appetite increases irrationally, demanding high-calorie food in large amounts. Practise self-control (perhaps with someone's help) in order to cultivate rational dietary habits.

- **Get physical exercise.** Vigorous physical exercise that causes you to perspire is an ideal remedy for depressive symptoms, which are very commonly experienced by those in the midst of divorce. Choose one activity you enjoy; practise it five or six times a week. For example, you may enjoy gardening, sports, hiking or gymnastics. Or you may take time to play with your children, which will help them and yourself.

- **Develop spirituality.** Keeping spiritually fit is wise, especially when your mood is going through delicate times. Pray to God, read and reflect on Bible messages, participate in a devotional or worship activity with other people. Listen or play music that elevates your spirit.

self-help

RELATING TO THE EX-SPOUSE

Many would like to rub out the previous stage and start a new life altogether, but that is impossible, as children continue to be lawful children of both and the responsibility towards them may prolong for many more years. Accept this reality and cultivate a cordial relation with your previous wife or husband.

- **Discuss matters in private and in neutral territory.** Whenever there is the need to talk on a common item, make arrangements to be alone, away from the presence of children, preferably outside the home. It is recommended that you find a public place (snack bar, park or hotel lobby) in order to discuss matters in peace and reach agreements without the danger of getting excited.

- **Display a serious, natural and correct behaviour.** When you meet him/her, do it as if the encounter were a business meeting: be cordial, distant and restrain feelings. Above all, avoid ardour. Before the meeting, prepare yourself mentally, breathe in deeply, and warn yourself: 'Keep calm, do not get excited.'

- **Commit agreements to writing.** When you sit to negotiate, before and after divorce, clearly write down your mutual agreements. Share them with your ex-spouse so that there is proof of your consensus.

- **Remember that your children are likely to lose out.** Arguments and rows with your 'ex' will increase the psychological risks to your children. Avoid heated discussions of any kind, especially if children are around.

- **Look for someone to help arbitrate your differences.** Sometimes it is necessary to resort to an impartial arbitrator. For example, a common friend, a psychotherapist or a lawyer may be able to suggest reasonable agreements to both parties.

- **Be reliable and faithful to the agreements.** Once agreements have been reached, submit to them to keep your own conscience healthy and for the protection of your children.

5.09
Single-parent families

- **Singleness:** commonly the mother has had an undesired pregnancy during her teen years.

- **Divorce**, leaving children under the care of one of the parents.

- **Abandonment** of the family by one of the parents.

- **Death** of one parent, leaving behind widow/widower and orphans.

- **Family violence**, causing the perpetrator to be separated from the family.

- **Emigration** of one of the parents.

- **Adoption** carried out by a single mother or father.

- **Maternity**, where a single woman has a child through **artificial insemination**.

- Death of both parents, leaving a **grandmother, aunt, or relative in charge**.

The challenge of these circumstances is colossal. The parent in charge lacks the physical and emotional support found in a loving couple. He/she also has less time to attend to demands of children and work.

House chores become more taxing. Income is reduced causing financial difficulty. And to top it all, the relationship with the ex-spouse tends to be very unpleasant.

In addition to the practical arrangements, the person (most often the mother) experiences **loneliness and sadness** caused by the lack of emotional support.

Sometimes, the mother tries to use children to meet her need for social interaction. This is risky, as pointed out in the box on the adjoining page.

Just a few decades ago, single or divorced motherhood was an isolated and occasional occurrence.

Today, if single-parent families are grouped, we will find that, in many communities, their frequency is similar to (and sometimes higher than) traditional families. Single-parent families have a variety of forms and causes:

DO NOT FORGET THAT YOUR CHILDREN ARE JUST CHILDREN

A single mother works very hard without much opportunity to relate and communicate with adults. When she gets home, she finds her children waiting for their natural needs (play, laugh, talk about trivialities, etc.) to be satisfied. There is the risk of using children as source of emotional and interpersonal support. If you have noticed that you spend too much time talking to them about your problems and conflicts, remember that:

- Your children do not possess the emotional capacity to play an adult role.
- You will not only bore them, but you may also confuse them when you project your frustration upon them.

- Your children's needs as children must be met and you are the best instrument for them to attain the goal.

The best thing to do is for you to focus on the child's level. At the same time, seek **adult company** through friends and family in order to meet your own emotional needs.

Facing single-parent stress

Among the top 5 to 6 most stressful occupations is that of mothering small children. If we add the condition of single parenthood, we reach dangerously high levels of stress. If you are in this circumstance or have someone near who is, consider the following advice in order to prevent and to face advanced conditions of stress:

- **Seek reliable help.** Even though you feel strong enough to face all tasks by yourself, be realistic. It is nearly impossible for a single parent to make it without help. Seek support from relatives or friends. If your finances permit it, pay someone you trust to help you with domestic chores.

- **Organise your life systematically.** Set up a fixed routine and do not abandon it, even though it may be monotonous. Regularity in daily activities transmits security and stability to children and makes tasks easier and simpler.

- **Do not ignore your children's questions.** Your children will ask questions about their father or mother who is absent. Answer truthfully and with a calm, emotional tone, without exaggeration or anger. Use the most adequate level of explanation according to the children's ages.

- **Apply consistent and rational discipline.** Set up family rules and standards—few but well en-

forced. In the end, children will appreciate having limits in their lives. Teach them to work and cooperate from early life. Be consistent in the application of criteria and communicate your expectations to whoever helps you to take care of your children, your ex-spouse included.

- **Plan financial matters.** Insufficient financial resources are a typical cause of stress in single-parent families. Make a small budget or list of anticipated income and financial obligations. Be careful to avoid expenses until the time you have paid your debts. Explain to your children that they cannot always have what they ask for.

- **Spend time with your children.** They need you and it is worth sacrificing a few domestic chores in order to develop activities with the family: reading, playing, taking a walk, etc. Do not allow your children to watch too much TV, as you and your children need to strengthen family ties.

- **Take care of yourself.** Dedicate time to yourself, caring for yourself physically and emotionally. If you get sick, you will feel emotionally weak and your family will suffer. Set aside time to be alone and also with other adults. In this way, you will preserve your physical and mental health.

5.10

Violence at school and in the street

SYMPTOMS THAT MAY FAVOUR VIOLENCE

If you observe any of the following symptoms (especially three or more) in your children, try to carefully apply the tips given on these pages in order to prevent violent behaviour:

Primary school child	Adolescent
• *Has an attention and concentration problem.*	• *Is too rebellious with parents, teachers and other adults.*
• *Tends to annoy and provoke other children.*	• *Does not respect others' rights.*
• *Tends to fight with other children at school and in the streets.*	• *Drinks alcohol or uses drugs.*
• *Gets bad marks consistently.*	• *Misses classes without a good reason.*
• *Loses control and becomes very angry if others tease him/her.*	• *Complains too much that he/she is treated unfairly.*
• *Is rejected by other children because of his/her attitude.*	• *Becomes friends with other problem youth.*
• *Is cruel with pets.*	
• *Is not patient and gets very frustrated when things do not work out.*	

Due to the increase of urban population as well as other factors, violence in the streets and at all levels of school has multiplied. This is a very serious problem requiring the intervention of the local authority as well as parents and teachers. Violence can only be eradicated when it becomes incompatible with one's **personal values.** There is a tendency for violent behaviour to appear at the preschool age in many children. But it is desirable to channel this energy toward dialogue, tolerance and respect towards others, instead of using physical violence when differences appear.

Preventive measures

Parents of small children are in the best position to guide their children in the path of peaceful relationships. Teachers of preschool children can also take this important role. These are the children in need of greater care:

• Children who often display **temper tantrums for more than 15 minutes.**

• Children **fighting** other children **without apparent reason.**

• Children **lacking affective links with their parents** (do not hug them, are not loving, they do not feel the need to remain close to them in unfamiliar places).

• Children who regularly watch **violent programmes** on TV or the computer.

To help these youngsters who have problems controlling their impulses, consider the following tips:

• **Use a peaceful emotional tone.** Do not shout or threaten. Instead, use a soft tone of voice. Relate to the child in a caring, supporting and understanding way. Show a calm and relaxing attitude in your own behaviour.

• **Supervise constantly.** Avoid leaving the children unsupervised. In such situations, young children end up fighting. The presence of the adult helps them control their impulse. If you leave your child with other family members, make sure that the environment is safe, respectful and free from violent examples.

• **Limit the use of violent TV and DVDs.** When you buy or rent DVDs, they should be appropriate for children, and it is the same for TV programmes. Watch them together with your children and talk to them about what is happening

RESEARCH RESULTS

TV causes long-term violence

There is an extensive research tradition showing a relationship between violent TV programmes and aggressive behaviour in those watching them.

A University of Michigan study (Huesmann *et al.*, 2003) revealed that aggressive behaviours performed by adults in 2003 were linked to TV scenes watched prior to 1977.

Data gathered in 1977 from over 500 children aged between 6 and 10 years of age were compared to the level of violence 25 years later.

Results were amazing. Those exhibiting a high level of violence in adulthood were precisely those witnessing the highest level of violence on TV when they were children.

Within this latter group, 42% of males (40% of females) had violently pushed or shaken their spouse, and almost 70% said they had shaken someone else at least once in the last twelve months.

in the show or movie. Make sure they understand that violence is unacceptable.

• **Spend time with your children.** Talk to them, listen to them, play and carry out tasks with them. Get involved in as many of their activities as possible.

• **Avoid physical punishment.** Using the belt, slapping, pulling ears and other forms of violent punishments bring about obedience. However, these methods have serious drawbacks. One of them is the violent example exhibited which may encourage children to imitate it. Replace this method with that of withholding privileges (not allowing them to play, or to go out, or to play on the computer or to watch TV).

- **Be consistent in the application of discipline.** Family rules should be few and well respected. Unacceptable behaviour is always unacceptable. Being irregular with rule implementation produces insecurity, irritation, frustration and eventually aggression.

How to transform violent behaviour

A **relaxing environment** where civilised and peaceful conduct is displayed is a powerful way to weaken violent behaviour. Teaching **programmes that promote peaceful interactions** are also very useful. These programmes may include teaching youth about the reality of violence, its origin and consequences, as well as helping them to learn more about:

- The option we all have of choosing **dialogue** instead of violence.

continued on page 280

Gems of Ancient Wisdom

'The Lord was grieved that he had made man on the earth, and his heart was filled with pain. [...] The earth was corrupt in God's sight and was full of violence' (Genesis 6:6, 11).

'Train a child in the way he should go, and when he is old he will not turn from it' (Proverbs 22:6).

'As charcoal to embers and as wood to fire, so is a quarrelsome man for kindling strife' (Proverbs 26:21).

PREVENTING BEING VICTIMS

Children, women and the elderly tend to be the main target of violent individuals.

To avoid this, consider the following pieces of advice and teach them to those prone to become victims:

- In the daily travel routines, **do not follow the same route every day**. Use alternative ways, streets and transportation options. Do this randomly.
- **Do not go by yourself.** Seek the help of a friend or companion.
- **Never provoke others**, especially members of other ethnic or racial groups, **with your attitude, words or looks**.
- **Have a pre-arranged plan.** What would you do if attacked? What phone number would you use in case of emergency? How would you react to someone with doubtful intentions?

- **Do not open the door until you are sure who is on the other side.** Use the peephole, chain, voice, etc. before opening.
- **Do not talk to strangers.** This is especially recommended to children, but the expanding number of dangerous subjects makes it valid for many adults in many places.
- **Turn to the community:** friends, neighbours... and participate in projects oriented to neighbourly living—voluntary activities, altruistic service to the needy, etc.

SUBJECTS AT HIGH RISK OF DISPLAYING VIOLENCE

Alcohol and psychoactive substance users. People under the effect of these substances take unnecessary risks and end up being violent or victims of aggression.

> *What can you do?* Avoid the use of substances. Do not support them and do not buy products sponsored by alcoholic firms. Be an example of sobriety to your children and other minors.

Adolescents and youth. Violence at school and in the streets is normally performed by groups or gangs harassing or abusing a boy or girl chosen as a victim. Preferred victims are the bookish, those who are too thin or too fat, and those dressing or behaving differently.

> *What can you do?* Seek a good environment for minors; pick a school where respect and intolerance of violence is part of the ethos. Advise youth not to be boastful or to provoke violence in any form. Oppose violence and become active in the development of rules and regulations to suppress violent behaviour.

Males. Males of any age are more likely to display violence than girls and women. However, we need to remember that women use psychological violence: hurting words, hatred, resentment, slander, lies…

> *What can you do?* Organise small groups of youth as large groups are more given to violence. Teach respect, understanding and tolerance. Invite young people to postpone the exclusive friendship between male and female, as early couple relationships bring about greater violence.

Members of large families. Those growing up in families with many children, especially those with scarce resources, use fighting as a way out of their conflicts. Force becomes normal and it is used in a variety of contexts.

> *What can you do?* Carefully teach good manners, dialogue, negotiation and generosity as civilised ways to face conflict and competition and to reach goals.

Those watching violent programmes. The presence of violence in the media is out of proportion and the probability of children and youth being affected is high (see the box on page 277).

What can you do? Reduce the amount of programmes and video games, both for you and your children. Choose contents able to promote togetherness. Suggest alternatives, such as games and sports in the open, social activities in the community, reading and handicrafts, which do not carry the risk of violence.

Sayings of Jesus

'"Put your sword back in its place," Jesus said to them, "for all who draw the sword will die by the sword"' (Matthew 26:52).

continued from page 278

- The **danger of psychological violence** by means of words and a hurtful attitude.

- The **value of being peacemakers**, mediators in others' conflicts.

Conflict resolution

Seminars and classes on conflict resolution are a rational approach and a good alternative to violence. A conflict resolution **plan** normally includes how to:

- **choose the best moment to dialogue**; know how to wait for the best emotional state; avoid confronting the opponent in times of 'anger.'

- **use 'I-messages'** such as 'I believe that…' 'This makes me feel…'

- **avoid 'you-messages'** such as 'You think that…' 'You believe that…'

- **listen attentively** and make sure you understand.

- **dialogue on possible solutions**, assessing advantages and disadvantages.

- **use a positive attitude**, affirming and forgiving the opponent.

- **conclude with a shared solution**, without winner or loser.

Sayings of Jesus

'You have heard what it was said, "Eye for eye, and tooth for tooth." But I tell you, Do not resist an evil person. If someone strikes you on the right cheek, turn to him the other also' (Matthew 5:38, 39).

self-help

HOW TO FACE A VIOLENT SITUATION

Unexpected violent situations in the adult world are difficult to face.

Before a threatening or violent person, consider the following strategies:

1. **Do not challenge or resist.** Instead, use a soft tone of voice to prevent the escalation of violence.

2. **Cooperate.** Show yourself as friendly and natural as possible. Cooperate with the person in what you can.

3. **Buy time.** Act slowly and with calm. This will allow time for help to arrive or for the aggressive person to calm down.

4. **Once out of danger, avoid repeating the event.** If the violent person is unknown, strengthen your safety precautions. If the person is known (for instance, a family member), use the following preventive measures:

- Find a good moment to talk about what happened. Do not fall into the mistake of thinking that, if you are quiet about it, it will not happen again.

- Speak about the reasons causing the incident and how to avoid them.

- Show your position firmly and clearly—this is unacceptable behaviour and cannot be tolerated.

- If things do not get better, seek professional help, because, if properly treated, violence can be reduced and overcome.

If you are a witness of any violent act, even if it is not targeted at you, do not support it. Do not stand watching as if it were a show. Look for someone who can help or call the police. Be serious about your opposition to aggression and violence.

TEST YOURSELF ::

This is a questionnaire for adults. Answer sincerely True or False to the following statements:

Am I inclined to violent behaviour?	T	F
1. When I oppose others, I feel palpitations.		
2. I have a history of violence in my family (parents, grandparents, uncles).		
3. I frequently experience mood changes: sometimes I feel wonderful, but later I may be full of hatred towards someone.		
4. I have lost my temper more than once, shouting, slamming doors, or breaking something.		
5. In a quarrel I used my hands, and hit or pushed my opponent.		
6. When I get angry, I blame others.		
7. I am very jealous.		
8. I am very envious.		
9. I tend to control my spouse in everything he/she does (spending, contacts with others...).		
10. In my disagreements with my companion or spouse, I use threats.		
11. I drink alcohol or use drugs.		
12. I tend to insult or humiliate my opponent (or spouse).		

Interpretation:

- **0 to 3:** Little or no tendency to be violent.
- **4 to 7:** Warning. You have the tendency to become violent and should do something to control this dangerous impulse. You can try by yourself, but if this is not sufficient, you should seek outside help.
- **8 to 12:** Your situation is very dangerous. Your tendency to become violent has been consummated and you need external help. Seek a psychological or psychiatric professional, or a social worker. Your problem has a solution, but with the use of appropriate help.

Gems of Ancient Wisdom

'He is the God who avenges me, who puts the nations under me, who sets me free from my enemies. You exalted me above my foes; from violent men you rescued me' (2 Samuel 22:48-49).

'The LORD works righteousness and justice for all the oppressed' (Psalm 103:6).

'The ruthless will vanish, the mockers will disappear, and all who have an eye for evil will be cut down' (Isaiah 29:20).

5.11
Natural disasters

Many parts of our globe are susceptible to earthquakes, tidal waves (tsunamis), floods, volcanic eruptions, hurricanes, torrential rains, fires... They all leave a long list of people affected, many helpless and without preparation to face the calamity.

Consequences of natural disasters

Consequences include the loss of human lives and material damage of great cost. Survivors tend to face one or more of the following sequels:

- **Deep sorrow**, due to the loss of loved ones.
- A very intense state of **emotional shock**.
- **Denial**—not wanting to believe or accept what has just happened.
- Deep-seated **nervousness**.
- **Anxiety** at the possibility of the event (or something of the kind) happening again.
- **Depressive symptoms:** insomnia, lack of appetite, of energy, of motivation and of hope; depressive mood, and desire to die.
- Involuntary memory **retrieval of horrific scenes**, sometimes accompanied by palpitations, sweat and trembling.
- **Nightmares** with the theme of those scenes.
- **Difficulty** concentrating and **remaining attentive**.
- **Panic** reaction to **conditioned stimuli**; for example, sirens or alarms elicit the recall of the event.
- **Problems** in **interpersonal relationships**.
- **Somatic reactions:** headache, backache, dizziness...

People going through anxious situations do not normally read books like this in order to practically apply the advice given. These tips are therefore for those nearby willing to help: neighbours, relatives, primary help providers, volunteers...

If you ever have the opportunity to help personally and directly the victims of a catastrophe or natural disaster, bear in mind the pieces of advice outlined below.

How to help the victims

Aside from the medical care and practical help that victims may receive, there are a number of mental health tips that can also be applied:

- **Remember that mental healing takes time.** Persuade the affected individual that, in the same way that physical sores take time to completely heal, psychological traumas also take time. Unfortunately, sometimes this means months or even years. However, the healing process is progressive and includes a small step each day.

- **Invite the person to talk about the experience.** Talking about what has happened may become highly therapeutic. Whenever possible, encourage victims to share their testimony. Try it in a peaceful and relaxing environment, without any rush, and with total devotion and empathy on your part. If the victim does not wish to talk about the disaster, wait for a better moment, and do not force this form of therapy.

- **Look for self-help groups.** It has been proven that the support of other surviving victims in the context of a self-help group is a very effective treatment. Remember that the group should be led by a group counselling expert. Help the victim to search for an already existing group, or else try and organise one.

- **Initiate the surviving person into a routine.** After the first few days of shock, the person should retake his/her daily life, or part of it, with specific routines, based on tasks that may serve as distraction. This is a way to avoid excessive rumination and to restore self-confidence and hope in the future.

- **Watch out for your health.** It is very important that survivors from catastrophes practise healthy habits, including eating wholesome and appealing food, getting regular sleep, doing physical activity and following a systematic lifestyle.

- **Avoid important decisions.** The period of recovery from natural disasters does not permit important decision-making tasks regarding the profession or relationships of the affected person. Such decisions must be taken after the healing process is over.

DEALING WITH OTHER'S MISFORTUNES

There are people who are too sensitive to others' misfortunes, even though they may be far away. They suffer from not being able to offer support or because it seems an injustice which is impossible to solve. What can one do in these cases?

- **Take a break from news,** TV, radio or newspapers.
- **Convince yourself that you are *not* responsible** and that events have nothing to do with you.
- **Gain perspective.** Reflect on the importance of your work or your duties in the place where you live. Think of your usefulness here and now and in your long-term values.
- **Help somehow.** If not directly, at least via a donation.
- **Pray to God for those who suffer.** Faith is not inhibited by distance and your prayers may benefit others as well as yourself.

Gems of Ancient Wisdom

'Praise be to the God and Father of our Lord Jesus Christ, the Father of compassion and the God of all comfort, who comforts us in all our troubles, so that we can comfort those in any trouble with the comfort we ourselves have received from God' (2 Corinthians 1:3-4).

5.12

War

War is a frightening experience, especially to those living near the conflict.

Its effects have a great outreach, as there are wars somewhere in some part of the world at any time. This means that wars touch, directly or indirectly, almost any family on earth.

The effects of belligerent actions upon mental health are even more devastating than the sequels left behind by natural disasters.

Unlike a hurricane or earthquake, victims of war see themselves as the target of **deliberate human intervention**. The person argues: 'With dialogue and negotiating efforts perhaps the war could have been avoided; but that did not happen and I am now the victim.'

War hostilities affect people differently, depending on their personal strength and style. Also, effects depend upon the degree to which each one gets involved in the war.

Combatants, in principle, receive the most impact, but those in the rearguard are also touched. And, in modern wars, civilians, children, seniors and the sick often pay a great toll. War also affects people living hundreds and thousands of miles away, especially loved ones, exiled members of the war-torn community, and highly sensitive people.

How to diminish the effects of war

The impact of war is such that the person needs to adopt measures in several areas of life during and after the hostilities. If you have the chance to help someone living in those difficult moments, or if you want to be prepared for the future to face them yourself, bear the following principles in mind:

Mental attitude in face of the conflict

- **Decide that you are going to survive.** The desire to live and the firm mental determination to survive will help you to gain strength and maintain a positive psychological state. Do not fall into the trap of thinking that the end is near. Gaze at the future with excitement, examine your plans and purposes and consider them a real and authentic possibility.

- **Retrieve pleasant memories.** There are in your mind images, words, experiences, persons, events... that may bring a smile to your lips. Dwell in those happy memories. Treasure them and rehearse them in your head. When the present is disturbing, you must hold onto the pleasant past.

- **Preserve a healthy self-concept.** Try not to ruin your self-esteem because it is your lot to suffer for awhile. Your value is the same; your dignity, untouched. Your principles, your skills, your education, your goals continue to be firm and nobody can snatch them from you. You may have lost property (money, real estate, etc.) but that does not take away your personal value. Remember that there is hope where there is life and one can get a fresh start towards the original plans.

- **Filter war propaganda.** Protect yourself from the effect of war propaganda. Its messages are so strong and the emotional state so intense that people often end hating even their loved ones if falsely accused by the opposite side. Other times propaganda makes people change their most precious ideologies. Hold tight to your beliefs, your values and your principles. Contrast them with propaganda and make your decision conscientiously and harmoniously.

- **Redirect your feelings and emotions.** It is normal that you feel frustrated and angry with the situation. It is not easy to reject those thoughts, but you can manage the turbulence by engaging in activities and keeping in touch with a close friend or relative.

- **Enhance your spiritual life.** Wars and their turmoil are times when supernatural power is needed. Approach your God, your Creator and Heavenly Father through prayer. Reading and meditating on the Holy Scriptures is also a source of mental health, peace and calm in moments of anxiety.

Behaviour during the conflict

- **Show maximum discretion.** Expressing opinions in times of war is very dangerous. Be discrete and quiet. If in doubt, it is best to remain silent.

- **Keep yourself updated.** Search for reliable sources of information in order to have up-to-date information, but do not allow yourself to be consumed by information overload. Information saturation may increase your discomfort and discouragement.

- **Offer your help.** Although you may be suffering yourself, there will always be others worse off. Help them, listen to them and make provision to meet their needs whenever possible.

- **Care for your health.** Even in the midst of want and disorder, you can remember the basic principles of health and hygiene, diet, exercise and rest.

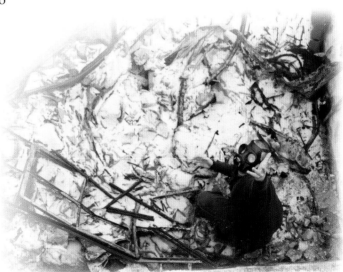

IMPACT ON COMBATANTS

The many wars of the 20th century have left millions of people with trauma of various kinds. This has permitted researchers and observers to follow up on war survivors, especially ex-combatants.

These are the problems experienced by ex-combatants at a rate of double or triple that of the general population:

- **Alcohol and tobacco** abuse.
- **Post-traumatic disorder** symptoms.
- **Feeling of insufficient happiness** and personal satisfaction.
- Frequency of **physical ailments**, such as coronary disease, asthma, diabetes, cancer, duodenal ulcer, and deafness.
- Frequency of **mental disorders**, especially depression and anxiety.

- **Spend time with your family.** During war, family relationships are essential to preserve mental heath. Strengthen your family ties and find refuge in friends and loved ones.

- **Talk about your experience.** Within your family or in a context of safe friendship, take the opportunity to verbalise. This will provide release for your spirit to help you to maintain your mental health.

- **Remember that your relational needs may vary.** With the war trauma you may end up feeling closer or more distant from loved ones. Even your sexual needs may change. These are normal variations and, with time, adjust themselves.

After the conflict

Once the war ends, psychological sequels remain and cause great difficulty in people's daily lives. During this time, it is necessary to maintain proper mental attitudes in order to prevent a collapse after the physical threat has gone:

- **Accept that healing takes time.** Emotional recovery after war hostilities takes time: months and even years. In order to avoid relapse, you must understand this long-term process. It is not easy to free oneself from anxiety, from resentment, from those involuntary memories, from asking yourself why, from fear of new wars, from regrets about this or that, etc. But with self-confidence and an attitude of hope, you must be sure that things will progressively improve.

- **Prepare for those stimuli that will cause memories to return.** Even long after the war, you will have moments when recollections will take over your mind. Prepare strategies to reject those thoughts or at least to approach them with growing calm. Anniversaries and other environmental or media events will rekindle your memory, but this may become therapeutic if you are able to review them calmly.

- **Adopt a hopeful attitude.** You must maintain firm hope in a good future at all times. Think confidently that your problems will get better and better or that your ability to face them will increase. In any case, seek God to obtain peace and hope in the future, including eternity.

RELIABLE PROMISES

In the midst of wars and disasters, the Bible has been for many the anchor allowing them to preserve their mental and spiritual wholeness. The reading of and reflection upon hopeful biblical passages, with assured faith in God and his infinite love, constitutes an ideal defence against the craze and frustration of war. The following promises are but a small sample of God's revelation to a weak, oppressed and hurting human being:

Psalm 37:24
'Though he [man] stumble, he will not fall, for the LORD upholds him with his hand.'

Psalm 46:1-3
'God is our refuge and strength,
an ever-present help in trouble.
Therefore we will not fear, though the earth give way
and the mountains fall into the heart of the sea,
though its waters roar and foam
and the mountains quake with their surging.'

Psalm 55:18
'He ransoms me unharmed from the battle waged against me, even though many oppose me.'

Psalm 91:3-6
'Surely he will save you from the fowler's snare
and from the deadly pestilence.
He will cover you with his feathers,
and under his wings you will find refuge;
his faithfulness will be your shield and rampart.
You will not fear the terror of night, nor the arrow that flies by day,
nor the pestilence that stalks in the darkness,
nor the plague that destroys at midday.'

Psalm 138:7
'Though I walk in the midst of trouble, you preserve my life;
you stretch out your hand against the anger of my foes, with your right hand you save me.'

Lamentations 3:31-33
'For men are not cast off by the Lord for ever.
Though he brings grief, he will show compassion, so great is his unfailing love.
For he does not willingly bring affliction or grief to the children of men.'

John 16:33
'I have told you these things, so that in me you may have peace.
In this world you will have trouble.
But take heart! I have overcome the world.'

Chapter Summary

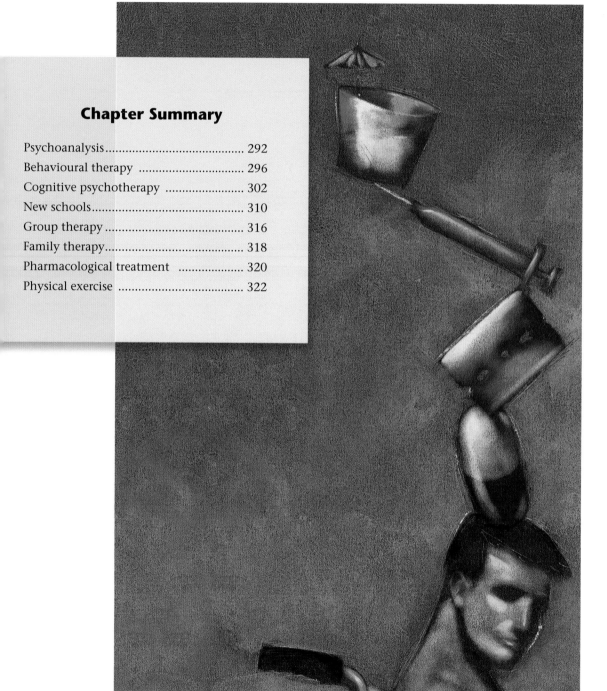

Therapies

6

Mildred, married and mother of two children, has a cleaning compulsion. She is afraid of getting infected with poisonous germs from house dirt and food. There are days when, as soon as she finishes cleaning the house, she feels the urge to do it again. She admits it does not make sense, but she goes on and repeats the process from beginning to end. She does the same thing with food; and even so, she eats with some apprehension, fearful of the germs that she might be ingesting. When she is invited to eat out, she does not enjoy herself because she is assaulted by worry over lack of hygiene. Soon she completely loses her appetite and feels nauseous.

Mildred consulted a psychologist, and received the diagnosis of obsessive-compulsive disorder. The psychologist is an expert in cognitive-behavioural therapy (units 6.02 and 6.03). She introduced Mildred to thought-stopping techniques to prevent her obsessive ideas. Mildred also watched some DVDs of people carrying out house and kitchen cleaning activities in a satisfactory manner without anxiety or unnecessary repetition. These persons enjoyed their free time and ate with gratitude and satisfaction, without suffering from scruples or fears. Lastly, Mildred talked to the psychologist about things that happened years before and cause her discomfort even today. All this helped her control her behaviour and the number of occurrences declined.

Chapter Highlights

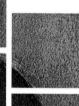

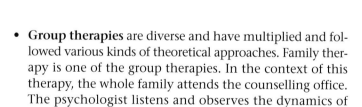

- According to **Freud**, mentally healthy individuals enjoy **equilibrium between these three components**: *ego*, *superego* and *id*. However, when there is a conflict between them, psychological disorders take over.

- **Behaviour modification** (one of the behavioural techniques) programmes are developed utilising all types of available consequences and positive reinforcements.

- **Cognitive restructuring** is based on the assumption that people who are prone to emotional imbalance tend to look at things in a negative way. The goal is to restructure the way of shaping judgments in order to adjust them to reality.

- Positive psychology is centred on **positive emotions** and optimism as a remedy to the majority of personal problems.

- **Group therapies** are diverse and have multiplied and followed various kinds of theoretical approaches. Family therapy is one of the group therapies. In the context of this therapy, the whole family attends the counselling office. The psychologist listens and observes the dynamics of family relations.

- Aside from psychotherapy and other alternative remedies, drugs serve as a **good complement** in the treatment of psychological problems.

- The **healing and stabilising effects** of physical activity are seen as an unquestionable fact in the circles of both the mental and physical health professions.

A whole variety of therapeutic approaches

This unit contains a series of widely used psychotherapies that apply to mental disorders. They are grouped into eight categories according to type of therapy. Much of the advice offered can be practised **by the person him/herself**. In other cases, however, more complex techniques require the presence of a **specialised psychotherapist**.

The oldest clinical therapies used nowadays belong to the field of **psychoanalysis** (unit 6.01), which centres on problems whose roots are in the past, generally in the stages of infancy or childhood. The goal of the procedure is to reach the person's subconscious to find the original cause of the disorder. It is a long and laborious process. Before beginning, the patient needs to ask the right questions—how it works and for how long it is likely to last.

Behavioural therapy is one of the most popular forms of treatment today (unit 6.02). The goal of this procedure is to eliminate undesirable behaviours through rewards and habit changes. Emotional problems are often manifested by automatic behaviours, by impulse or habit. Behavioural therapy works well in these cases.

Cognitive therapy (unit 6.03) is also very popular. In fact, it is very commonly used together with the behavioural approach, as they complement each other. Without any doubt, this combination represents the highest percentage of all treatments used in psychotherapy today. Cognitive therapy centres on mental processes, as it assumes that undesirable behaviour happens because of erroneous thinking. Therefore, the majority of cognitive techniques are geared to controlling, guiding, or modifying thinking and thoughts so that they do not lead the person to psychopathological manifestations.

Over the last few decades **new schools** of psychotherapy (unit 6.04) have emerged. The following are included under new schools: **Neuro-linguistic programming, positive psychology, resilience** and **spiritual psychotherapy**. These new approaches have been welcomed by many, as they emphasise health and mental well-being over psychological illness and they anticipate high success levels. They are also attractive because they use easy-to-understand processes and carry a high rate of effectiveness, especially for mild disorders, which are the majority.

Group therapy is also presented (unit 6.05) as it contributes to the healing of problems and conflicts. The advantage of this technique lies in the effect that the group produces upon each participant. Because members face a common problem, all learn from each other. They are willing to make group covenants, and this gives strength to each individual to face barriers whenever left alone.

A special modality of group therapy is **family therapy** (unit 6.06). This form of intervention is built upon the idea that the family is a social system where people with problems can worsen or get better according to family dynamics. The psychotherapist requires the participation of all family members who are living under the same roof. This is done in order to understand interrelations and to prescribe steps aimed towards solving the problems.

Another form of psychological treatment is **drug therapy** (unit 6.07). This approach, even though it does not heal, provides the necessary support for the patient's well-being and sustains him/her while under one form or another of therapy or while waiting for stressors to vanish.

Lastly, a new form of therapy is included—**physical exercise** (unit 6.08). There is no doubt among the scientific community of the multiple benefits that physical activity offers to mental health. Very common problems, such as stress, depression and anxiety weaken considerably when exercise and physical activity are integrated in the psychotherapeutic strategy.

Fortunately, today there are many options for the treatment of psychological disturbances. There are a variety of possible interventions both for severe problems and for those arising from temporary circumstances. We invite the reader to explore those presented in this book and to learn more from other sources in order to apply them to their lives and preserve a good state of mental health.

6.01
Psychoanalysis

Psychoanalysis is the oldest form of psychotherapy. Austrian psychiatrist **Sigmund Freud** (1856-1939) created the theory and practice of psychoanalysis. To Freud, human beings are by nature **irrational, impulsive and selfish**. Their behaviour is determined by impulses and sexual and aggressive instincts. The environment, through the influence of culture, customs and education, shapes those basic instincts into acceptable behaviour in the framework of existing rules.

These are, according to Freud, the **personality components**:

- The *id*, or human instinctive energy. It contains the most selfish and primitive tendencies of hu-

man nature. It is an internal force within the person, but the person is conscious of it.

- The *superego*, which is the person's conscience. It represents values, principles and standards of behaviour acquired through family, society and the culture where one lives.

- The *ego*, or rational structure of personality. It encompasses thought and conscious personal decisions. The ego is the balance between aggressive force (id) and moral strength (superego).

Mentally healthy individuals enjoy equilibrium between the three components above. On the other hand, when there is a conflict between them, psychological disorders take over.

Psychoanalysis attributes **present conflicts** to **past experiences**, especially from infancy and early childhood. When bitter experiences (for example, threats, abuse, terror, etc.) remain unconsciously in memory storage for a long time, the person runs a high risk of psychological imbalance.

The fundamental goal of psychoanalysts is, therefore, to facilitate the transfer of bad memories from the unconscious to the conscience. This is the beginning of the healing process.

Psychoanalytic techniques

The object of all psychoanalytic techniques is to reveal unconscious conflicts in order to *verbalise* them and eliminate their effect. How is this intervention carried out?

Traditional psychoanalysis occurs in a clinical room with a couch where the patient lies. The analyst sits by the headboard, out of the patient's sight, to favour free and fluent expression. Four to five weekly sessions are held, each an hour long. **Psychoanalytic therapy** (contemporary version of classical psychoanalysis) does not use a couch, but a face-to-face interview. It also reduces the sessions to one or two per week.

These are the most widely used psychodynamic techniques:

Free association

In a peaceful and relaxing environment, the patient expresses his/her thoughts and feelings in a spontaneous manner as they come to mind. Other times, the analyst says common words and the patient responds with whatever verbal expression may come to his/her mind.

This activity reveals unconscious information. The therapist interprets these messages, which most often point to the person's remote past (for example, when the patient was a small child). Both talk about the past events that have presumably produced the imbalance. This interaction about remote events brings about an unloading or **catharsis**, which contributes to the patient's recovery.

Dream analysis

For the psychoanalyst, dreams contain relevant information from the unconscious. If the patient manages to retrieve the contents of a dream, the therapist may interpret the meaning.

Patients are therefore asked to sleep with notebook and pencil at hand. At the time of waking up, without any delay, they are to remember and write down the basic dream content they just had.

PRACTICAL CASE

Free association applied to the feeling of emptiness

This is an example of a woman patient in the first stages of psychoanalysis. She verbalises whatever comes to her mind and the therapist intervenes only sparingly to facilitate fluency of ideas.

Patient: Well... if I am here it is because I feel an inner emptiness... I do not find satisfaction. This makes me anxious... Will it be like this for the rest of my life? As a little girl I was very energetic, loving, enthusiastic and full of life... How much I have changed! But, why has this happened? When did it all start? I got married five years ago and I was excited about marriage... I wanted to develop professionally [she stops for a moment and thinks; then she continues]. Frankly speaking, I don't think it is my husband (poor thing!) or my job [She sighs]. I have a friend, Sarah. She is very happy, always radiant. I am so jealous! Why not me? I feel something is lacking.

Therapist: So you were happy as a child...

Patient: Yes, absolutely.

Therapist: Always? During all of your childhood? What about later on?

Patient: Hmm... Well, as a child I was very lively and did what I wanted... I was free! Though I should admit that this was not welcome by my parents. They were lenient with me and I took advantage... I had a good time. I was a little crazy, and they disapproved of my behaviour. In sum, I suppose I ought to recognise that I was not a model daughter.

Therapist: How do you get along with them now?

Patient: (increasingly restless and with teary eyes): They died six years ago... It was a terrible accident.

As the dialogue—almost a monologue—progressed, the patient searched for the key to her problem. She ruled out certain options. In the end, with the analyst's discrete but highly valuable help, a sudden association of ideas seemed to orient her in the right direction.

Use of insight in agoraphobia

The insight technique aims at a sudden 'inner vision' of elements hidden to the conscience. Let's examine an example where this is sought through a discussion held in an advanced stage of psychoanalysis.

Patient: As I have told you I am terrified to go out... My breathing only returns to normal when I get to my door and get in the lift... Once at home, I feel totally relieved.

Therapist: You are afraid of people. I know that. What we need to find out is the origin of your fear.

Patient: I think it is my fault. I am the inhibited, insecure type, just as others are intrepid, cold-blooded... I have always seen it as a matter of temperament.

Therapist: Always? Since when? Since the time of your birth? Please, think about it.

Patient: Excuse me, doctor, but there is nothing to think about. I am like that. That's all.

Therapist: So, were you born inhibited?

Patient: Correct! My father was not a tyrant, if that is where you are going.

Therapist: And your mother?

Patient (hesitant): My mother...? She used to show authoritarianism and excessive devotion to me. Just because she wanted to overprotect me; she saw me as weak...

From here on, the therapist prolonged the conversation to find out to what extent the last piece of information was relevant. In other words, the meaning of the relationship between the patient and his mother, as this could be the cause of his agoraphobia, or at least a contributing factor.

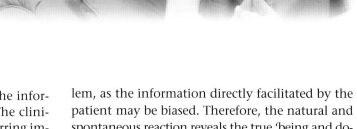

This is done for a number of days and the information is taken to the psychoanalyst. The clinician identifies patterns, themes, and recurring images from the dreams. Then hypotheses are drawn with possible internal and unknown conflicts that affect the patient. Once these contents are identified, the patient talks in depth about them until emotional balance is restored.

Transference

There are **behavioural patterns or feelings** (for example, hostility or affection) normally used by the patient towards a close person. These same feelings or behaviours are transferred to the analyst.

Without planning for it, the patient behaves with the therapist as if he were his/her father, husband/wife, or opponent. Transference helps the psychoanalyst to interpret the nature of the problem, as the information directly facilitated by the patient may be biased. Therefore, the natural and spontaneous reaction reveals the true 'being and doing' of the patient.

Insight

This is a type of **discovery** that takes place in a sudden and casual manner in the context of analytic psychotherapy.

The therapist helps the patient to verbally express an opinion on an emotionally-charged topic. Both engage in a debate that may bring to the surface the personal style of the patient; and this may be the deep cause of the problem.

This insight or revelation allows the patient to transform unconscious contents into conscious ones and begin recovery through talking about the topic.

Psychoanalysis and addictions

Marlo and Kalinian's study (2003) about the effectiveness of psychoanalysis on the treatment of drug and alcohol addictions shows how psychoanalytic therapy works well with certain individuals, especially those inclined to use drinking and drugs to alleviate pressure from a strong sense of guilt.

Highly effective therapies, such as Alcoholic Anonymous (see page 133), do not work well with this type of person, as any relapse will make him or her feel like a total failure. The addict then enters into a vicious circle that perpetuates addiction.

Psychoanalytic therapy uses a less guilt-ridden and more tolerant system, with a high success rate in cases of substance dependence. The study states that psychoanalytic therapy benefits from its application together with cognitive-behavioural strategies (see the next two units).

COMPLEXITY OF PSYCHOANALYSIS

Psychoanalysis is a complex process that cannot be carried out through self-help or without the direction of a trained individual. The intervention of a psychotherapist with the necessary experience is therefore necessary in order to count on a high probability of success. On the other hand, it is known that psychoanalysis...

- is usually **long** and can lag on for years.
- is the most **expensive** form of therapy due to its length and the training of the psychoanalyst.
- has a high level of **dependence on the psychoanalyst**.
- is often **questioned** for its **lack of scientific support**.

Gems of Ancient Wisdom

'I do not understand what I do. For what I want to do I do not do, but what I hate I do. [...] What a wretched man I am! Who will rescue me from this body of death? Thanks be to God—through Jesus Christ our Lord!' (Romans 7:15, 24-25).

6.02
Behavioural therapy

Observable behaviour is the most important factor for behavioural therapy. Once the undesirable conduct is identified, it can be modified with the application of appropriate techniques.

This therapy recognises feelings, thoughts and personal values, but does not consider them highly when applying intervention. In fact, according to behavioural theory, there is no need to change them. Having altered the behaviour, feelings and thoughts will start to change.

But this does not always happen. That is why, over the last few years, the combined cognitive-behavioural approach has been emphasised to use both cognitive and behavioural therapies, as explained in the next unit.

Behavioural therapy works well by itself when the problem does not have deep roots. It is especially adequate under the following circumstances:

• **When the cause of the problem is a learned behaviour.** Undesirable conducts learned by repetition or observation are more easily modifiable than those appearing as a result of trauma or of consolidated personality. If, for example, a depression comes as a result of living together with a depressive person and observing and imitating that individual, behavioural therapy will be quite useful.

• **When rewards and prizes are appropriate.** If a child with enuresis (see page 183) is under treatment, one could use a point system wherein the child is given one point for each night without wetting the bed and later on the points can be exchanged for toys.

• **When punishment is avoided.** For example, in an intoxication treatment, it is better to reward abstinence for two months than to punish a relapse.

• **When the desirable behaviour can be learned by imitation.** For example, an adolescent displaying violence will change more by observing the normal behaviour in other adolescents than from receiving a sermon.

Psychotherapeutic techniques

These are very widely used behavioural techniques:

Systematic desensitisation

It is a useful technique for those suffering from anxiety towards objects and situations such as travelling by plane, speaking in public, receiving an injection, being in a high place, meeting people, using a lift, etc.

It can also be successfully applied in cases of insomnia, stammering, alcohol abuse, anger, and asthma attacks. The procedure is based on the fact that anxiety and relaxation are incompatible and, with sufficient practice, relaxation prevails (see the box on the right).

Behaviour modification

This form of therapy is utilised to eliminate undesirable behaviours, especially in children. For example, temper tantrums, disobedience, untidiness, etc. It is also useful to extinguish habits such

continued on page 298

CORRECTING BAD TEMPER

If you are given to bad temper in your dealings with others, try to change tactics and see the results. Make a point in practising the following behaviours during an entire day:

- Smile and adopt a pleasant facial expression.
- Show genuine interest in others.
- Display kindness and courtesy.
- See the humourous side of things.
- Gaze at life's positive aspects and talk to others about them.

Carefully observe **other people's reaction**. Many will display the same kind and positive behaviours as you. Is it any easier for you, then, to practise the acts from the list in view of the reactions of others?

Behaviour modification (especially in connection with relationships) can begin with small acts until it becomes a habit of correct and polite interaction.

Systematic desensitisation for social phobia

Jason was elevated to department head at his company. However, the position required that he addressed groups of people and Jason suffered serious anxiety in front of an audience. In spite of preparing himself thoroughly, at the time of making the presentation, he lost control and experienced sweating, stuttering and ended up reading his paper too quickly and with mistakes.

He decided to go to the psychologist and received the diagnosis of social phobia. The psychotherapist applied a systematic desensitisation plan with the following steps:

1. Jason learned progressive relaxation in the clinic and practised it at home for several days. This technique is based on the tension and relaxation of different muscle groups (see page 40).

2. With Jason's help, the psychologist developed an anxiety scale from situations of little anxiety up to those producing a great deal of fear:

*	He is told to present a report (*minimal anxiety*)
**	Preparing his presentation
***	Walking to the boardroom
****	Hearing his name announcing the presentation
*****	Beginning his speech in front of the audience
******	Questions asked by those in attendance (*maximum anxiety*)

3. After a relaxation session, the therapist helped Jason imagine the first scene in detail. He was surprised to notice that he remained relaxed. The same was repeated with the second situation in the list; then the third, and fourth. At the fifth scene, Jason could not tolerate imagining the faces of the executive directors looking at him. The session was stopped at this time.

4. The next appointment began with relaxation followed by the visualisation of pending scenes. When difficulties were encountered, the session would stop and continue at the next appointment.

5. After having managed to visualise all scenes in a relaxed state, Jason went to the actual boardroom (without people) and practised his speech.

6. On the day of his presentation he thought of the achievements of previous days and, even though he felt a certain amount of anxiety, he made an acceptable presentation.

continued from 297

as fingernail biting or telling lies, especially when they are not prompted by deep emotional problems.

The technique requires studying the environment in order to identify the stimuli that push the person to the questionable behaviour. In addition, it is necessary to find out what the person likes in order to design a good reinforcement plan. The consequences of the behaviour also need careful study, as they will vary depending on whether the effects are painful or pleasurable (see the Self-help box on the previous page).

Behaviour modification programmes are developed utilising all types of available **positive reinforcements**:

- **Material reinforcements:** Toys, sweets, colouring books, etc. in the case of children. Clothes, books, flowers... for adults.
- **Token economy:** Vouchers, coupons, tokens and other forms of credit can be accrued in order to exchange them for valuable objects or reinforcing activities.
- **Reinforcement activity:** Watch TV, go out with friends, attend a play, go out to dine in a restaurant or play a favourite sport.
- **Social reinforcements:** Praise, messages of encouragement, smiles, hugs, etc.

It is advisable to use material rewards in the initial stages of treatment. As the process moves on, social reinforcement is introduced to reach the final goal—maintain the desirable behaviour through internal (and not external) motivation.

PUNISHMENT OR REWARD?

Beware of choosing a punishment that is actually a reinforcing experience!

For example, to punish a child to go to the loft (or the cellar) when he is bad may become a 're-ward' instead of a punishment. There may be many attractive and amusing objects in the loft that will provide full entertainment to the child.

If this is so, he/she will do anything possible to 'be bad' in order to receive such attractive punishment.

Behaviour modification for temper tantrums

Four-year-old Alfred was always an easy child. However, since his little brother was born, everything changed. Alfred used to lose his temper far too often—sometimes 5 or 6 strong episodes in the same day. He also lost his appetite. Finally, his parents went to the psychologist for help.

The psychologist visited their house two afternoons. Without talking much, she observed life in the family and took some notes. She held two interviews with the parents and one with Alfred. It became clear that Alfred's mother was reinforcing the boy's inadequate behaviour. He had learned that he could attract his mum's attention when she was taking care of the baby. He only had to throw himself to the floor, scream and kick and say that he did not want to eat. Straight away, his mother left the baby to affectionately attend to Alfred.

The behaviour modification **plan** had two objectives:

1. To eliminate temper tantrums.
2. To return to normal eating habits.

This was the counsel to follow:

1. **Do not pay attention** to Alfred when he throws a temper tantrum.
2. **Devote exclusive time** to him every day, showing that, in spite of the arrival of the baby, his parents' love and care have not diminished. Do not show approval and affection when Alfred has a temper tantrum or when he refuses to eat.
3. **Encourage him to participate in the care of the little one.** This will make him forget about himself.
4. **Do not pay attention to him when he refuses to eat.** Do not permit him to eat between meals so that he will be hungry at the table. Start the plan with his favourite recipes.
5. Use a **token economy.** Alfred is to receive tokens for obeying, for helping with small tasks, for eating well, for not having tantrums, etc.
6. Whenever a whole week passes with good eating habits and without temper tantrums, Alfred can visit and play with his cousins for a whole day as a **reward**.

The plan worked well to the point of reaching the objectives within the first week. There were minimal relapses, and after one month, the problem was considered solved.

Self-control technique

With the help of a clinician or with adequate materials, the person learns principles and skills to be his/her own therapist. The subject keeps an eye on himself/herself, controls himself/herself, and administers rewards to himself/herself.

In order to carry out this technique, a good measure of **discipline** is necessary. But the pressing need to abandon certain habits has given strength to many, so that they help themselves by following the self-control principles.

This technique is **highly recommendable** for those who need to **abandon substance addiction** (alcohol, tobacco) or to acquire good habits of study, eating, organisation, etc.

Modelling or imitation

This technique is based on the idea that many behaviours originate from observing other people. Therefore, adopting new behaviours or modifying existing ones may be successfully attained through observation and imitation.

The following models are the most likely to be imitated:

- influential
- attractive
- powerful
- of the same social or ethnic group
- of the same age and gender

PRACTICAL CASE

Self-control to correct eating anomalies

In a medical check-up the doctor warned Beth that at her age of 50, and given her increasing weight gain, she was becoming a firm candidate for heart attack. With the help of a friend who knew the psychological principles of self-control, Beth managed to lose weight progressively and definitely. Aside from the diet prescribed by the doctor, self-control techniques demanded an initial change of habits, a new lifestyle. See the list of habits in the lower section of this box.

Beth attached a copy of her diet on the refrigerator door together with the list of new behaviours and a chart to record her weight data. She weighed herself every week. Each time she was able to record a half-kilo loss, she used her savings from not buying sweets and junk food and rewarded herself with the following:

- Cinema or theatre ticket.
- Natural fruit juice in a nice snack bar.
- Massage in a sauna parlour.
- The latest book by her favourite author.
- Musical CD.
- A new item of clothing for her new shape.

In a natural and spontaneous way, the words of admiration from friends and relatives were added ('Your figure is stunning!'), thus affirming in Beth the new dietary habits, which, in the end, produced health and happiness.

Old habits	New behaviours
• *Eating hundreds of calories alone.*	• *Eating with her family or a friend.*
• *Using pre-cooked fast food.*	• *Using time and effort to prepare food.*
• *Going to supermarket while hungry.*	• *Going to the supermarket after eating.*
• *Cooking in large amounts.*	• *Cooking just for one meal.*
• *Eating very fast.*	• *Taking double the time to eat than before.*
• *Eating while watching TV.*	• *Not eating outside the dining table.*

A contract to solve marriage conflict

Martha and Gabriel recounted their experience two years after their wedding. Their relationship problems had grown to the point of almost producing separation. Martha suggested going to a counselling centre. Gabriel disagreed, but he was eventually convinced.

The sessions were tense in the beginning. Gabriel thought that the counsellor was on Martha's side. And she suspected that the professional was favouring Gabriel. After four sessions, dynamics started to take a hopeful turn. After having listened extensively to both parties, and having assessed the situation, the counsellor stated the fundamental problems. The couple confirmed that her hypothesis was correct.

These were the **areas** producing **most frustration** in Martha:

• She hardly received demonstrations of love and affection from her husband.

• Gabriel did not show interest in her side of the family and was indifferent towards his parents-in-law.

• He did not help with house chores.

Gabriel's major sources of frustration regarding Martha were:

• Martha did not consider his opinion when spending money; however, he always checked with her when making important purchases.

• Their sexual life had vanished some time after their wedding and she did not show much interest in sexuality.

The contract itemised each one's responsibilities. It was agreed for him to be more gregarious with his parents-in-law, but they had to plan together all activities regarding this matter. She would be more sexually active, but he was responsible to 'prepare for sex' with his verbal messages of care and tenderness. All the fundamental areas received attention in the contract. A few things required negotiation, but the counsellor helped as arbiter, adding a good sense of humour.

Lastly, the contract was signed. The couple soon started to change behaviours and to adopt new habits of mutual interaction. The marriage had been saved thanks to expressed negotiation reflected in a written document.

How is this idea taken to the psychotherapeutic context? The application modalities are diverse:

• The therapist demonstrates the behaviour to be imitated. The person observes, reproduces and rehearses the behaviour in the safe environment of the counselling room.

• Other subjects (actors) serve as models. They can be real or be in a video or DVD.

• Examples, stories or books may serve as a source of inspiration and imitation.

• Dramas are observed by the client, sometimes played with the client's participation.

Modelling can be used to teach various social skills, ways to manage stress, alternatives to face anxiety, etc.

(See the case of Mildred, given at the beginning of this chapter, page 289, where behavioural modelling was applied to her cleaning obsession).

Contracts

Behavioural contracts are extremely useful when facing problems that affect two or more persons.

Couples, families, classrooms or work teams are the contexts where this method establishes the steps necessary to attain harmony and restore damaged relationships.

The document, usually drawn in the presence of someone acting as arbiter, describes the agreements and specifies the consequences of abiding or not abiding by the covenant. The contract should be stated in specific, reasonable and positive terms. (See the box above).

Behavioural medicine

Behavioural medicine is focused on identifying and modifying habits and thoughts directly affecting a specific organic illness. It also prepares the patient to avoid environmental conditions that may impinge upon the illness. The psychologist's participation in the medical team is becoming increasingly common, as it has been confirmed that conventional medical treatment may be significantly enhanced by behavioural medicine.

Many organic responses, such as the dilatation of blood vessels or intestinal spasms, are affected by the person's behaviour. By means of behavioural medicine, the individual receives instruction to face circumstances in a healthier way.

In order to ascertain the specific processes affecting the organism, as well as their extent, behavioural medicine utilises sophisticated systems of biological feedback. By means of **sensors**, the patient receives direct information from the painful areas and can see the connection between the available data and his own behaviour, thought or circumstance. This is not always practical and many times the traditional paper-and-pencil method is used to record environmental events and symptoms. Examining these records, we can establish cause-effect relationships in order to apply treatment. The box on the right illustrates how this form of therapy is carried out.

Behavioural medicine for a case of irritable colon

Margaret was undergoing irritable colon treatment over two years without noticeable improvement. She tried several types of drugs, but her condition did not improve. She continued to experience strong abdominal pain, which appeared and disappeared without apparent reason, along with attacks of diarrhoea.

In partnership with the doctor, the psychologist established a **plan** whereby Margaret would follow these tasks:

- **Hourly record of her routine activities** plus out-of-the-ordinary events.
- **Record her symptoms** (intestinal pain, diarrhoea…) and intensity.
- **Record her mood** as influenced by symptoms and events.
- **Identification of stressing activities** with date and time.

After studying all data, physician and psychologist observed a close relationship between visiting certain, excessively demanding clients (Margaret worked in sales) and the worsening of symptoms. To avoid any clashes, she remained quiet before their demands (mostly inappropriate). The intervention plan included **assertiveness** training so that she would express her viewpoint and communicate with clients the things that could be done, as well as the limitations. Intestinal symptoms improved in a few weeks as Margaret became prepared to face her discomfort.

LIMITATIONS OF BEHAVIOURISM

Behavioural techniques focus on behaviour, not on the root of problems. There are therefore many cases where this type of treatment is insufficient.

When Henry, a stammering 11-year-old boy, was prescribed a treatment, he was taught pronunciation techniques in a specialised laboratory where he automatically responded to computerised stimuli. In three weeks his problem was practically taken care of.

However, a week later, the problem reappeared with similar intensity. It was then confirmed that the problem was with his two older brothers, who embarrassed him and ridiculed him causing insecurity and stammering.

In this case, together with the behavioural treatment, **therapies focused on his feelings**, his self-concept and interpersonal conflict resolution. The results were successful.

6.03
Cognitive psychotherapy

Cognitive psychotherapy focuses on mental processes. This approach teaches that thoughts precede behaviours. Therefore, those with the tendency to worry excessively due to trivial things can learn to manage thinking processes and focus them on topics adjusted to reality. If the way one thinks is changed, the manifestation of those thoughts (the anxious and worrying behaviour) will also change.

The **goal** is to **instruct the person to control his/her mind and thoughts** in order to produce alternative ways of judging and behaving.

Cognitive psychology has worked well for many kinds of mental disorders. Depression, anxiety, anger, stress, insomnia, traumatic experiences, and chronic pain are examples.

This approach to therapy is not infallible, as thoughts do not always translate into actions and results. Besides, it is difficult to utilise cognitive techniques with certain persons (see the box 'Limitations...' on page 309). Nevertheless, clinical experience has shown that cognitive psychotherapy works well in many cases and the duration of treatment is relatively brief.

Psychotherapeutic techniques

The following cognitive techniques are very widely used:

Self-talk

This is a self-help technique and can be practised individually without professional support. Basically, it consists of encouraging oneself and giving commands to oneself in order to face tense situations, to avoid undesirable behaviours or to attain control over impulses.

When Sylvia, mother of three small children, is about to get angry, she tells herself (quietly and inwardly): 'Sylvia, calm down. These children do not understand. Some day they will grow and become well behaved. Remember the last time you became too upset.'

After having given herself a few such messages, she breathes deeply and feels encouraged to proceed.

The formal clinical self-talk process follows four distinct steps illustrated in the box below.

PRACTICAL CASE

Self-talk for a case of shyness

Stanley was so shy that very rarely would he approach a young lady to talk with her. He read about self-talk in a book and decided to try it in order to approach Barbara, an attractive peer. Although a difficult task at the beginning, Stanley began to leave behind his inhibition whilst focusing on the steps to follow:

1. **Identification of destructive or negative thoughts.** For Stanley, typical sentences were: 'She is going to say "no" and that will ruin me.' 'She will even laugh at me together with her girlfriends. How embarrassing! How awful!'

2. **Transformation of such thoughts into practical ideas and solutions.** Stanley said to himself: 'Instead of anticipating failure, I will do something to avoid it. I will prepare what to say. I will rehearse in front of the mirror. I will wear new clothes and perfume. I will keep calm at all times.'

3. **Use positive thinking on oneself.** Stanley was shy basically because he con-

sidered himself inferior when compared to others. He started to use thoughts such as: 'I am a good student. When I get set to do something, I tend to do it well. I do not play football too badly. I do not have many friends, but those I have appreciate me. And as far as my looks, I am not so ugly as to scare Barbara away.'

4. **Success visualisation.** The last step was for Stanley to imagine the success he would achieve in meeting Barbara. He envisioned himself as relaxed, approaching her naturally, and speaking to her with a bright smile. She seemed happy to see him and her way of responding favoured an open and frank conversation. After some conversational time, he would say: 'The other day I heard you say that you would like to attend a concert. I have purchased two tickets for Sunday and I would like to take you. What do you think?

Stanley was surprised at how he carried out his objective in an unprecedented calm; all because he prepared himself mentally following this simple advice.

Gems of Ancient Wisdom

'Finally, brothers, whatever is true, whatever is noble, whatever is right, whatever is pure, whatever is lovely, whatever is admirable— if anything is excellent or praiseworthy— **think about** such things' (Philippians 4:8).

'There is deceit in the hearts of those who plot evil, but joy for those who promote peace' (Proverbs 12:20).

Cognitive restructuring

This technique is based on the assumption that people who are prone to emotional imbalance tend to look at things in a negative way. The goal is, therefore, to transform or restructure the way of shaping judgments in order to adjust them to reality, rather than to negativism.

Based on his clinical experience with depressive patients, psychiatrist **Aaron Beck** concluded that the onset and development of depression depended greatly on how the person interpreted life events. In sum, he verified that negative thoughts pose the main barrier to recovery.

Through his interviews with patients, Beck found a great deal of **perception and judgment errors**, and most of them could be changed. These are a few examples:

- **Assess matters in extreme terms.** 'Either I do my work to perfection or I do not do it at all.' 'My girlfriend's love is not passionate—she must hate me.'

- **Generalise.** 'Everybody rejects me.' 'I am going to fail all my subjects,' 'My boyfriend left me—all men are the same.' 'Things always turn out wrongly.'

- **Exaggerate.** 'I made a mistake on my income tax form—I will end up in prison.' 'I have eaten unwashed fruit—I will become ill.'

- **Draw illogical conclusions.** 'I have found cigarettes in my son's room—he is hooked on drugs.' 'Those two individuals in the corner have looked at me—no doubt that they are talking about me.'

In addition, Beck discovered that these pessimistic and catastrophic thoughts were on the following **three areas**:

- **Oneself.** The person looks at himself/herself in a pessimistic way: 'I will not attain it.' 'I am too stupid.' 'These things are not for me.'

- **The world.** In her pessimistic analysis, the person moves on to others and the general environment. 'They only wish to take advantage of people.' 'Circumstances are so difficult that there is no possible solution.' 'His attitude shows that his only purpose is to hurt others.'

- **The future.** The person views the future hopelessly: 'I will never find a job.' 'My son will have an accident any day.' 'My father died young; it will soon be my turn.'

Cognitive restructuring has, therefore, **two major aims**:

1. **Identify the patient's erroneous thought.** The person is not usually aware of the negative thoughts and the help of a second person (generally a psychotherapist) becomes necessary in order to identify them.

2. **Offer more balanced judgment options.** The therapist shows the patient's irrationality and proposes healthier judgment alternatives.

P R A C T I C A L   C A S E

Cognitive restructuring for depression

Michael's symptoms (weakness, insomnia, loss of appetite, guilt, inferiority…) led the psychiatrist to diagnose depression, and she prescribed adequate drugs but warned that the tablets were not sufficient and that he needed psychological treatment.

He visited the psychologist, who soon concluded that Michael needed to change his way of thinking. For example, one of his main problems was to get discouraged because of his work. Any change of circumstance would make Michael think that something horrible was about to happen. The therapist would demonstrate to him that his attitude lacked logic; so the clinician showed Michael that his past experiences revealed the nonsense of his fear.

Another problem was that he would take seriously any comment from his friends or family. Something as simple and humourous as: 'Michael, you are going to become bald,' would make him worry a great deal.

The role of the psychotherapist was to persuade him that his thoughts were unfounded and illogical. He also asked Michael to keep a **record of all negative thoughts** that overtook him between sessions, as well as any **incidents and ideas that preceded** the thoughts. This information revealed the situations that caused negative thinking. It took twelve sessions to solve all the conflicts, but eventually Michael became aware of what produced his depressive symptoms and how to prevent them.

self-help

ANALYSE YOUR THOUGHTS

This exercise will help you to identify your negative thinking and to look for alternatives. Read the example and think of a real situation in your life. Identify negative thoughts and substitute them with positive alternatives. Repeat the exercise, applying it to new situations.

Situation: 'Next week we are going on holiday to a foreign country'	
Negative thoughts	**Adaptive responses**
'We will forget something'	'We will make a list of necessary things'
'We will lose our passports'	'We need to be cautious'
'They will steal something from us'	'Theft is improbable if we stay in a group'
'The language is going to be a problem'	'We are going to have a wonderful time!'
Consequences	**Consequences**
Discouragement, headache, worry	Happiness, excitement, well-being, anticipation

Situation: [Another one]	
Negative thoughts	**Adaptive responses**
...	...
...	...
...	...
Consequences	**Consequences**
...	...

Thought stopping

Thought control or thought stopping (also see page 146) is a simple technique that can be practised individually with great possibilities of success, provided there is determination.

The majority of behaviours have their origin in the preceding thought. This usually lasts long enough for the person to realise what is coming. The technique consists of stopping the chain of thoughts in time to avoid the behaviour.

The **process** includes four steps:

1. **Discover the thought** that produces stress or leads to the undesirable behaviour.
2. **Identify the links** or clues that announce the thought.
3. **Say: 'STOP!'** at the first sign of the link or clue.
4. **Fill the mind with an edifying topic** previously prepared for this purpose.

(The box on the adjoining page illustrates how this technique works).

---

self-help

STOP YOUR NEGATIVE THOUGHTS

Thought stopping is a very useful preventive measure. The majority of undesirable behaviours are preceded by thoughts. The goal is to detect ideas and mental processes that come before problem behaviour.

Carol had a tendency to experience feelings of inferiority when she observed other people perform tasks well. With the years, she had accepted (inadvertently) the belief that any task she would initiate should end up in absolute success. Of course, there were times when Carol failed. This would cause her great discouragement.

One day, as she was talking to a friend whom she admired for her achievements, Carol discovered that her friend also failed at times... This piece of information made her question her illogical belief and she managed to free herself from this harmful idea.

Aaron Beck suggested some of the irrational beliefs found in his patients:

- 'In order to be happy, I must succeed in any activity I initiate.'
- 'In order to be happy, I must always be accepted by everybody.'
- 'If I make a mistake, it means I am inept.'
- 'If someone disagrees with me, it means that he/she does not like me.'
- 'My value as a person depends on what others think of me.'

Do you share some of these irrational beliefs? Do you have other such thoughts in your life? Discover them. Try to reject them following the thought-stopping steps.

Thought stopping for a paedophilia case

Carl was a single man; he was kind, courteous, humourous, and liked by everyone. He lived with his mother and worked in a factory. On the weekends, he was a volunteer youth leader with the local boy scouts. After returning from a camping trip, a group of 10- to 12-year-old boys told their parents that Carl, between jokes and laughter, had hugged them and touched their genitals. Apparently, it was not the first time that this had occurred, but nobody had been brave enough to tell.

Carl was reported to a court and sentenced to pay a fine and to undergo psychological treatment. He did not take it wrongly. He was aware of his unacceptable impulse and wished to correct it. In fact, he had tried on several occasions, but to no avail.

In the counselling room he had ample opportunity to recall past events that could have been the cause of his paedophilia. He experienced a great relief to verbally express these things. But talking was not enough. He needed to be equipped with skills that he could utilise whenever his impulse took over. The psychotherapist taught him the thought-stopping technique:

1. **Discover the thought leading to behaviour.** His physical contact with the boys tended to occur soon after his indulging in certain fantasies—he envisioned himself naked caressing the boys. The longer the time spent in those thoughts, the more difficult it was for him to resist his impulse to seek contact with minors.

2. **Identify the links that announce such thoughts.** The mere observation of groups of boys was the beginning of his fantasies. Thus Carl, during the treatment, would avoid walking near schools, sports centres, etc.

3. **Say: 'STOP.'** Aware that one thought would lead to the next; he would say to himself 'STOP!' as soon as his mind would get busy with images of boys.

4. **Fill the mind with another topic.** Once the chain of thoughts was stopped, Carl would think of alternative images. To help himself, he would use small cards (kept in his pocket) where he had written some pleasant memories: 'the cottage of my uncle and aunt,' 'a card game,' 'the day when I was promoted,' 'my dog Laika.'

This technique helped Carl to free himself from the habit. He continued to use it after the treatment, although over time he needed to use it less frequently.

Problem resolution

This is a common form of cognitive therapy. It consists of performing a logical and rational analysis of any problem situation in order to choose the best possible solution.

As a general rule, the person in the midst of difficulties lacks the necessary resources to assess or solve his problem in a quiet and reflective way. It is therefore useful to count on **someone outside oneself** to provide guidance. Four steps are suggested for problem solving:

1. **Isolate the problem** with sufficient clarity.
2. **Suggest** as many **alternatives** as possible.
3. **Assess the proposed options**, their application, and possible consequences.
4. **Choose** the best option.

(The box on the next page exemplifies these steps for a specific case).

Sayings of Jesus

'Therefore I tell you, do not worry about your life, what you will eat or drink; or about your body, what you will wear. […] But seek first this kingdom and his righteousness, and all these things will be given to you as well' (Matthew 6:25, 33).

---

self-help

ORGANISE YOUR PROBLEMS

List your life problems in the spaces provided. Then think of the best solution.

Severity of problem

Severe problems
that *cannot be changed*

• *Death of a loved one*
• *My unhappy childhood*
• _____
• _____
• _____

Advice: Accept reality and organise your life in a rational manner. Challenge your negative thoughts. Forget yourself and help others.

Severe problems
that *can be changed*

• *My tobacco dependence*
• *Low self-confidence*
• _____
• _____
• _____

Advice: You should solve these problems. Do not wait for too long. Seek professional help or social support. Decide firmly to face them.

Susceptibility to change

Unimportant problems
that *cannot be changed*

• *My mother-in-law's eccentricities*
• *Traffic jams*
• _____
• _____
• _____

Advice: Ignore these problems. Do not let these trifles ruin your life. Smile, breathe deeply and enjoy life.

Unimportant problems
that *can be changed*

• *The untidy loft*
• *The errand I have being postponing*
• _____
• _____
• _____

Advice: Sit down and develop a plan to solve these small problems. And if they are not really important, let them stay as they are and do not torture yourself.

PRACTICAL CASE

Problem resolution in career choice

The year before beginning college, Pamela was confused about choices for her career. So she sought the help of Flora, an expert in career counselling. In one afternoon of intense work, they solved the problem.

The first task was to confirm that Pamela's grades would give her entrance into the majority of studies. Her problem was precisely that, among so many options, Pamela felt attracted to many of them.

Next, in order to encompass everything, they wrote down the study areas that Pamela liked best: information technology, social work, law, public health, and environmental studies.

The third stage was the hardest. She had to answer the following questions one by one:

- Why take career X?
- What types of subject areas are dominant in that line of studies?
- What is my intellectual ability to face those subject areas?

- What are the employment opportunities for that line of studies?
- Is this a career dominated by individual effort or by teamwork?
- What are the facts in terms of remuneration, social rewards and personal satisfaction of that profession?

Answers were written down to be revised later on.

Lastly, after having weighed all options with their advantages and disadvantages, Pamela concluded that environmental studies would fit her ability and would provide more short-, medium- and long-term satisfaction than any other line of studies. With this understanding, Pamela initiated her college studies with a good level of motivation and achievement. At times, she recalled with gratitude that brief and effective afternoon devoted to decide on her studies.

LIMITATIONS OF COGNITIVE PSYCHOTHERAPY

In order for cognitive psychotherapy to work, the client needs to be able to identify, assess, block and initiate thoughts at will.

These skills are learned, in part, in the counselling office, but there are **people with serious difficulties to understand** and apply these principles. These are the most resistant persons to cognitive psychotherapy:

- Children
- Uneducated or slow learners
- Those with a personality for action and not for thought analysis

If cognitive therapy is forced upon people, they may become frustrated and discouraged. It is better to apply other forms, such as behavioural psychotherapy, covered in the previous unit.

6.04

New schools

Neuro-linguistic programming (NLP)

This form of therapy was created by **Richard Bandler and John Grinder** in the 1970's. Both were psychotherapists, but their backgrounds were in computing and linguistics, respectively. They chose three great names in psychotherapy: **Erickson, Perls and Satir**. Observing the techniques from these great historic masters, Bandler and Grinder developed the theory and practice of NLP.

Neuro-linguistic programming is appropriate for the treatment of phobias, traumas and other personal barriers that prevent someone from reaching their goals. The method is targeted at **past experiences** as the origin of present trouble. These are the application steps:

1. **The psychologist helps the client to feel personally competent and strong** in order to face the problem. When sufficiently emphasised, this feeling prepares the client to be in control of the situation (for example, confronting the phobic object) in order to avoid trouble. The psychotherapist observes the client's mood via breathing, tone of voice, colour of the skin and general disposition. These help the professional know whether progress is actually taking place.

2. **Use of visualisation to move back in time and see when the trauma**, phobia or other disorders originated. Visualisation is multi-sensorial (colours, sounds, kinaesthetic sensations). The psychotherapist gives instructions so that the patient 'comes out of his/her body' (through imagination) and observes the situation as an outsider. This offers a new perspective, not from within, but from outside. This makes the observation more relaxed and anxiety-free.

The steps above, when practised several times, weaken the source of the disorders and help clients change their behaviour into a more adaptive one. The method widely uses non-verbal messages, as these bring about more precision to communicate feelings and emotions than mere words.

NLP strongly emphasises hope in the client's personal capacity to successfully change behaviour. Within the context of NLP, everyone can effect important changes; if there is a 'failure,' it does not matter, as it provides a source of information to continue to fight against the problem. Nevertheless, the method also has drawbacks (see the box below).

QUESTIONABLE USE OF HYPNOSIS

As in the case of psychoanalysis, NLP strives to reach the **unconscious level of the mind** in order to go back to the remote past and the ultimate root of the problem. This difficult task may produce errors.

In addition, when patients by themselves cannot achieve this, the psychotherapist uses hypnosis (a process that makes many people uncomfortable and which can be used unethically).

NLP also requires the presence of a therapist with a great deal of training and its complexity makes it impossible to use as a self-help technique.

Positive psychology

Martin Seligman, a professor of psychology at the University of Pennsylvania, is the name that most clearly represents this new school. Positive psychology was formally born in 1998 when Seligman met with two of his colleagues in Akumal, on the Mexican Yucatan peninsula, to draft the foundations of this new psychological branch.

Ever since that moment, the popularity of positive psychology has been growing tremendously. This is perhaps because, unlike traditional psychology, positive psychology is centred on positive emotions and optimism as a remedy to the majority of personal problems.

These are the **core ideas** of this psychology:

- **Optimism** (see pages 20 and 48) **provides the means to prevent and fight mental as well as physical illness.** Pessimism is the cause of many mental disorders, especially depression.

- **Optimism may be learned utilising cognitive therapy techniques.** Namely, focusing on the temporary nature of negative events, and also on the stable aspects of positive occurrences.

- **The analysis of past, present and future** must be done in an **optimistic** and hopeful way.

- **Hope** (see page 64) **is necessary to preserve mental health.** Positive therapy teaches patients to think kindly (not harshly) of themselves.

- **Competitiveness** (page 230) **does not cause the victory of many; rather the defeat of the majority.** Cooperation is therefore a preferred association.

- **Control over thoughts** (pages 146 and 306) **is the recommended technique to free oneself from undesirable ideas** of oneself, the environment and the future, as these ideas favour pathological behaviours.

Laughter therapy

As a supporting therapeutic approach based on positive psychology, laughter is highly beneficial. Several things are attained through laughter: release of energy, exercise of numerous muscles, release of endorphins, deep breathing and strengthening of defences. All of the above have a beneficial effect upon mental health.

Norman Cousins tells his story in his book *Anatomy of an Illness as Perceived by the Patient*. This experience impacted medical science and illustrated the advantages of a determined, non-passive attitude.

Cousins, editor of the *Saturday Review*, was diagnosed with ankylosing spondylitis, a severe illness that follows a process of progressive general paralysis out of which only 0.2% of the patients have managed to escape.

Cousins decided to be one of those rare exceptions. Based on the idea that negative emotions and stress weaken the human organism, he concluded that **positive emotions** should favour the body. As a result, he substituted the strong tablets he was taking with increasing doses of vitamin C and particularly with the use of positive thinking. Given his beliefs, he commented: 'It was easy to have faith, love, and hope but, what about laughter? There is nothing less funny than lying on your back with painful bones. The appropriate thing to do was to follow a systematic programme. I thought it would be good to start with a few funny movies.'

That was the beginning of a treatment that would end being called laughter therapy. Results were very successful; **laughter** had **analgesic effects** and **favoured sleep**. In addition, blood tests started to show a decrease in blood infection.

Little by little he recovered his skeletal mobility, could sit up in his bed and managed to walk without crutches. In sum, he recovered.

His experience was published in the prestigious *New England Journal of Medicine*, and his book became a best seller for several years.

THE OUTREACH OF POSITIVE PSYCHOLOGY

The great advantage of positive psychology lies in its **scope and versatility**. Everybody can apply many of its techniques and integrate them into their daily lifestyle. Its principles are useful for the prevention and healing of emotional problems. They are also effective for nourishing relationships and enjoying life experiences thoroughly, as well as increasing professional and academic achievements. These are some of the positive psychology rules you can use on yourself:

- **Practise gratitude.** Instead of complaining about life, be grateful for the good things it provides, for what you are, for what you have and for what you can get. Take bitter moments patiently and when they pass away (because they always do), show gratitude once more.

- **Forgive whoever wronged you.** Being forgiven causes relief, but granting forgiveness brings about even greater emotional well-being. Practise it and observe the results. This will make you feel better and help improve your relations.

- **Look at the past without resentment.** The past is the origin of many disorders, but the way of approaching it will make a difference. Do not fall into the trap of lamenting what others, or circumstances, did to you. Accept what happened (the past cannot be changed) and redo your life, as nobody can take your happiness away.

- **Enjoy the present.** There are reasons in your life today to consider yourself happy. Enjoy daily activities. Positive psychology distinguishes body pleasures from high-order pleasures. Both are acceptable, but while the first are short-lived, the second are long-lasting and go beyond the level of the senses to reach the cognitive realm—the sensation of well-being, contemplation, and relaxation… These are superior pleasures.

- **Assess the future with hope.** Reject catastrophic thinking towards the future. Do not generalise ('Everything always goes wrong with me everywhere I am'). Think that events may go wrong, but they also may go right. Therefore, trust that things will go alright and do what you can to make it a reality: prepare yourself, be cautious to attain your goal and anticipate complications.

- **Identify your strong points.** Positive psychology helps a person to assess strengths: enthusiasm, sympathy, valour, creativity, intelligence, empathy, kindness, precision, good will… Knowing your strong points, you can channel your life towards a successful future.

- **Reject catastrophic thinking.** Negative thinking is the cause of pessimism and of depressive symptoms. Learn to identify them from the beginning and push them aside following the steps of cognitive restructuring (see page 304).

- **Practise the 'super-virtues.'** Seligman studied a great number of sacred and philosophical writings (for instance, Confucius, Buddha, Lao-tzu, Aristotle, Plato, the Bible, the Samurai Code, Patristics, the Qur'an, etc.). Among the over 200 virtues identified in those writings as being of superior moral quality, the most valued ones by all sources were:

  ✓ Wisdom
  ✓ Courage
  ✓ Charity
  ✓ Justice
  ✓ Temperance
  ✓ Transcendence

  Choose these virtues as aims for your life. This may bring changes to your lifestyle, and, at the same time, it will bring about unprecedented satisfaction.

Resilience

Resilience is the ability to face highly stressful situations without falling into psychological dysfunction (see chapter 5, page 240). In addition, resilient persons gain additional strength from difficult situations, thus increasing their ability to endure and recover.

Resilience is characteristic of a certain type of person who has an increased sense of tenacity to compensate for deficiencies. Nevertheless, ***everybody can strengthen this trait*** through learning and practice (see the box below). The following are ways to increase resilience:

- **Understand that suffering is a form of learning.** There is no human way to eradicate suffering and adversity. Accept, therefore, that difficulties provide a way to help you endure occasional, unavoidable pain.

- **Secure a good social support system.** The social component is perhaps the strongest factor to increase resilience. Meet with people who face similar struggles or accept the help that others may offer you. Find support from these persons throughout the difficulty.

- **Enhance your level of resistance.** We all possess a comfort zone, an area where we feel well. Try to broaden that comfort zone. Practise patience when confronting nuisances and worries.

- **Consider problems as opportunities.** Do not view yourself as a suffering martyr. Instead, look at the problem as a challenge and take the opportunity to successfully handle it. With your victory, you will develop your resilience.

- **Patience and perseverance.** Even the hardest trials have an end. With this in mind, practise patience, together with the corresponding remedial measures. Then observe how the storm passes in the end.

- **Hold fast to a faith and belief system.** Extreme difficulties require supernatural help. Trust in God as an omnipotent and loving being who will provide the way out of the adversity in due time and in the best way.

Gems of Ancient Wisdom

'I can do everything through him who gives me strength' (Philippians 4:13).

RESEARCH RESULTS

Resilience can be learned and taught

Martin Seligman and a team of experts at the University of Pennsylvania (USA) created a resilience program to help school-aged children to develop this trait. They used traditional stories where characters were able to reach great goals, in spite of their size, weakness or lack of experience. This plan was carried out with children between 6 and 12 years of age coming from an adverse family situation that placed them in a position of high risk for depression. For 12 weeks they were taught several methods to resist pessimistic and negative thoughts. They were expected to analyse, answer and evaluate questions such as:

What is the worst thing that could happen to you? What is the real probability for that to happen?

Many of these activities were carried out in group, studying others' arguments, confirming or rejecting them. They also learned problem-solving strategies.

Two years later, researchers found that 22% of the children following the program suffered from depression. Meanwhile, the control group made up of children with similar problems but without treatment showed a 44% rate of depression. The success of this programme made it popular in ten other locations throughout the USA. And it also reached Canada, Australia and China.

Spiritual psychotherapy

Spiritual psychotherapy has advanced a great deal during the last few years. In the past, the scientific community rejected cases that involved the effect of prayer, meditation and other forms of spiritual action. However, many psychologists and therapy groups now integrate religion, spirituality and mental health.

A good number of psychotherapies (and even physicians) are now recommending to their patients some of the following measures:

- **Forgiveness.** If you have feelings of guilt for not having forgiven or for not having been forgiven, use forgiveness. Forgive the offences that others may have done to you and ask for forgiveness if you are the offender. Also ask God to forgive you and rid yourself of the burden of guilt.

- **Love.** Love as principle, not only as impulse, can be a decisive factor to achieve mental health. Love your dear ones and even the undeserving ones. You will notice a sensation of joy and well-being.

- **Prayer.** Pray to God with the faith and innocence of a child. This will lighten your emotional burden. You will also observe that God always provides an answer, even though it may not be to your liking. Praying for others also causes wonderful results. Several studies have revealed the efficacy of intercessory prayer (see the example in the box on the adjoining page).

- **Meditation.** It is known that meditation improves one's general physical state and particularly relieves high blood pressure and reduces tachycardia. When meditation has a solid spiritual component (for example, reflection upon Bible passages), it becomes more significant. Spiritual meditation has the ability to cause even better results than secular meditation (see the box on the next page).

- **Private or group worship.** Participation in religious worship can also exert a great therapeutic effect. Private worship brings about a state similar to meditation. Group worship carries a higher level of joy due to the inspiring effect of other believers.

- **Dependence upon a Supreme Being and his presence in your life.** Feeling the presence of an all-powerful being greater than self is an unspeakable sensation. Seek that presence in the silence of a church, in nature, in prayer or in Bible reading.

- **The hope of salvation.** The certainty that God wishes you to be eternally happy is a positive factor in present and future mental health. Explore further and search for provisions and ways to enjoy the divine gift.

The effects of intercessory prayer and spiritual meditation

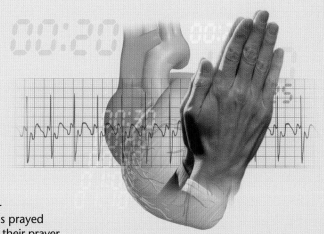

W. S. Harris and his team investigated the effects of prayer on a group of patients (Harris *et al.*, 1999) from the coronary unit at the Mid-America Heart Institute in the city of Kansas (USA). Participants were patients admitted for cardiac ailments. They were assigned to two groups: those who would be prayed for and those who would not be prayed for (control group). Patients did not know they were participants in the study. Physicians did know of the investigation, but did not know to which group patients had been assigned.

During their stay in hospital, a group of believers from various religious denominations prayed systematically for those patients included on their prayer list. The result showed that those patients who were prayed for **recovered their health in a quicker and more lasting way** than did those in the control group.

Additionally, **Amy Wachholtz and Kenneth Pargament**, of Bowling Green University in Ohio (USA), studied the effects of several types of meditation (Wachholtz and Pargament, 2005). They assigned students to two random groups and instructed them in two forms of spiritual meditation: using the name of God and secular meditation. They also designated a control group who only received information about relaxation and how to reject stressful thoughts. There were no ethnic or cultural differences among participants; nor were there differences in the knowledge of meditation techniques. They were all asked to practise their respective techniques for 20 minutes each day for two weeks.

Results showed that the spiritual meditation group had **less anxiety and a more positive mood** that the other two groups. Furthermore, in an additional pain resistance test (keep their hand in a bucket with crushed ice until they could not resist any longer), the spiritual meditation group resisted double the time as compared to the remaining participants.

6.05
Group therapy

Group therapy is conducted with a set of people (six to eight) sharing a common condition. The psychotherapist, who is especially trained in this approach, leads the interaction and provides common advice.

Group therapies are diverse and have multiplied and followed various kinds of theoretical approaches. Experience has demonstrated that this form of therapy may become superior even to individual therapy, especially when the goal is **to learn social skills or to solve interpersonal problems**. In these cases, the group is an ideal context to try, rehearse, learn and share together (see the advantages of this procedure in the box below).

Group therapy is particularly useful in cases of low assertiveness, anxiety, phobias, obesity and all types of addictions: alcohol, tobacco, drugs, gaming, Internet, etc. This technique also has its drawbacks (see the box 'Group therapy limitations' on the adjoining page).

Gems of Ancient Wisdom

'Carry each other's burdens, and in this way you will fulfil the law of Christ' (Galatians 6:2).

Does it make sense to open up to a group?

If it is difficult for many to relate their intimate issues to a single person, how much more difficult must it be to share them with a group of unknown individuals! However, group therapy includes a number of significant advantages that match the effectiveness of conventional therapy:

- Each person **feels understood** and appreciated by those suffering from the same problem.
- It causes a therapeutic reaction in the patient that makes him/her feel less alone in his/her suffering and helps to develop an **attitude of solidarity**.
- It **favours learning** through listening to how others face the same difficulties.
- It facilitates **skills rehearsal** in an accepting and understanding context.
- It is **cost-effective** as the professional attends a greater number of individuals without much increase of cost.

Group therapy for lack of self-confidence

Arthur was a university student attending a therapeutic group for a few weeks. Participants had a common problem: low self-confidence and social inhibition. The group met two hours a week and Arthur was happy with the results.

There were eight young people like him from the university, aside from the psychotherapist. At the beginning the group seemed unable to start up… Everyone was reluctant to tell their experience, but once the ice was broken, everyone followed. Soon the group became cohesive to the point of providing a strong support to all participants.

Arthur said: 'The strength communicated by a group like this is remarkable. At the last session I confessed that one of my internal conflicts was the disagreement I held with one of my professors and my inability to face him. His approach to teach was totally atheistic and I had good reasons to defend my perspective as a believer in God. The group encouraged me to affirm my position in front of the teacher and my other peers. I committed myself publicly to do it and I did it. I did not only state my position clearly, but several other students from the class said they agreed with my point of view. This and other experiences have helped me to leave behind my insecurity. And the group was decisive for the change.'

SPONTANEOUS GROUP DEVELOPMENT

Danielle and Marsha were friends since adolescence. They kept their friendship even after they married and had children. As the years passed, both were affected by divorce and their connection served as a source of support through the circumstances. They purchased a self-help book for divorced mothers and they invited other lady friends who were also recently divorced mothers. Without realising, they had formed a successful therapeutic group meeting one afternoon each week.

If you have a problem that is common to other people near you, why not try to form a **self-help group**? Many groups are already working successfully: alcoholics, divorced, family violence victims, sufferers from sexual abuse to minors, family of Alzheimer patients, etc. In addition, there are groups of patients with common medical ailments—arthritis, breast cancer, pre-menstrual syndrome, irritable colon, AIDS, schizophrenia…

GROUP THERAPY LIMITATIONS

In spite of the advantages of group therapy, there are also a few limitations that need to be considered:

- **Lack of confidentiality.** There is a likely risk of information leaking out of the group. This may produce embarrassing situations in small communities where everybody knows each other.
- **Lack of personalised attention.** There are cases where clients need to talk widely and unload their burdens. In these instances, group therapy is very limited as available time is to be shared with everyone in the group.
- **Presence of a pseudo-leader.** In all groups, there is the risk that one of the members tries to take up the entire time to talk or take leadership in the group.

6.06
Family therapy

Individual therapy is applied to the person who supposedly has the problem; the family is not considered at all.

However, this has limitations and it has been demonstrated that treatments work much better when all members of the family unit are involved. After all, the family is a nucleus where the problems of one affect the rest and where all contribute to aggravate or to soothe each other's problems.

In the context of this therapy, the whole family attends the counselling office. The psychologist listens and observes the dynamics of family relations. Each member is also submitted to an individual interview. At times, the professional may visit the home and, during a few hours, will silently observe the family as they interact.

Once the information is gathered, the therapist presents his/her hypothesis to the family members and they offer their opinion and participate in the shaping of the final diagnosis.

In the presence of the psychologist everyone better understands each other's positions and reasons.

Then, agreements are reached and each family member commits to abide by them. Week after week, follow-up takes place and expectations are modified until the adequate behaviours become part of the routine.

RESEARCH RESULTS

Family therapy for depressive patients

A team of clinical researchers at Brown University School of Medicine (USA) proposed a specific family therapy model (Keitner *et al.*, 2003). This model has worked effectively for the treatment of patients with chronic depression and seems superior to individual therapy. It includes the following steps:

1. **Family evaluation.** Using appropriate scales, the clinician discovers the particular solving-problem strategies used by families, as well as their communication style, how they display affection, the role of each member, the type of behaviour conducted and the degree of control upon such behaviours.

2. **Contract.** At the second or third session, a contract is developed with the consensus of the whole family. The contract stipulates the urgent agreements to improve the depressive person's health from the beginning of psychotherapy.

3. **Treatment.** In the following sessions, people discuss the previous week with its difficulties and any progress made. Various future expectations for the family to support the depressive member are identified. Negotiations take place and improvement options are considered. They agree on avoiding certain behaviours and promoting others. The depressive person progressively abandons his/her role of patient and starts adopting the role of a normal family member. Sessions become more spaced and termination of treatment draws near.

4. **Conclusion.** With the improvement of depressive symptoms, there is dialogue about the therapeutic activity and achievements. The group discusses future alternatives and draws an independent plan to support the family member with depression.

Family therapy provides continuing help not only with depression but also with a variety of other disorders. This is because it can reach out beyond the mere psychological intervention of the traditional sessions.

PRACTICAL CASE

An ignored
and overburdened woman

Sonia is a housewife married to Mark, and they have two adolescent children. Mark works long hours as a bank employee and the children hardly stop by the house. For no apparent reason, Sonia started to feel weak and discouraged. She lost her appetite, her sleep and some weight. Her doctor referred her to the psychiatrist, who diagnosed depression. The treatment included anti-depressive drugs as well as psychological treatment.

After the first session of therapy, the psychologist asked that husband and children also attend the next session. The professional explained that, in order to achieve the greatest effectiveness, she needed to know Sonia's family setting.

Once the family session ended, the therapist conducted one separate session with each member of the family. She confirmed that the problem was not only Sonia's. The intense commitment to work on the part of her husband was the precipitating cause of her depression.

The children also had their share of blame... They did not help in the house, and as typical adolescents, they did not share their problems with their mother anymore. These circumstances caused Sonia to feel exhausted, rejected and useless.

However, Sonia was not free from responsibility. Her pessimistic and sombre style kept her family away. She tended to emphasise the negative aspects of life and her conversation was depressing. As a result, her husband preferred to put in overtime at the bank and the boys to stay out longer.

This family configuration required a global approach where everyone accepted responsibility and remained committed to do their part. Therefore, an action plan was developed to assign specific tasks to each of the family members. They read the document and, with a few amendments, they agreed and signed the behavioural contract (see page 300). After a few weekly sessions, Sonia felt much better. For the future, family members knew what they had to do in order to avoid problems.

Gems of Ancient Wisdom

*'**Wives**, submit to your husbands, as is fitting in the Lord. Husbands, love your wives and do not be harsh with them. **Children**, obey your parents in everything, for this pleases the Lord. **Fathers**, do not embitter your children, or they will become discouraged' (Colossians 3:18-21).*

Pharmacological treatment

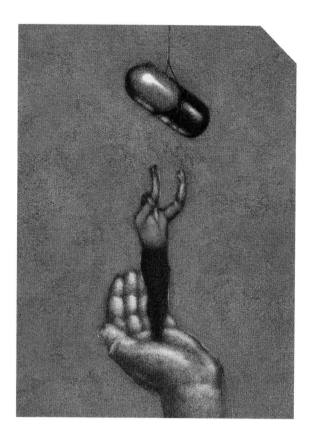

and bringing relief to those suffering from the painful symptoms of depression. These are examples: Tryptizol®, Norpramin®, Pertrofana®, Sinequan®, Tofranil®, Aventyl® and Surmontil®. *All should only be taken under medical supervision.*

Anti-depressive medication works differently in different patients and the reason is not exactly known. It is therefore common that the psychiatrist prescribe one and then change to another and so on in order to find the best chemical to meet the patient's personal needs. Depending on which type of drug is used, there are a variety of side effects, which make treatment more unpleasant: loss of memory, dryness of the mouth, thirst, tremors, drowsiness, bradycardia, constipation... Improve-

Aside from psychotherapy and other alternative remedies, drugs serve as a **good complement** in the treatment of psychological problems. Medication should never be rejected in the course of mental health. Although it is well known that they do not cure disorders, they do provide well-being to the patient, favour psychotherapeutic intervention, and in many cases provide a safeguard against suicide. This unit describes the drugs utilised for the treatment of the most common mental illnesses—depression, anxiety and stress.

Depression treatment

Anti-depressive drugs have been used for several generations; today they provide a good degree of effectiveness. These medicines act upon the central nervous system, altering the brain's chemistry

Anxiolytics	
Type of anxiety	**Drugs**
Panic attack	*Alprazolam (Xanax®, Trankimazin®, Zolarem®, Zoldac®): Works as a sedative. It is metabolised in the liver, causing some complications in elderly patients and in those with hepatic sensibility. When its use is interrupted, insomnia and original symptoms may reappear.*
Phobia	*Phenelzine (Nardelzine®, Nardil®): It is especially effective to treat social phobia. Side effects: dryness of mouth, blurred vision, drowsiness, urinary retention, constipation, seasickness, insomnia, decrease in sexual potency, weakness and sweating.*
Generalised anxiety	*Buspirone (Ansial®, Buspar®): It is an effective anxyolitic for the treatment of generalised anxiety disorder. Side effects include: seasickness, drowsiness, nausea and headaches.*

HOW TO QUIT TRANQUILLISERS

Quitting the use of tranquillisers necessitates medical and psychological help. The following advice will help you:

- **Set up a plan to progressively reduce the dosage,** cutting down to half the dose of a single day of the week, next week cut down two, etc. until you have reduced the dose of each day over seven weeks. Then reduce to one-fourth to leave the tablets completely behind.
- **Substitute the drug.** It is not sufficient to remove the medication. It must be replaced by something. Medicinal herbs, such as Valerian, Lavender and Passion Flower are good examples of sedative and tranquillising herbs.

- **Practise relaxation daily.** Set aside 20 minutes after work in order to find relaxation and enjoy silence. This will help you feel in control of yourself, of your impulses and habits.
- **Get physical exercise daily.** Walk briskly or practise a sport. Worries tend to produce catecholamine and increase stress levels. Physical exercise (see page 322) aborts the process and favours self-control.
- **Initiate new habits.** Break with the routines that make you dependent on tranquillisers. Start a healthy and natural diet, with plenty of water. Include new activities in the open. Develop a positive attitude towards others, and a good sense of humour. Get to bed early to assure enough rest.

ment is generally not seen for the first two or three weeks of drug treatment.

Anxiety treatment

Practically all anxiety cases include pharmacological treatment as an initial measure to reduce anxiety levels. At the same time psychotherapeutic action must be initiated and can be extended for weeks or months (Clark *et al.*, 1999).[1] Drugs for anxiety are called anxiolytics (see the table on the previous page).

Stress treatment

The most commonly prescribed drugs for the treatment of stress, insomnia and nervous agitation are called tranquillisers. Their usage is very widespread, hence the long list of commercial names, such as Valium®, Librium®, Restoril®, Rivetril®, Serax®, Tranxilium® and many others. All of them belong to the pharmacological family of **benzodiazepines**. These medicines work as muscular and affective relaxants. In many cases, they are unnecessary, as focusing on the psychological

and relational problems causing the symptoms would suffice to correct the nervous discomfort.

As with any other drug, these medicines must be *administered under medical supervision*. It should be remembered that tranquillisers cause dependence and, when discontinued, may cause withdrawal symptoms such as tremors, headaches, nausea, and reasoning and perception distortions (see the box above to know how to quit tranquillisers).

---

1. *The brief treatment consists of 12 to 15 one-hour sessions. However, there are psychoanalytical forms of treatment that can last for years.*

6.08
Physical exercise

Can physical exercise be included among the various forms of therapy? Today, the healing and stabilising effects of physical activity are seen as an unquestionable fact in the circles of both the mental and physical health professions.

The Medline database (2005) shows more than 20,000 references to studies where 'physical exercise' appears in the publication title. And the vast majority of these studies portray the benefits of adding physical activity to our daily lives. This is not only to prevent but also to heal illnesses of a physical as well as mental nature.

Our body machinery is designed for **activity**. If we did only a fraction of the physical exercise done by our great-grandparents, the amount of physical and mental illnesses we suffer from today would be reduced to half. Nobody would talk about the beneficial effect of exercise, as it would be integrated into a life without lifts, cars, washing machines, tractors, etc.

It is no wonder that the World Health Organization (WHO) has declared **sedentary life** as *one of the greatest public health enemies of our day*. Therefore, physical exercise has become, by default, a form of therapy, especially in the context of mental health.

In spite of the overwhelming evidence of the goodness of physical activity, many people resist including it in their lifestyles. Many fear that something unexpected and undesirable may occur to them. That is perhaps why a number of myths have been perpetuated (see the box below) that should be rejected.

Physical exercise myths

1. **It is only for young people.** Although the possibilities of extreme types of physical exercise decrease with age, it is never too late to start an adequate exercise plan. Today, there are many physical exercise plans for people of 60, 70 or 80 years of age, and beyond. Even muscular tissue has been found to develop in elderly people involved in supervised exercise.

2. **It is dangerous and may be harmful.** Complete sports such as cycling, jogging or swimming carry minimal risks. But if you are afraid to practise a sport, simply walk. If the exercise causes pain, you may be doing something wrong, or reaching the limit of your ability and you need to incorporate changes. In any case, there is more risk of illness from staying on the sofa than in exercising.

3. **It takes too much time.** It is true that exercise takes some time, about 20 minutes a day. However, exercise yields agility, good mood and helps one to lose weight. These will help you save time in other tasks, as you will do them with greater speed and effectiveness.

4. **It is boring.** It does not have to be. Practise the physical activities you enjoy most. Include other people you like to be with, add music, and do it as you work. The Self-help box on the adjoining page can give you some ideas.

5. **It exhausts you.** You need to practise it for a while in order to reach fitness and experience a light and pleasant fatigue. And remember: the quality of sleep increases with exercise, so you will end up feeling more rested.

WATCH OUT FOR EXCESSES

There are those who do not get physical exercise at all. Others, perhaps encouraged by so much publicity on the beneficial effects of activity, go too far. Excessive exercise may cause...

- chronic fatigue
- significant mood alterations
- addiction risks (in individuals with anorexic tendencies)
- muscular lesion risk
- risk of osteoporosis and interference with ovulation (in women)

Exercise and physical health

The dividends yielded by regular and moderate physical exercise, which in turn favour mental health (see pages 24 and 52), are many. These are the most significant:

- diminished risk of heart attack
- diminished risk of thrombosis
- prevention of high blood pressure
- prevention of osteoporosis and diabetes
- reduction of obesity

The problem is that many do not make up their minds to get up off the sofa and begin some sport, exercise or physical activity to obtain the expected benefits. Do not think that exercise is unpleasant. Soon after you begin, you will have a hard time quitting because of how good it makes you feel.

self-help

MAKE IT FUN

Exercise does not need to be boring or difficult, nor should it be too complicated or expensive. Although there may be discomfort in the beginning, it becomes pleasant as it **enhances your self-esteem and reduces tension and anxiety**. If you persevere, your own body will reward you with an additional dose of **endorphins**, causing well-being and pain relief. Try these suggestions and add your own:

- Play tennis with your best friend/s and use the time going and coming to talk.
- Clean your windows or the floor with rhythmic music.
- Do not use the lift and climb the stairs singing a children's song.
- Pedal on a stationary exercise bike while you watch a funny movie.

- Go running with your digital audio player and change the route once in a while.
- Join your children in a game and make the decision to laugh as much as you can.
- Change your exercise pattern on Monday, Wednesday and Friday.
- _____
- _____
- _____

RESEARCH RESULTS

Exercise and memory

One of the latest research findings is the relationship between physical exercise and mental capacity. **Woo and Sharp** (2003) recruited teen and adult participants who were submitted to physical exercise as well as several mental tests.

The influence of physical exercise upon mental test results was not clear in all areas, but it did improve a number of test scores. Specifically, young people experienced increased ability to recall data classified under categories.

Adults under the exercise regime obtained better results in verbal memory.

Exercise and mental health

Moderate physical exercise increases energy (necessary to avoid depression). Vigorous exercise decreases tension (necessary to fight anxiety). And all types of exercise improve one's mood. Today there is no doubt about the direct relationship between physical activity and mood. It is for each individual to try different types of activity and degrees of intensity to observe the results.

The following psychological conflicts/disorders may be prevented or improved by including physical activity in one's lifestyle:

- depression
- anxiety
- stress and tension
- worries or uncertainties that cause mental ailment
- aggressiveness and rage
- feelings of low self-esteem
- cognitive ability (see the box on the left)

Occupational therapy

Keeping mentally and physically active is not only convenient; it can be therapeutic in a number of circumstances and disorders. The science of profitably applying the benefits of activity to health is called 'occupational therapy.'

The beginnings of this approach were started by French psychiatrist **Philippe Pinel** (1745-1826), who opposed the tradition of keeping psychiatric patients chained. He worked towards the integration of useful activities into the patient's routines.

The use of this therapy goes beyond the limits of psychology and requires the intervention of an occupational therapist, a professional with a medical background and specialisation in this particular area of health.

Occupational therapists try to help people **develop skills and overcome inabilities**. They first assess the patient's deficiencies (and degree of dependence) as well as his/her potential to overcome them.

Hence the common use of this form of therapy for **disabilities** (physical and mental), **co-dependence**, **addictions** (of psychoactive substances), **paediatric problems**, **old age complications**, neurological and mental health disorders, including **depression**, and many others.

Appropriate therapeutic activities are prescribed in order for patients to develop skills and abilities in the mental, motor, social, physical and psychological areas. In mental health issues, this form of therapy also favours relaxation, helping the patient to direct his/her attention away from obsessive thoughts.

self-help

HOW TO KEEP ONESELF MOTIVATED

Once exercise has begun, it is important to maintain the motivation in order to avoid inactivity relapse. To motivate yourself, think of the following statements, which are probably all true:

- I am feeling a general sense of well-being since I am getting exercise
- I have lost some weight
- I now sleep better at night
- I am building up my defences, and am less susceptible to illness

- My appetite is adequate and much better controlled than before
- The two hours following my physical exercise are the most pleasant of the day

- _____
- _____
- _____

RESEARCH RESULTS

Brief and moderate exercise, highly beneficial

Robert Thayer, in his book *Calm Energy* (2001), describes one of his studies where he measured the effect of 10-minute brisk walks (no running) upon participants. He measured at 30-, 60-, and 120-minute intervals after the exercise.

Results showed that energy rose over the first 60 minutes and lasted up to 120 minutes. It is remarkable that only 10 minutes of exercise can exert such as lasting result.

A number of investigations carried out by Thayer and others led him to propose his theory: moderate exercise burns energy, but also adds a different kind of energy—**calm energy**, a necessary ingredient to achieve **positive mood**, sense of humour, and a less voracious appetite than when exercise is not practised.

Gems of Ancient Wisdom

'Those who hope in the LORD will renew their strength. They will soar on wings like eagles; they will run and not grow weary, they will walk and not be faint' (Isaiah 40:31).

Bibliography

American Psychiatric Association. *Diagnostic and Statistical Manual of Mental Disorders* (4th Edition) – DSM-IV, 1994.

Bachofen, M. *et al.* Home self-assessment and self-treatment of obsessive-compulsive disorder using a manual and a computer-conducted telephone interview: replication of a UK-US study. *J Clin Psychiatry*, 60:545-549 (1999).

Barker, M.G. Unpublished lectures, Bristol University, February 1995.

Barrera, M.E. *et al.* The effects of interactive music therapy on hospitalized children with cancer: a pilot study. *Psychooncology*, 11:379-388 (2002).

Barsky, A.J. and Ahern, D.K. Cognitive behavior therapy for hypochondriasis: A randomized controlled trial. *Journal of the American Medical Association*, 291:1464-1471 (2004).

Bayle, F.J. *et al.* Psychopathology and co-morbidity of psychiatric disorders in patients with kleptomania. *American Journal of Psychiatry*, 160:1509-1513 (2003).

Benson, H. *Timeless healing*. New York, Scribner, 1996.

Buckner *et al.* Characteristics of resilient youths living in poverty: the role of self-regulatory processes. *Development and Psychopathology*, 15:139-162 (2003).

Campbell, D. *et al.* Effects of patient-controlled music therapy during coronary angiography on procedural pain and anxiety distress syndrome. *Critical Care Nurse*, 23:50-57 (2003).

Carnwath, T. and Miller, D. *Behavioural Psychotherapy in Primary Care: A Practice Manual*. London, Academic Press, 1986.

Carrel, A. *Man, The Unknown*. New York, Harper & Brothers, 1939.

Cheek, J.R. *et al.* Using music therapy techniques to treat teacher burnout. *Journal of Mental Health Counseling*, 25:204-217 (2003).

Cheng, H. and Furnham, A. Attributional style and self-esteem as predictors of psychological wellbeing. *Counselling Psychology Quarterly*, 16:121-130 (2003).

Christensen, L. Effects of eating behavior on mood: a review of literature. *Int J Eat Disord*, 14:171-183 (1993); Christensen, L. The effect of carbohydrates on affect. *Nutrition*, 13:503-514 (1997); Christensen, L. and Redig, C. Effect of meal composition on mood. *Behavioral Neuroscience*, 107:346-353 (1993).

Clark *et al.* Brief cognitive therapy for panic disorder: a randomized controlled trial. *J Consult Clin Psychol*. 67:583-589 (1999).

Cohen, S. *et al.* Emotional style and susceptibility to the common cold. *Psychosomatic Medicine*, 65:652-657 (2003); Cohen, S., Tyrrell, D.A.J. and Smith, A.P. Psychological stress and susceptibility to the common cold. *The New England Journal of Medicine*, 325:1991, 606-612.

Crocker, J. The cost of seeking self-esteem. *Journal of Social Issues*, 58:597-615 (2002).

Danner, D., Snowdon, D. and Friesen, W. Positive emotions in early life and longevity: findings from the nun study. *Journal of Personality and Social Psychology*, 80:804-813 (2001).

Daw, J. Eating disorders on the rise. *Monitor on Psychology*, 32:21 (2001).

Dew, M.A. *et al.* Healthy older adults' sleep predicts all-cause mortality at 4 to 19 years of follow-up. *Psychosomatic Medicine*, 65:63-73 (2003).

Dzurec, L.C. Relationship as an inherent component in healthy women's fatigue. *Western Journal of Nursing Research*, 24:441-454 (2002).

Escandón, R. and Gálvez, C., *Free from Drugs and Addictions*, Madrid, Safeliz, 2005.

Furnham, A. and Petrides, K.V. Trait emotional intelligence and happiness. *Social Behavior and Personality: An International Journal*, 31:815-824 (2003).

Gerst, D. Preventing teen hate crimes: Our role as NPs. *Nurse Practitioner*, 30:62-63 (2005).

Goleman, D. *Emotional Intelligence – Why it can matter more than IQ*. New York, Bantam Books (1995).

Goodman, W.K. Obsessive-compulsive disorder: diagnosis and treatment. *J Clin Psychiatry* 60 Suppl 18:27-32 (1999).

Gottlieb, S. Cognitive behaviour therapy can reduce hypochondriasis. *British Medical Journal*, 328:725 (2004).

Greenberg, M.A. and Stone A.A. Emotional disclosure about traumas and its relation to health: effects of previous disclosure and trauma severity. *Journal of Personality and Social Psychology*, 63:75-84 (1992).

Griffin-Shelley, E. The Internet and sexuality: a literature review—1983-2002. *Sexual and Relationship Therapy*, 18:355-371 (2003).

Gupta, R.K. and Moller, H.J. St. John's Wort. *European Archives of Psychiatry and Clinical Neuroscience,* 253:140-149 (2003).

Hall, N.R.S., Altman, F. and Blumental, S.J. Mind-body interactions and disease and psychoneuroimmunological aspects of health and disease. *Proceedings of a Conference on Stress, Immunity and Health Sponsored by the National Institutes of Health.* Orlando, Florida, USA, Health Dateline Press, 1996.

Harker, L. and Keltner, D. Expressions of positive emotion in women's college yearbook pictures and their relationship to personality and life outcome across adulthood. *Journal of Personality and Social Psychology*, 80:112-114 (2001).

Harris, W.S. *et al.* A randomized, controlled trial of the effects of remote intercessory prayer on the outcome of patients admitted to a coronary care unit. *Archives of Internal Medicine*, 159:2273-2278 (1999).

Hart, S. and Carrington, H. Jealousy in 6-month-old infants. *Infancy*, 3:395-402 (2002).

Hay, D.F. *et al.* (2003). Pathways to violence in the children of mothers who were depressed postpartum. *Developmental Psychology*, 39:1038-1094 (2003).

Hoffman H.G. *et al.* Use of virtual reality for adjunctive treatment of adolescent burn pain during wound care: A case report. *Pain*, 85:305-309 (2000); Hoffman H.G. *et al.* Water-friendly virtual reality pain control during wound care. *Journal of Clinical Psychology*, 60:189-195 (2004).

Hohagen, F. *et al.* Combination of behaviour therapy with fluvoxamine in comparison with behaviour therapy and placebo. Results of a multicentre study. *Br J Psychiatry* Suppl 35:71-78 (1998).

Huesmann, L.R. *et al.* Longitudinal relations between children's exposure to TV violence and their aggressive and violent behavior in young adulthood: 1977-1992. *Developmental Psychology*, 39:201-221 (2003).

Karlin, W.A., Brondolo, E. and Schwartz, J. Workplace social support and ambulatory cardiovascular activity in New York City traffic agents. *Psychosomatic Medicine*, 65:167-171 (2003).

Kasser, T. *et al.* The relations of maternal and social environments to late adolescents' materialistic and prosocial values. *Developmental Psychology*, 31:907-914 (1995).

Keitner, G.I. *et al.* Family therapy and chronic depression. *Journal of Clinical Psychology*, 59:873-884 (2003).

Kochanska, G. *et al.* Guilt in young children: development, determinants, and relations with a broader system of standards. *Child Development*, 73:461-482. 2002.

Lam, S.F. *et al.* The effects of competition on achievement motivation in Chinese classrooms. *British Journal of Educational Psychology*, 74:281-296 (2004).

Lange, A.J. and Jakubowski, P. *Responsible assertive behavior: cognitive-behavioral procedures for trainers*. Campaign, Illinois, USA, Research Press, 1976.

Larson, D.B. Associations between dimensions of religious commitment and mental health, *American Journal of Psychiatry*, 149:557-559 (1992).

Lepine, J.P. and Pelissolo, A. Social phobia and alcoholism: a complex relationship. *J Affect Disord.*, 50 Suppl 1:S23-28 (1998).

Levy, B. *et al.* Longevity increased by positive self-perceptions of aging. *Journal of Personality and Social Psychology*, 83:261-270 (2002).

Leymann, H. *Mobbing. La persécution au travail*. Paris, Éd. Du Seuil, 1996.

Lin, H.R. and Bauer-Wu, S.M. Psycho-spiritual well-being in patients with advanced cancer: an integrative review of the literature. *Journal of Advanced Nursing*, 44:69-80 (2003).

Lucribier Y. and Weiller, E. Co-morbidities in social phobia. *Int Clin Psychopharmacol.*, 12 Suppl 6:17-21 (1997).

McCaffrey, R., Effect of music on chronic osteoarthritis pain in older people. *Journal of Advanced Nursing*, 44:517-524 (2003).

Markus, C.R. *et al.* Does carbohydrate-rich, protein-poor food prevent a deterioration of mood and cognitive performance of stress-prone subjects when subjected to a stressful task? *Appetite*, 31:49-65 (1998).

Marlo, H. and Kalinian, H. Utilizing psychoanalytic psychotherapy in the treatment of substance abuse. *Clinical Psychology and Psychotherapy*, 9:211-223. (2002).

Marriott, L. *et al.* Long-term estrogen therapy worsens the behavioral and neuropathological consequences of chronic brain inflammation. *Behavioral Neuroscience*, 116:902-911 (2002).

Medline: www.nlm.nih.gov/medlineplus (17.5.2006); medline.cos.com/cgi-bin/search, 2005.

Melgosa, J., *Less Stress!*, Madrid, Safeliz, 2000; Melgosa, A.D. and Melgosa, J., *To Couples*, Madrid, Safeliz, 2004.

Mikkelsen, E.G. and Einarsen, S. Relationship between exposure to bullying at work and psychosomatic health complaints: The role of state negative affectivity and generalized self-efficacy. *Scandinavian Journal of Psychology*, 43:397-405 (2002).

Murray, C.J.L. and López, A.D. *The global burden of disease: A comprehensive assessment of mortality and disability from diseases, injuries, and risk factors in 1990 and projected to 2020. Summary.* Cambridge, Massachusetts, Harvard University Press, 1996.

Nickel, A.K. *et al.* Music therapy of children with migraine. *Psychotherapeut*, 47:285-290 (2002).

Nolen-Hoaksema, S. and Morrow, J.A prospective study of depression and distress following a natural disaster: the 1989 Loma Prieta earthquake. *Journal of Personality and Social Psychology*, 61:105-121 (1991).

Nordin, K. *et al.* Discrepancies between attainment and importance of life values and anxiety and depression in gastrointestinal cancer patients and their spouses. *Psychooncology*, 10:479-489 (2001).

O'Connor, K. *et al.* Cognitive-behaviour therapy and medication in the treatment of obsessive-compulsive disorder: a controlled study. *Can J Psychiatry*, 44:64-71 (1999).

O'Leary *et al.* Treatment of wife abuse: a comparison of gender-specific and conjoint approaches. *Behavior Therapy*, 30:475-505 (1999).

Olive, K.E. Religion and spirituality: important psychosocial variables frequently ignored in clinical research. *Southern Medical Journal*, 97, 1152-1153 (2004).

Peplau, L.A. Human sexuality: how do men and women differ? *Current Directions in Psychological Science*, 12:37-41 (2003).

Perkins, K.A. *et al.* The subjective and reinforcing effects of visual and olfactory stimuli in alcohol drinking. *Experimental and Clinical Psychopharmacology*, 11:269-275 (2003).

Raine, R. *et al.* General practitioners' perceptions of chronic fatigue syndrome and beliefs about its management, compared with irritable bowel syndrome: qualitative study. *British Medical Journal*, 328:1354-1357 (2004).

Rippere, V. Dietary treatment of chronic obsessional ruminations. *British Journal of Clinical Psychology*, 22:314-316 (1983).

Riu, E. El suicidio, cómo advertir el riesgo y prevenirlo. *El País*, 24.2.2004.

Salaberria, K and Echeburúa, E. Long-term outcome of cognitive therapy's contribution to self-exposure in vivo to the treatment of generalized social phobia. *Behav Modifi*, 22:262-284 (1998).

Seligman, M.E.P. *Authentic Happiness.* New York, Free Press, 2002.

Schumaker, J.F. *Religion and mental health.* New York and Oxford, Oxford University Press, 1992.

Shahar, G. *et al.* Perfectionism impedes social relations and response to brief treatment for depression. *Journal of Social and Clinical Psychology*, 23 (2):140-154 (2004).

Singh, Y.N. and Singh, N.N. Therapeutic potential of Kava in the treatment of anxiety disorders. *CNS Drugs*, 16:731-743 (2002).

Sobel, D.S. and Ornstein, R. *The Healthy Mind, Healthy Body Handbook.* Los Altos, California, Ishk Book Service, 1997.

Smith, S. Compulsive Cybersex can jeopardize marriage, rest of life. *Monitor on Psychology*, 34 (9):20 (2003).

Solantaus, T., Leinonen, J. and Punamäki, R.L. Children's mental health in times of economic recession: replication and extension of the family economic stress model in Finland. *Developmental Psychology*, 40:412-429 (2004).

Sorkin, D., Rook, K. and Lu, J. Loneliness, lack of emotional support, lack of companionship, and the likelihood of having a heart condition in an elderly sample. *Annals of Behavioral Medicine*, 24, 290-300 (2002).

Spunt, B. Pathological gambling and substance misuse. *Substance Use and Misuse*, 37:1299-1305 (2002).

Stallard, P., Velleman, R. and Baldwin, S. Recovery from post-traumatic stress disorder in children following road traffic accidents: the role of taking and feeling understood. *Journal of Community and Applied Social Psychology*, 11:37-41 (2001).

Stein, M.B. *et al.* Social phobia in the primary care medical setting. *J Fam Pract.*, 48:514-519 (1999).

Stravynski, A. and Greenberg, D. The treatment of social phobia: a critical assessment. *Acta Psychiatr Scand.*, 98:171-181 (1998).

Taillefer, S.S. et al. Correlates of illness worry in chronic fatigue syndrome. *Journal of Psychosomatic Research*, 54:331-338 (2003).

Tansella, M. Gender differences in mental health. *World Health*, 51:26-27 (1998).

Thayer, R.E. *Calm Energy: how people regulate mood with food and exercise.* Oxford, Oxford University Press, 2001.

Wachholtz, A.B. and Pargament, K.I. Is spirituality a critical ingredient of meditation? Comparing the effects of spiritual meditation, secular meditation, and relaxation on spiritual, psychological, cardiac, and pain outcomes. *Journal of Behavioral Medicine*, 16:369-384 (2005).

Waller, J. *Children of Cain: How Ordinary People Commit Extraordinary Evil.* New York, Oxford University Press, 2001.

Wallman, K.E. *et al.* Graded exercise improves attentional performance in chronic fatigue syndrome patients. *Australian Journal of Psychology*, 55:220-225 (2003).

Williams, D.R. The health of men: Structured inequalities and opportunities. *American Journal of Public Health*, 93:724-731 (2003).

Woo, E. and Sharps, M.J. Cognitive aging and physical exercise. *Educational Gerontology*, 29:327-337 (2003).

Young, S.N., The use of diet and dietary components in the study of factors controlling affect in humans: a review. *J Psychiatry Neurosci.*, 18:235-244 (1993).

Zhu, J.-N. *et al.*, A sex difference in the human brain and its relation to transsexuality, *Nature* 378:68-70 (1995).

ALPHABETICAL INDEX